HARPER OF DETROIT

THE ORIGIN AND GROWTH
OF A GREAT METROPOLITAN HOSPITAL

by

Frank B. Woodford and Philip P. Mason

DETROIT 1964

WAYNE STATE UNIVERSITY PRESS

CONTENTS

ILLUSTRATIONS

PREFACE

No book of this kind can be considered complete without the authors' acknowledgment of the help of many people who gave freely of their time, advice, materials, and specialized knowledge. Without them, the end product would be much less than it is.

There were, for example, Miss Christine Colditz, of Philadelphia, and Harold J. Bean, of Sandusky, Ohio, who aided us in obtaining data about the location and description of Walter Harper's Philadelphia property. Philip Langwald, secretary of the Detroit Board of Water Commissioners; Harold Glassford, vice president of the Burton Abstract & Title Company, and Hazen E. Kunz, president of the Michigan Historical Society, provided valuable information regarding the Harper-Martin properties in Detroit and Michigan.

Miss Geneva Kebler, archivist for the Michigan State Historical Commission, Lansing, furnished us with copies of pertinent documents, particularly with reference to the military aspects of Harper Hospital and the Soldiers' Home. Her knowledge of available material, and her unfailing promptness in responding to demands for it, make Miss Kebler a researcher's delight. James M. Babcock, chief, and his associates of the Burton Historical Collection, particularly Mrs. Bernice Sprenger, also furnished help in locating material which has earned them an admirable reputation for scholarly assistance.

Robert Warner and Miss Ida C. Brown of the staff of the University of Michigan Historical Collections gave us access to their rich resources and helped particularly in locating necessary Civil War records.

Charles J. Meyers and Robert Spiro, of Detroit, directed us to several important research collections relating to Harper Hospital. Frank X. Scannell and Mrs. Esther Loughin of the Michigan State Library, Lansing, facilitated our work by locating numerous government documents.

Miss Mary Peltier, librarian for the Detroit Board of Health, and Mrs. Fannie Anderson and Vern Pings, librarians, Wayne State University College of Medicine, gave valuable assistance in running down answers to questions regarding general hospital and health matters in Detroit. Russell J. Chambers, Detroit Housing Commission project manager for the new Medical Center, proved a source of important information concerning that phase of the Harper story. On the same subject, we relied heavily upon Dr. Gordon H. Scott, dean of the Wayne State College of Medicine. Henry Alexander, of Michigan Medical Service, was most generous in supplying background material on Blue Cross.

A special word of thanks is due Professor Leslie L. Hanawalt, of Wayne State University. Dr. Hanawalt has for some time been gathering material about the University's medical school and its predecessors, the old Detroit Medical College and the Detroit College of Medicine. Whatever we needed, he gave us without stint, and that in advance of the publication of his own work on the history of the institutions mentioned. That is pure generosity, and our gratitude goes far beyond our ability adequately to express it.

Wherever we turned to members of the medical profession, the response was prompt and rewarding. Among those we relied upon for authoritative information, both regarding Harper Hospital specifically, and professional matters generally, were Dr. Louis J. Hirschman, of Traverse City, Michigan; Dr. Henry R. Carstens, of Birmingham; Dr. Kenneth Krabbenhoft, Dr. William J. Stapleton, Jr., and Dr. J. Milton Robb, of Detroit. A very special word of thanks is due Dr. William S. Reveno whose wise counseling, frequently at the sacrifice of his own time and convenience, helped us over some of the most troublesome parts of this undertaking.

Finally, we must express our profound gratitude to the people at Harper Hospital itself. Their enthusiasm, always a sustaining ingredient, was matched only by their co-operation in making available everything we asked for, and in giving us free use of the Hospital records and facilities. Mrs. Barbara Coe Johnson, director of the Harper Hospital libraries, and her efficient staff cheerfully acceded to our every demand, however unreasonable. It was a delight to work with George E. Cartmill, director of the Hospital. Not only did he make us feel, as we were overrunning his premises, that we were part of the Harper family, but he also read the manuscript in rough form. As a result, he made several extremely helpful suggestions and, in more than one instance, saved us from grievous error.

We are grateful, too, to Mrs. Patricia Higgins and Mrs. Mary Anne Harrison who typed the manuscript, cheerfully working under that kind of pressure which harassed authors commonly apply.

Finally, we acknowledge the counsel and encouragement given us by Dr. Harold A. Basilius, Director, Wayne State University Press, and Mrs. Patricia Davis, editor.

To all those mentioned, as well as others whose help and encouragement it is less easy to pinpoint, our heartfelt appreciation.

F. B. W.
P. P. M.

Chapter 1

THE MEETING IN THE PARLOR

Darkness was settling
on Detroit in the late afternoon of February 3, 1859. The lamplighters
were making their rounds, touching the corner gaslights into amber
life. Where they passed, yellow circles of reflected light spilled on the
snow which lay thick and heavy along the fashionable stretch of Woodward Avenue just above Grand Circus Park.[1] The substantial citizens
were making their ways home. In their offices and stores, well downtown, their clerks would have another hour or so of work before they
could cover up the stock, dot the last sentences of the legal papers, snuff
out the lamps, and make their separate ways home.

It was a sharp, cold evening, with a promise in the air that it would
soon be even colder. There had been a heavy snow, three to four inches,
the day before. The newspapers commented about the recent run of
cold nights. Carriages and other wheeled equipages had been put away
in barns, coach houses, and livery stables; sleighs and cutters had been
brought out. The Detroit River had frozen over solidly, stopping the
car ferries. Traffic between Detroit and the Canadian shore was over
the ice.[2]

In front of the residence of the Rev. Dr. George Duffield, there was
unusual activity. A half-dozen men arrived, singly or in pairs. Their
sleighs drew up before the house, buffalo lap robes were pushed aside,
and blankets were thrown over the horses. The Duffield residence stood
on the west side of Woodward on the corner of High Street which, in
time, would become Vernor Highway. Across the street, in a spider web
of scaffolding and piles of building material, was a new structure,
St. John's Episcopal Church, nearly completed and waiting for April
when its congregation would occupy it.

A couple of blocks west, at the intersection of Park Avenue and Duffield Street, was a small frame building, soon to be taken over by one of the Duffield sons, Dr. Samuel P. Duffield. There, in partnership with Hervey C. Parke and George S. Davis, he would manufacture a line of pharmaceutical supplies. Eventually the firm would evolve into Parke, Davis and Company.[3]

The Duffield residence was imposing by any set of standards, past or present. It was a square, brick building of two main stories, with a small penthouse which gave it a partial third floor. Architecturally, it might be described as federalist. A high iron fence ran along the Woodward Avenue side, and the spacious yard was shaded by tall evergreens and maples.[4]

As the manse of the First Presbyterian Church of Detroit, the residence might have appeared pretentious to some people, although no one knowing Dr. Duffield ever would have voiced the thought. Dr. Duffield was a preacher, but not a poor one. His church was wealthy, and his parishioners included some of the most substantial Protestants in Detroit. His salary, $2,500 a year, was generous and permitted him to live on an equal social footing with the best families in town—most of whom, incidentally worshiped regularly at his splendid church on the northwest corner of Farmer and State (now Gratiot), a site presently occupied by the J. L. Hudson Company.

Dr. Duffield had raised and educated a family of five sons and a daughter. By 1859, they were grown and were making their respective ways in the world. Soon they would be as distinguished as their father. But even when the demands of a growing family were heaviest, Dr. Duffield was far from the overworked, worried, half-starved preacher who existed on a meager Sunday collection of small change, supplemented by barrels of apples donated by parishioners, or with labor in his own cornfield to feed himself and his brood.

His was a gracious, hospitable home that these half-dozen substantial citizens entered. Most, if not all, of them were deacons and elders of Dr. Duffield's church. Inside, he was awaiting their arrival with his second son, Divie Bethune Duffield, who was already reputed to be a brilliant young man and one of the most capable attorneys in Detroit. While anticipating this meeting, which he and his son had called, Dr. Duffield was in a somewhat introspective mood, his thoughts divided between the physical ailments which afflicted him and the material blessings which Providence had showered upon him. It was about this time when he noted in his diary that he had been bothered with "a run of ailments" for more than a year. He did not specify their nature, but they were troublesome. He was glad they were not as violent as those which had afflicted him for several months a year before, and he was grateful that they did not interfere with the discharge of his duties. He wrote:

The Lord in some respects greatly prospered me. In temporal matters, he has enabled me to meet all my debts beside having several thousand dollars (five) to draw interest and stock that at this time might be converted into money, to the amount of $16,000—five hundred shares of Quincy Mining stock at $33 par value. How great are His mercies to me and mine.[5]

Thus, there was a certain air of complacency and well-being, mixed with proper humility, awaiting the visitors of Dr. Duffield and his son that cold February evening. But any feeling of self-satisfaction did not assume precedence over the serious business at hand. It was the Lord's work, and with Dr. Duffield that always came first.

The six men trooped into the house, shedding their greatcoats, fur gloves, and fur hats. If they tramped snow onto Mrs. Duffield's carpets, nothing was said. Isabella Duffield had been mistress of a minister's home too long not to be accustomed to comings and goings in all sorts of weather, with whatever minor disruption of her housekeeping such traffic created. She was gracious; they were welcome.

With murmured amenities about the weather, and perhaps a comment or two about the Dred Scott decision which Chief Justice Roger Taney had just handed down, and which was taking up a good deal of space in Detroit's newspapers, the men were ushered into Dr. Duffield's study. It is easy to picture a warm, friendly fire in the fireplace, the gaslights glowing, and the room lined with shelves of books denoting a wide range of intellectual interest. As Dr. Duffield looked at his visitors —all old friends and church associates—he must have been impressed with the solid character of the men. They were truly representative of the breed which was transforming Detroit into a vigorous, progressive community. The city was prospering under the leadership of shrewd, able businessmen such as they. The lifeblood of the town was trade and most of the prosperous businessmen were merchants. Some of them had founded establishments which still exist, in one form or another, to this day. Detroit had not yet become a factory town. There was some light industry, of course, and a beginning had been made toward the development of heavy industry. The latter was represented in the group by Dr. George B. Russel, a respected physician whose interests extended beyond the practice of medicine. Some six years earlier, he had organized a company to produce wheels for railway cars. In time, it would develop into a division of the American Car & Foundry Company. He had also built an iron foundry in Hamtramck Township, one of the first plants of its kind in the Detroit area. Among his other enterprises was the operation of a ferry service between Detroit and Windsor. That had been going for at least seven years, and his vessel, the "Ottawa," was a busy river craft.[6]

The others present were merchants, builders, or dealers in real estate, a fairly lively occupation as the town grew in population and the demand increased for house lots, homes, and farms. Representative of this group was Buckminster Wight, a pillar of the First Presbyterian Church, who had erected the first brick row "terrace" on the north side of Jefferson Avenue between Riopelle and Russell and who was a partner in a prospering lumber business.[7] There was David Cooper, a builder and real estate man. Frederick Buhl, of Pennsylvania Dutch stock, was in the fur business and was taking over what remained of the American Fur Company. Alexander C. McGraw owned a shoe store; he was prosperous and eminently respectable. Jacob S. Farrand, who in time would perhaps be the best known of any of them, was the senior partner in a busy drug firm which continued to be a leading Detroit enterprise until just a few years ago.

The character of all these men was revealed by something else. They were all "town boosters." They would have delighted a chamber of commerce secretary. Each acknowledged a civic responsibility; each had served, or was serving a public function. Frederick Buhl had been mayor in 1848, and an alderman before that. Dr. Russel had served as health officer and as inspector of the Detroit House of Correction. Farrand had been a member of the Water Commission (his father, Bethuel, built Detroit's first public waterworks), an alderman, and president of the Common Council. Wight, too, had been an alderman. The others had served as school inspectors, assessors in their home wards, or in other public capacities.

Most of them were full of good works. Their names appeared on the rolls of the volunteer fire companies; Buhl was a proprietor of the Grand River plank road; and like Jacob Farrand who found time in a busy life to be president of the Presbyterian Session, treasurer of the Detroit Evangelical Alliance, and secretary of the Detroit Young Men's Temperance Society.

In politics, most if not all had been Whigs; now their attention was turning toward the newly founded Republican party which two years before had scored so well in Michigan, electing the party's first governor. They were staunch Union men at a time when the rift between North and South was widening. Wight was perhaps more outspoken than the others; he was an avowed and uncompromising abolitionist. For a time he had been affiliated with the Free Soil party. A former state senator, he had been part owner of the *Peninsular Freeman,* a radical abolitionist publication.[8]

They were, indeed, solid men who could be relied upon to give the full measure of their talents and energies to any worthy cause. That was why Dr. Duffield had summoned them to meet at his house that evening.

There was one other man waiting with Dr. Duffield and Divie. He was somewhat nondescript in appearance—certainly he did not wear the broadcloth of prosperity like the others did. He looked more like a small neighborhood merchant, or possibly a farmer. He was known to all the others, but they did not know him well. Nobody did. His name was Walter Harper. He was there for a very special purpose. In fact, he was the reason for that gathering. He had come to give away his extensive property holdings—to endow those other men and their successors as his trustees. To Detroit, which was scarcely aware of his existence, he was about to give the largest gift it had ever known.[9]

When the assembled gentlemen had taken their seats on the straight-backed chairs or horsehair divan, the usual accessories in a proper Victorian household, Divie Duffield stood up, a paper in hand, and explained the purpose of the meeting. It is always a dramatic and solemn occasion when a lawyer reads a legal document to an interested gathering, whether it be a will, a contract, or a trust agreement as this one was. He had the close attention of his audience, despite the fact that all present knew the general contents of the document. It had been under discussion for weeks; their individual parts in the matter at hand had been carefully explained and their approval and participation had been solicited and granted. Nevertheless, they followed closely every word of Divie Duffield's strict legal terminology:

Witnesseth that whereas it is the wish and desire of the party of the first part [meaning Walter Harper] from his property hereinafter described, or the avails thereof, to contribute toward the erection and maintenance of a hospital for the benefit and relief of the sick and aged poor within the limits or adjacent to the said city of Detroit . . . , which hospital shall be under the direction and management of persons of the Protestant faith, and whereas by reason of advancing age he is unable personally to initiate such charity but, on the contrary, is anxious to entrust the same to such parties as are herein named as the parties of the second part, and those who may become their successors in the trusts hereinafter created . . . I do hereby give, grant, transfer, alien and convey . . . forever all the right, title and interest which I . . . own and claim in and to the following described lands and premises.[10]

The "parties of the second part" in this instance were Dr. Duffield, Dr. Russel, McGraw, Farrand, Wight, Buhl, and Cooper, nominated as the Board of Trustees to see that Walter Harper's wishes were carried out.

Harper had entensive property holdings. It might almost be said that he was land poor. Yet, all of what he had was handed over in that trust agreement. It was described in detail—864⁴⁴⁄₁₀₀ acres located in the Ten Thousand Acre Tract in Greenfield Township, Michigan, on the outskirts of Detroit; 80 acres in Oakland County, Michigan, and 3 lots with buildings in the heart of Philadelphia. There were no strings attached as far as the manner in which this property could be used or disposed of by the trustees. They, and their heirs and assigns after them, in carrying out the purpose of the trust, could "keep, manage, preserve, sell, mortgage or exchange, or otherwise dispose of said real estate and property, or any part thereof, and invest and reinvest the proceeds thereof. . . ." Lawyer Duffield had carefully plugged all loopholes.

The "whereases" and "wherefores" continued with a set of conditions which, said the *Detroit Daily Advertiser* a few days later, "are few and easy to be complied with." First, Harper specified that the trustees would pay him an annuity of "two thousand dollars during my natural life." Of that amount, $1,000 was to be used to pay off mortgages on his Philadelphia property which was encumbered to the extent of about $8,000. Second, the trustees, while serving at no fixed rate of remuneration, were to receive reasonable compensation for their time and expenses in carrying out the terms of the trust. Third—and this was the meat of the whole—the trustees were directed to erect and maintain a hospital in or near Detroit "for the succor, care and relief of such aged or sick persons as shall apply for the benefit of the same, and who shall seem to my Trustees hereof to be proper subjects for such and, as their means will enable them to afford." The hospital, its site, and operation were to be left to the trustees' discretion, saving only that they should observe "a reasonable simplicity and economy, both in design and management." As soon as it was ready to receive patients, a medical chief was to be appointed. But it was specified that he must be a practitioner of "the regular or old school system of medical practice." No homeopaths, naturapaths, operators of magnetic tractors, or devotees of the more esoteric cults, of whom there were many at that time, were welcome.

In addition to the purely medical functions of the hospital, Harper slipped in another clause which provided for the establishment, as part of the institution, of "a school for the instruction of youth in different arts and trades after the manner of what is known in Prussia as 'The Fellenburg [*sic*] School.'"

The model for this vocational school had been established at Hofwyl, near Bern, Switzerland in 1799 by the Swiss educator, Philipp Emanuel von Fellenberg. Believing that the old system of training through apprenticeship was no longer effective, von Fellenberg endeavored to train young people for industry and agriculture under a community system. The product of their labor would cover the expenses of their education. While his plan was at first ridiculed, it eventually caught on, and pupils came to him from all over Europe, not only to learn trades, but also to benefit from the high moral standards which he endeavored to maintain.[11] (This, incidentally, was the only provision of the Harper trust which was not carried out to the letter. The Hospital eventually performed important educational functions, but they were of a somewhat different nature than Harper envisioned, and bore no resemblance to the Fellenberg system.)

A key provision of the trust dealt with the manner in which vacancies on the Board of Trustees were to be filled. It was specified that whenever a member of the board, each of whom was to have life tenure, died or resigned, the pastor and session of the First Presbyterian Church *

---

* Gathered together in the Appendix is certain information which would interrupt the flow of the narrative but which may be of interest to readers. Topics which receive such additional treatment in the Appendix have been marked with an asterisk.

should submit the names of three suitable replacements. The remaining trustees would select one of the nominees to fill the vacant place. Theoretically this clause gave the First Presbyterian Church a degree of control over the affairs of the Hospital. Although the provision has been observed, it soon became customary for the trustees to submit to the church's governing body the names of persons whom they would like to have nominated, and their wishes have been followed.

Finally, it was urged that as soon as possible the trustees should apply to the legislature of the state of Michigan for an act of incorporation. This was eventually done. On March 20, 1863, a special act "for the incorporation of Hospitals or Asylums," specially tailored for Harper Hospital, and including the salient features of the trust, was adopted.[12]

Having read the lengthy document, Divie Duffield paused and looked around the room. There was no dissent; one by one the newly named trustees put their signatures to the deed to which Walter Harper had previously affixed his name. When the pen had scratched the last signature, Harper Hospital had become a legal reality.

Duffield later told how he had read and explained the deed to all present "and especially to Mr. Walter Harper, the Grantor." He asked Harper if the deed expressed his wishes in all respects. Harper replied that:

. . . it was exactly what he wished, that he gave his assent to it with all his heart . . . that he had been contemplating such disposition of his property for many months past, and if the gentlemen named were only willing to oblige him by serving as Trustees, in pursuance of the conditions of the deed, he would be very grateful, and feel relieved of that which had long been resting upon his mind as a thing incomplete, viz, a desire in some manner to appropriate his property for the relief of the sick and aged poor of Detroit and vicinity.[13]

On a still later occasion, Duffield stated that Harper had read and signed the document prior to the February 3 meeting, "that he knew its contents, that the deed expressed his wishes in all respects—that there was nothing in it he desired to alter and that he acknowledged it to be his free act and deed, and with all his heart placed it in the hands of the Trustees." [14]

C. N. Ganson, a notary public, was called in to witness the signatures. Thereupon, Duffield noted, "the company dispersed." The following day, the document was recorded in the office of the Register of Deeds for Wayne County, Michigan.[15]

Within a few days, the Detroit newspapers learned about Walter Harper's gift and, although they admitted knowing very little about the donor personally, they were lavish in their praise of him and devoted considerable front page space to describing the trust. "Within a day or two," proclaimed the *Detroit Daily Advertiser* on February 8, "this individual [referring to Harper] who will henceforth be regarded in Detroit as one of the most munificent benefactors of his species known in the annals of American philanthropy, has made a donation for the establishment of a much-needed charity, that will astonish as much as it will gratify our citizens, and which could hardly be believed if the records of the Register's office did not testify to its truth." The *Detroit Daily Advertiser* then took a blind shot at estimating the value of the donation. "We have heard the value of the property estimated to be exceeding one hundred thousand dollars." For good measure, a guess was tacked on that the Philadelphia property was worth not less than forty thousand dollars.[16]

The trustees certainly had no objections to Walter Harper receiving full credit for his generosity. Neither could they object to the details of a public trust being known. They were, however, disturbed by the estimates of the value of the property which had not yet been accurately appraised. To avoid any possible later misunderstanding or repercussions, they determined to give the local press an official statement of the terms of the Harper deed and the trustees' intentions. This was done on February 9, and appeared over the names of the trustees. "We are sure," said the statement, "our citizens will rejoice that so bountiful a gift, for so noble an object, has been entrusted to appreciative and faithful guardians."[17]

It was the trustees' hope, they continued, to initiate the trust "at the earliest possible period, so as to receive the greatest amount of present and permanent good to the community in the midst of which we dwell." As a caution against wild speculation about the value of the Harper property, it was stated that "the land in this vicinity is at present unproductive and unimproved." Finally, the board promised:

... at an early period to organize and open "The Harper Hospital" and in due season a school, also mentioned in the deed of trust and directed to be organized and conducted upon the plan of the institution at Hofwyl, in Switzerland, as also in Prussia, agreeably to the system and object of Emanuel von Fellenberg, for the benefit of poor and deserving youth, who find that among us, the learning of the ordinary arts and trades by means of an apprenticeship, is becoming constantly more difficult, and so as to be almost unattainable.

This statement was drafted at the first meeting of the Board of Trustees on the evening of February 7 at the Duffield residence. The board took this occasion to organize itself formally, electing Dr. Duffield president; David Cooper, treasurer; and Divie Bethune Duffield, who was not a member of the board, secretary.[18] Ten days later, on February 17, the board convened for the third time. Divie Duffield had some interesting news to report. Mrs. Ann Martin, or Nancy Martin, by which name she was better known, the housekeeper for Walter Harper, had decided to emulate him and add something of her own to his original gift. "Some conversation occurred," reported Duffield, "relative to a proposal on the part of Mrs. Ann Martin to convey on certain terms a five acre lot and a fifteen acre lot situated at different points on Woodward Avenue . . . for the purposes of the Harper Hospital." [19]

A committee, consisting of Farrand and Cooper, was appointed with instructions "to wait upon Mrs. Martin and arrange with her for the acceptance of the property referred to, and for the purposes named."

The committee found Mrs. Martin more than willing to co-operate. Farrand and Cooper, on February 28, reported that Mrs. Martin did indeed desire to turn over "the five acres on Woodward Avenue on which she now lives, and also the fifteen acres owned by her and lying on the Pontiac Road nearly four miles out of the city." There were, they said, certain conditions which would have to be met, just as Walter Harper had imposed conditions. First, Mrs. Martin demanded an annuity of $600 "during my natural life," payable in quarterly installments.[20] Perhaps, however, the most significant condition of her offer was that the hospital, when built, should stand on her five-acre tract. All property not required as a site could be disposed of at the discretion of the trustees. That lot, or part of it at least, became an historic site, because on it Harper Hospital was erected. Next, Nancy Martin wanted a place to live and specified that:

. . . after the erection of the Hospital building, hereinafter referred to, or at such time prior thereto as said parties of the second part the trustees may elect, to erect and finish upon some portion of the said five acre lot, convenient to the city water pipes, a cottage house costing three hundred dollars or thereabouts, and which with suitable yard privileges, the said party of the first part shall be permitted freely to use and occupy for and during the term of her said natural life.

This was an easy condition to meet. After all, the land was there; five acres looked like more than enough for a hospital building with room to spare for a cottage and yard or garden. The water pipe presented no difficulties because, although the location was regarded as being far out in the suburbs, a four-inch water main had been installed on Woodward Avenue in 1855, extending north to Alexandrine Street, one of the few side streets which had been opened off Woodward up to that time.[21]

Just as Walter Harper insisted upon inclusion of the Fellenberg system, so did Mrs. Martin require that when the Hospital was built, "suitable provision be made for the bestowal of such medical care and accommodation as is usually afforded by institutions known under the name of 'Lying-in Hospitals.' " Aside from these specific conditions, the Martin deed supplemented Walter Harper's and was contingent upon carrying out the terms of his trust.

Frederick Buhl made a motion, quickly adopted, that Mrs. Martin's offer be accepted. While the deed was dated March 10, 1859, it was not signed by the various parties until March 15, at another trustees' meeting at which Mrs. Martin was present. As he had done when they met with Harper, Duffield read and explained the terms of the trust.[22] He recalled that three years previously, Mrs. Martin had made a will, leaving her property to charity, the kind and purpose not described. Walter Harper's gift had persuaded her to make a similar one, supplementing his. By this act, her earlier will was invalidated and replaced by the Hospital deed. Later, she executed another will, dated February 12, 1864, providing for the distribution of property not covered by her 1859 deed.

At that same meeting on March 15, the trustees resolved to pay an "early" visit to the Martin five-acre lot, which they apparently had not previously inspected, "for the purpose of defining a site for the Harper Hospital." They also instructed the secretary to offer for sale as soon as possible the eighty-acre Harper lot in Oakland County. The first installment of Harper's annuity had fallen due on March 1, and the board members—with the Rev. Dr. Duffield being excused—agreed to pay it

out of their own pockets. [23] Obviously, that could not be allowed to re-
cur. As trustees, they were richly endowed with non-productive land.
What they needed, and quickly, was cash to meet the obligations they
had assumed.

The press greeted the Martin grant with the same enthusiasm it expressed over the Harper gift. On April 5, the *Detroit Daily Advertiser*
said:

> Mrs. Martin has resided in Detroit for the past twenty-two years, having
> come here from Philadelphia. She has had a huckster stall in the market for
> a number of years and is known familiarly as "Nancy Martin."
> The value of the property is variously estimated; that four miles from
> the city is worth at least $1500, and the five-acre lot from $10,000 to $15,000.
> The site for the Hospital is a very beautiful one, there being at one end
> of it, a grove of oak, hickory, beech and other woods. Mrs. Martin, though
> rough in appearance, has a warm heart, and has done a great deal in the
> way of disbursing private charities and now, after making this munificent
> grant, she will be long remembered by not only the recipients of the benefits
> arising from it, but by the citizens generally.[24]

Feeling, perhaps, that it had not been sufficiently laudatory, the
Daily Advertiser had more to say on the subject in the following day's
edition.

> It strikes us that the people of Detroit owe it to themselves to give some
> public expression of the estimation in which they hold the noble act of Nancy
> Martin in presenting to this city, her beautiful lot on Woodward Avenue,
> as a site for the Harper Hospital. She has always estimated the value of the
> property at $25,000, and good judges of property assure us that it is well
> worth $20,000. She has reserved of all of it only a life interest of $600 annually,
> and a small residence. In consideration of this liberal act, can our citizens do
> less than raise this amount by subscription, and thus have the whole gift un-
> impaired for the object for which she designs it? We bravely make the sug-
> gestion, and if thought worth anything, it will probably be acted upon. But
> it seems to us that Detroit can afford to do this much towards the benevolent
> enterprise which she and Mr. Harper have so munificently endowed.[25]

There is room to suspect that this thinly veiled appeal was inspired
by Dr. Duffield and his fellow trustees. However, it elicited no known
response.

Chapter 2

THE OBSCURE MAN

In recounting
the origins of Harper Hospital, an old brochure has it that:

Years and years ago a lad roamed the highways and by-ways of Londonderry, Ireland, and at about the same time a girl was awakening into woman-
hood in sleepy Philadelphia. Through the fantasies of Fate, both found their
way ultimately to Detroit, and having accumulated a fair share of the world's
goods, and being inbred with a humanitarian spirit, they took the necessary
steps to lay the foundation for a hospital which would give aid to those sufferers who were unable to take care of themselves.[1]

This rather high-flown description of the two earliest benefactors
of Harper Hospital is typical of the romantic, storybook aura that always has surrounded them. Somehow it deprives them of the flesh and
blood to make them live as human beings. Instead, Walter Harper and
Nancy Martin were re-created as legendary figures and, unfortunately,
rather pallid ones at that. Although little is known about these two people, there is enough information available to make them much more
than wispy ghosts, who are remembered only for a single spectacularly
magnanimous gesture, or two unidentifiable people whose names somehow became attached to a hospital and a midtown street leading to it.

Walter Harper was an obscure man, at least as far as his life in
Detroit was concerned. Undoubtedly, he preferred it that way. There
is evidence that he lived almost the life of a recluse either from a natural
inclination to be self-effacing, or because of bitterness, frustration, and
disappointment, or probably because of all these factors. Up to the time
he gave away his property to the Hospital, his name was rarely if ever
mentioned in the newspapers or public records. He was called an ec-

centric.[2] George B. Catlin described him as "a virtual stranger in Detroit," who lived in obscurity.[3] Silas Farmer, who was Harper's contemporary and who knew something about everybody in Detroit, has almost nothing to say about Harper's origins, his early life, or his life in Detroit. Even the Harper trustees, at the time of the donation in 1859, felt it necessary, in announcing the gift, to explain rather apologetically that Harper had lived for several years in Detroit in "so quiet and reserved a manner that he has made few acquaintances." The trustees admitted there probably were few of his fellow citizens who had even heard of him.[4]

Such a retiring nature does not make it easy to do the man justice. As far as can be learned, he left nothing written, not even a signature beyond that on the deed to his property. Yet, it is impossible to believe he was either illiterate or ignorant. His ability to accumulate property suggests foresight, business acumen, and a large measure of shrewdness. That he was concerned with establishing a vocational school reveals an interest in education and the welfare of youth. To freely give so much property shows a humanitarian impulse although, in fairness, it must be conceded that the impulse may also have sprung partially from bitterness and disappointment in his children. If he felt he had to deprive them of sharing his estate, he at least had enough conscience to dispose of his wealth in a manner that would benefit the public.

Here and there we pick up scraps of information about Walter Harper. He was of Protestant Irish derivation, born in Londonderry, Ireland, March 17, 1789. He was the elder son of James and Margaret Harper. His mother was said to have been English, born in London. Altogether, there were three children. Nothing is known of the other two.[5]

About 1795, when Walter was six years old, the family crossed the sea and made a new home in Philadelphia. James Harper became a drover and cattle buyer, and while he is said to have made a comfortable living, he "never amassed any considerable amount of property, and his children made their own fortunes, such as they proved to be."[6] In those days, it was customary for buyers of cattle for the Philadelphia market to travel long distances, making their purchases from farmers in the western part of Pennsylvania, and even beyond in southeastern Ohio. They would then drive the herds on the hoof to Philadelphia and other populous seaboard cities to be slaughtered. It is pure speculation, but James Harper may have been one of those drovers who brought cattle East from the farther settlements, and whose accounts, on arriving home, of his adventures stirred the imagination of his young son and aroused in him an interest in the western country that ultimately caused him to go to Michigan. Perhaps—and this is still speculation—young Walter accompanied his father on one of his buying expeditions. At any rate, Walter Harper did become interested in the West and the opportunities which were opening up there.

But for the time being, that interest had to be pushed aside for more practical things. He was apprenticed, when he was about twelve or fourteen, to a Philadelphia coach maker. After six years of learning the trade, he was so skilled that he was hired by Conrad House as foreman at the then unusual salary of $2,500 a year. It is possible that House was the man to whom Harper was apprenticed. He remained with House, under contract, for ten years, which prompted the observation that this "demonstrates how skillful a workman and how excellent a manager he must have been." [7] The handsome wages which Harper received obviously permitted him to accumulate a considerable nest egg which he invested in Philadelphia property. For reasons unexplained, he retired from the coach building industry to devote himself, as the accounts of his life have it, to the mercantile business. What that really means is that he opened a grocery store in one of the buildings he had acquired and in which he also lived.

By this time Harper had married and was raising a family. His first wife, whose name is not known, bore him six children—three girls and three boys. Outside of one daughter, Margaret, who was born in 1813, the ages of the children are not given. The names of the others were Elizabeth, Walter, James, and Hugh. The fact that the name of the sixth child was not recorded suggests that the third girl may have died in infancy.

After a dozen years in the grocery business, Harper persuaded himself that there were golden opportunities in the West, and with his family he moved to Detroit. There, on November 10, 1831, he leased "a tier of rooms containing three rooms, one above the other" in the southwest end of Joseph Campau's red two-story dwelling house situated on Larned Street.[8] Once established in Detroit, Harper began looking for places to invest his capital. That was easy to do. By patent, signed by President Andrew Jackson, November 23, 1831, he took up in what is now the north end of Detroit 864⁴⁴⁄₁₀₀ acres for which he probably paid less than two dollars an acre. About the same time, and undoubtedly for less money, Harper also bought an eighty-acre farm in Oakland County, to which he soon moved his family. Meanwhile, he wisely held on to his Philadelphia property which he leased to various tenants, and upon which he obtained mortgages. The latter would appear to have provided him with the necessary funds to purchase his Michigan lands.

But something went wrong. The success he experienced as a coach maker and a grocer was not repeated on the farm, and Harper became discouraged. Exactly what happened cannot be learned, but after a year or two in Oakland County, he packed up and returned to Philadelphia, taking some of his children with him and apparently leaving others, the boys, behind. Whether his wife went back with him or not is equally unclear. She may have died in Michigan, although it is more likely that she passed away in Philadelphia soon after their return. At any rate, back in Philadelphia, Harper soon found himself a widower, and following the death of his first wife, Harper remarried, this time a Miss Mary E. Demer by whom he had one son, Charles. Restless and dissatisfied with life as he found it, Harper went once more to Detroit.[9] The elder children, or at least his daughter, Margaret, stayed behind. On the second trip he was accompanied by a servant girl, Ann Martin, whose life thereafter was to be closely linked to his.

If he were seeking peace of mind, Detroit offered him no more than Philadelphia, and his second trip was no more successful than the first. Exactly what happened during the visit is a mystery. There were veiled reports of "domestic troubles" and other circumstances on which it is not necessary to dwell at length.[10] There has been some talk that the domestic troubles were caused by Mrs. Harper's resentment of the presence of Ann Martin. All that is definitely known is that Mary Demer Harper died eleven months after their marriage. Walter Harper became estranged from his children, and "his household was managed by Mrs. Nancy [Ann] Martin," "who remained in her position, regulating his home." Although a comparatively young man, not yet in his fifties, Harper made no further effort to enter business or resume farming. Instead, he chose "virtually to retire from the world and live a life of seclusion,"[11] being content to exist "upon the competence which his labors had gained for him."[12]

According to an early city directory, in 1839 Harper and Mrs.

Martin were living on the "River Road near the sand hills, Spring-wells." [13] That would place them on what is now West Jefferson Avenue, near Fort Wayne. They must have resided there several years; when next located in 1857, Harper was listed as "boarding" with Mrs. Martin, whose small house stood on her lot just north of Brady Street, a block from where Harper Hospital stands today. In 1859, after each had signed over his property to the Hospital trustees, a cottage costing $450 was erected for them on the Hospital grounds. In 1864, the structure was moved to the north side of Fremont Street, which eventually was renamed East Canfield Avenue. There they continued to live, in almost complete obscurity, with Mrs. Martin looking after Harper until his death in 1867.

In his later years, Harper became more of a recluse than ever. Instead of enjoying public esteem for his endowment of the Hospital, he was seldom, if ever, recognized during the remaining years of his life for his generous act. That was of his own doing. He shunned attention, and after the first flurry of publicity attendant upon his donation, his name was rarely mentioned in the newspapers. That was simply because he refused to say or do anything noteworthy.

It is doubtful that he had many friends other than Mrs. Martin. Only one was ever mentioned. That was the Rev. Dr. Duffield in whom Harper seemed to place confidence. That Harper trusted and respected Dr. Duffield is attested by the existence of Harper Hospital. How this friendship began and how it flourished have never been explained. Perhaps Harper attended Dr. Duffield's church, although he was not a member, and Duffield once remarked that neither Harper nor Nancy Martin was a Christian in the sense of having a formal religious affiliation. The *Detroit Free Press,* in 1862 while Harper was still living, stated, "Though himself [Harper] a member of no church, he has been educated a Presbyterian." [14] The only person by the name of Harper listed in the membership book of the church was a Mrs. Janette S. Harper, who remains unidentified. She may have been the wife of one of Harper's sons.

The trustees of the Hospital, in order to honor Harper and Mrs. Martin, ordered portraits of them to be made and hung in the Hospital. Harper's shows a stern visaged old man with a crown of thick white hair. The face, although lined with age, is a strong one, with a wide, firm mouth, a rather long nose, and piercing eyes. Altogether, the portrait reflects intelligence and determination, but not much warmth.[15]

As the years passed on, Harper became feeble, and if contemporary accounts can be relied upon, he slipped into senility. In 1866, nearly a year and a half before his death, the trustees of the Hospital approved a bill of twelve dollars "for the services of a person employed to aid in the care of Walter Harper during his present feebleness." [16] Not until about a year before he died did the cause of his ill health become known. It was then discovered that he was suffering from "cancer of the face." It was too late, then, to do anything for him.* [17] He died at the home on Fremont Street, at 11:30 A.M., August 28, 1867. His age was seventy-eight years and five months.[18]

Detroit did its best to honor him. His funeral was held on August 29 from the First Presbyterian Church with Dr. Duffield preaching the funeral sermon. The Hospital trustees attended in a body to pay their respects. He was buried in Elmwood Cemetery, the last resting place of so many distinguished Detroiters. A large stone, provided by the trustees, was set upon his grave. At its meeting the day after the funeral, August 30, the board recorded the following on the pages of the minute book:

> As a matter of historical interest, it is here recorded, at the request of the trustees, that Walter Harper died in this city on the 28th of August 1867 and was buried from the 1st Presbyterian Church of Detroit on the 29th of August 1867; his remains were interred in Elmwood Cemetery and a monument is there erected to his memory—his birth being inscribed thereon as having occurred in Londonderry, Ireland in the year 1794.[19]

So little was he known that there could be no agreement even as to the year of his birth! The newspapers dutifully carried accounts of his death, reporting such scant details of his life as were known. But it remained for Detroit's historian, Silas Farmer, to sum up the salient fact of Harper's life better than anyone else has said it. "Walter Harper," wrote Farmer, "did not hold to his wealth as long as life lasted, but became his own executor, and lived to see his gift of a hospital in active operation." [20]

It is curious that when Walter Harper executed his deed of trust on February 3, 1859, he made no mention of his children or other heirs. This struck Duffield as curious, too, and he asked Harper about it. Noted Duffield later:

Supposed that he wished to make a will at that time—asked him how many children he had and in what manner he wished to divide to them his property—

He was silent for some time and then stated he had done for them all he ever would do—that they did not deserve anything at his hands in consequence of their unkindly treatment and that he wished to appropriate his property to some charitable or public use.[21]

There is no hint of what brought about Harper's disenchantment with his children. The only thing certain is that the break was complete and final.

At the time the trust was established, at least four of Harper's seven children were living—three sons in or near Detroit, and a daughter, Margaret. At least two of these, James and Margaret, survived him. Another daughter, Elizabeth, had moved to Windsor, Canada, where she married James Shipley, a tailor, but whether she still was living at the time of Harper's death cannot be determined. Two sons, Hugh and Charles, enlisted in the Fifth Michigan Volunteer Cavalry during the Civil War, and both were reputed to have died in action. Charles, at the time of his enlistment, lived in or near Fenton, Michigan. He joined up March 3, 1862. His age at the time was given as thirty-six years. He died May 17, 1862, of wounds received May 5 during McClellan's Peninsular Campaign near Williamsburg, Virginia.[22] Of Hugh's fate, nothing definite is known. The regimental records do not list a Hugh Harper, although he may have been carried on the rolls under a different name, perhaps a middle name. He may also have been in a different regiment. Many men by the name of Harper saw service with Michigan units.

Nothing more was heard from or about Harper's children until several years after the end of the Civil War. Then, on January 4, 1876, eight and a half years after Harper's death, A. C. McGraw called a special emergency meeting of the trustees in his office and laid before them a communication, the implications of which caused at least mild consternation.[23] A letter addressed to Postmaster Kaple at Detroit, said McGraw, had been handed to Buckminster Wight who had turned it over to McGraw. It had been written by a George Griffith, of Preston, Iowa, on behalf of Mrs. Margaret Latham, seeking information about Walter Harper. Mrs. Latham claimed to be Harper's daughter. Mrs. Latham, said Griffith, was old and destitute. She had heard, he added, that her father possessed considerable property. She was interested in determining whether she might not be entitled to share in his estate, and the trustees immediately had visions of a lawsuit to test the validity of the trust.

McGraw told the board that he had sent Griffith a cautious reply, "propounding certain questions for him to put to Mrs. Latham which would establish the fact as to whether she was really the daughter of the late Walter Harper as she claimed to be." [24] McGraw had received a reply from Griffith which left little doubt about the authenticity of Mrs. Latham's identity:

> Your letter came to hand about two weeks ago and I now endeavor to answer it. Mrs. Margaret Latham was born in Philadelphia October 4, 1813. She lived in Philadelphia until she was about 18 years of age, her father then moved to Detroit and lived there a short time and then moved about seven miles on what was then called the Pontiac Road and lived there awhile and then moved about 40 miles from Pontiac and staid there sometime, cannot remember the length of time, and then moved back to Philadelphia. He was no farmer, was usually employed in the mercantile business. He then remained there several years—his daughter Margaret lived with him during all this time. He then moved back to Michigan and she remained with a friend for awhile and then she went to Canada to live with a sister who was married and living there. Her sister dying sometime after that she returned to Michigan and was there married to Stanton A. Latham and moved to Iowa in 1855 and has lived there ever since—her husband left her about the time the Rebellion first began and she has never seen him since and she does not know whether he is dead or alive. She saw her father in Detroit last awhile before she was married. She has no children and never had. There was six children by Walter Harper's first wife, 3 girls and 3 boys, and one by his second wife, a boy. They are all dead except one brother and she has not heard from him for so long that she feels quite sure that he is dead. [25]

Mulling over this request for aid, the trustees felt a sense of responsibility which Walter Harper had never felt. Although they were quite convinced of the legality of the trust, they wished to avoid any troublesome litigation. Accordingly, they did what they considered the right and handsome thing. They wrote Mrs. Latham, through Griffith who may have been either an attorney or her pastor, offering her free board and housing in the Hospital for as long as she lived if she would return to Detroit. [26] That offer did not appeal to Mrs. Latham. Preston had been her home for a long time and, understandably, she did not want to leave and start a new life at her age among strangers. From the time her husband left her, she had been employed as a domestic servant. Apparently, she was well liked by her neighbors, and was affectionately known as "Auntie Latham." Having grown old, she was being cared for in the home of Charles Wager, by whom she had been employed.[27]

In turning down the Hospital offer, she made a counterproposal. She asked the Board of Trustees to grant her a modest allowance which would be enough to assure her care and provide for her needs among her friends. The matter dragged on for some time, until on June 12, 1877, the trustees voted to give Mrs. Latham "a small annuity" of $100, retroactive to May 1, 1877, and to be paid quarterly in advance.[28] This seems to have been satisfactory to Margaret Latham who received her pension regularly thereafter. She did not live to enjoy it for long, however. Early in January, 1879, Mr. Wager wrote, notifying the trustees of Mrs. Latham's death on December 31, 1878. Up to that time, she had received a total of $200.[29]

As a final magnanimous gesture, made at the suggestion of Mr. Wager, of Preston, the trustees appropriated twenty-five dollars for a tombstone to be erected over Mrs. Latham's grave. Carved on it was: "Sacred to the memory of Mrs. Margaret Harper Latham, dau. of the late Walter Harper, founder of Harper Hospital, Detroit Michigan." [30] The stone still marks the only known grave of any of Walter Harper's children. It remains a matter of considerable curiosity in Miles, a village near Preston, whose citizens derive a vicarious pride in their community's association with the great hospital in Detroit.[31]

A couple of years before the trustees heard about Margaret Harper Latham and granted her a pension, they had another scare. Rumors circulated that an attempt might be made to challenge Walter Harper's trust and have it set aside. The board was alerted by a news story which appeared in the *Detroit Free Press* about 1874.[32] It was learned, said the paper, that the heirs of Harper planned to contest his "will" because of action taken by the trustees to sell or rent a portion of the property on Woodward Avenue, "claiming thereby a violation of the terms of the behest [*sic*]." This, of course, was weak ground upon which to sue, because it was based upon several misconceptions. In the first place, Harper's deed specifically empowered the trustees with the right to "keep, manage, preserve, sell, mortgage or exchange" the real estate.[33] In the second place, the property then being offered for sale, the five-acre Woodward Avenue lot upon which the Hospital stood, had belonged to Nancy Martin and not Walter Harper. It was covered by her deed.

"Walter Harper," the *Free Press* continued, further garbling the facts, "had two children—a son who died without issue, and a daughter Elizabeth, who married George Shipley, for many years a merchant tailor in Windsor." It was unquestionably Elizabeth Shipley with whom Margaret Latham lived while she was in Canada. The paper went on:

Elizabeth Shipley gave birth to two children—George and Elizabeth, and in her father's will she was cut off without even the traditional shilling. Elizabeth Shipley, the daughter, married James McKenna, an engineer on the Great Western Railway, and resides in Hamilton [Ontario]. George Shipley, the son, recently died, leaving several heirs, two of his sons being in business on Sandwich Street, in Windsor, while a daughter is the wife of Laing, the grocer.

It was from these Windsor heirs that the *Free Press* reporter got wind of plans to contest the deed. Mrs. McKenna, he learned, had been in Windsor conferring with her nephews and niece, and together they had consulted a "prominent," but unnamed Detroit law firm. Apparently, the heirs themselves were not too sure of their ground. "They do not propose to invest any money on the suit unless necessary," the *Free Press* stated, "and thus present negotiations are directed toward retaining some reliable attorney who will conduct the case for a percentage of the property recovered."

There was a considerable misconception on the part of Mrs. McKenna and Harper's great-grandchildren about the value of the property covered by his trust. "They do not agree as to the present value of the estate, plus the income derived therefrom the past twenty years, but variously estimate it at from $2,000,000 to $3,000,000," the newspaper article pointed out. The trustees would have been only too happy if this guess had been even approximately correct.

As to the evidence upon which the heirs rely to substantiate their claim, they are quite reticent, but state that they have discovered an old French domestic who was in Walter Harper's employ at the time his will was made, and will swear that he was not in his right mind and had not been for some time. Also, a male witness who about that time saw Mr. Harper playing marbles with street boys, and wrangling and quarreling in true "knuckle down" schoolboy style.

The *Free Press* concluded:

Inasmuch as this litigation, if successful, would remove from Detroit one of its great beneficent institutions, the outcome of this movement will be attended with great interest.

Jacob S. Farrand was interviewed, as the spokesman for the Board of Trustees, and he disclaimed knowledge of any intention to test the trust, or even of any rumor of intent. For the reporter's benefit, he was inclined to wave it all off as a matter of no consequence or concern. But he was concerned, and so were the other trustees. Robert W. King, who was secretary of the board in 1874, sought out Divie B. Duffield, who had relinquished his secretarial post some years earlier, and obtained an affidavit from him concerning Walter Harper's condition at the time he deeded over his property to the Hospital.

"He was to all appearances as sound and sane as I ever saw or knew him to be," Duffield stated. "I have no doubt that he acted deliberately in this matter since it was in July or August [1858] he first spoke of this matter and at his own instance I called on him at his home with Father at that time at his own request." [34]

Duffield repeated his earlier statement: that he read the deed and explained it thoroughly to Harper who stated that it contained nothing that he desired to alter, and that it expressed his wishes completely. Harper further acknowledged, in the presence of witnesses, Duffield stated, that he acknowledged the deed to be his free act, and with all his heart was willing to place his property in the hands of the trustees.

Beyond that little flurry of excitement, resulting from the *Free Press* article and the Duffield statement, nothing further seems to have transpired. No suit was brought. Probably no Detroit attorney was willing to go to court on a "speculative" basis to attempt to win a chimerical twenty per cent of the proceeds if the case should turn out successfully for the heirs. Duffield's reputation as a lawyer who could draft an iron-clad document was so great that the gamble was hardly worth the effort. Nevertheless, the fear that someone would try to break the trust lurked in the back of the minds of the trustees. That, as well as humanitarian impulse, undoubtedly explains the alacrity with which Margaret Harper Latham's plea was answered.

Chapter 3

THE MARKET WOMAN

If Walter Harper
were a shrinking violet, Nancy Martin, co-benefactor of the Hospital,
most certainly was not. Her fellow citizens spoke of her in many ways,
but the terms *recluse* or *retiring,* or similar labels such as were applied
to Harper, were never used where she was concerned.

In many respects she was the very antithesis of the man with whom
she was so long and so closely associated. Her character and temperament might be regarded as the perfect complement to Harper's reticence
and lack of color, for she was ebullient, noisy, and quarrelsome. No one
ever accused Nancy of hiding her light under a bushel. "Few people
have lived any great length of time in the city of Detroit who have not
heard of Nancy Martin," said a Detroit newspaper.[1] Another paper,
on another occasion, put it more pointedly when it referred to her as a
"character."[2] She was an odd mixture of vigorous coarseness and big-
heartedness.

Her life began in the sordid surroundings of a Philadelphia slum.
She was born on June 25, 1799 of poor Irish parents in a run-down
part of the city near the waterfront, known as Bird's Alley. That
blighted place has since disappeared and even passed from local remembrance; Philadelphia directories and maps a few years later make
no mention of it. But if others forgot, Nancy did not. She carried the
mark of Bird's Alley as long as she lived. She never quite outgrew
being the child of the slums.

Her full name was Anna McCloud Powers.[3] That has the Irish
lilt to it, and it may be that she was born a Catholic. Her name, her par-
entage, and her birthplace combine to give weight to that presumption.

It is strengthened by the fact that in the moment of greatest need in her life, she turned for help to a Catholic institution.

What happened to her father is not known. Her mother ran a boarding house for sailors. It was not the best environment for a young girl, and it is not surprising that at the age of thirteen, she married a sailor, Charles Strickland.[4] The union was said to have been a happy one, lasting eleven years, although for much of that time, Strickland was away at sea. In 1824, while serving aboard a merchantman owned by one Benjamin Jones, a Quaker merchant from Philadelphia, Strickland was involved in a brawl with a drunken sailor and was murdered. His death supposedly occurred while the ship was in port as the murderer was described as a "pilot." [5] As far as can be determined, Strickland was a decent, likeable fellow. His death was a tragedy for Anna (or Ann—or Nancy, as she was later known), but the young woman did not permit it to put a blight on her spirit.

In 1827, she married again, this time James Martin, a friend of her first husband. Martin, also a sailor, shipped out three days after the wedding on a long voyage, not realizing that Nancy was pregnant. His ship was reported seven months later, and then never heard from again. Martin's unwritten epitaph, like that of so many seafarers, was "lost at sea." [6] The child, a girl, was born two months later, and Nancy named her Ellen. To support the baby daughter, she found employment in Philadelphia as a servant girl—an occupation which engaged her during the time when Strickland was away at sea. Sometime during those years, either before or after Ellen Martin's birth, Nancy worked in the households of Walter Harper, John Hare Powell, "and other prominent citizens." [7] That may have been after Harper returned from Detroit, following his unsuccessful attempt to establish himself there in 1831.

When the child was four years old, Nancy experienced a tragedy which was to affect her for the rest of her life. There are two versions of what happened. The first is that Nancy, being employed and unable to look after Ellen, placed the youngster in a Philadelphia convent where she was mistreated by a nun in such a manner as to cause her death. The other version has it that Ellen was stricken with a virulent disease, and Nancy carried her to a Catholic institution, only to be turned away by a nun. The result was the same. The child died. Whichever account is correct, Nancy Martin was overcome with grief, almost to the point of going out of her mind. She blamed the nun for the child's death, and in her irrational sorrow, built up a specter of cruelties inflicted on the little girl. Nancy swore vengeance. It is said she filed a complaint with the authorities, putting the responsibility for Ellen's death directly upon the sister. The nun was arrested; whether the complaint was dismissed, or whether the sentence, if there was one, was too light to satisfy Nancy's sense of justice, is not known. At any rate, Nancy vowed revenge if it took her entire life to achieve it, and she was heard threatening to take matters into her own hands, even to kill the offending nun.[8] One thing is certain. If Nancy was born a Catholic, she ceased to be one after her daughter's death. She is said to have "always cherished a strong antipathy toward all Catholics, and she took frequent occasions to denounce them." [9] Her disenchantment ultimately influenced her to endow a Protestant hospital.

Nancy's mother, who took these threats seriously, became worried about her daughter's frame of mind, and about the consequences if Nancy ever got the opportunity to carry out an act of violence. Mrs. Powers appealed to Harper for help. He was preparing to return to Detroit and he provided the solution. He offered to take Nancy Martin with him as a servant, which would prevent her endangering herself or others. There is an element of confusion in this history of Nancy Martin's despair. Ellen must have died around 1831, when Harper first went to Detroit. It would have been logical for Nancy to have accompanied him at that time. George B. Catlin, citing no authority, says "this strange couple" did go to Detroit together in 1831. But proof is lacking. Other versions offer 1837 as the correct date for her first appearance in the city in which she was to make her home. Margaret Harper Latham said nothing about Nancy accompanying the family West. It is possible, of course, that Harper sent her on ahead a year or two before he returned in 1837. On this entire question, Nancy, who supposedly "related the story of her life to a gentleman of this city," was completely silent.

But as a memento of her love for her child, and as a mark of her sentimentality, she brought with her from Philadelphia her baby's high chair, and kept it in her home as long as she lived. After her death, it was preserved in Harper Hospital—a memorial to the woman who helped create the institution.[10] Also, remembrance of the child is said to account for the stipulation in her deed that the Hospital, when established, should have a lying-in department.

Nancy Martin was an enterprising woman. Although she had been a servant girl in Philadelphia, and went to Detroit with Walter Harper in the same capacity, she soon ceased to rely upon him either for employment or support. Before long, she was peddling garden produce from door to door, working up a steady clientele. With her savings she purchased the lot on Woodward Avenue which she later gave to the Hospital. There she built a small house and cultivated a garden. Within a short time, she graduated from peddling vegetables and notions from door to door, to going into business as "a green grocer." In 1839, she occupied at least part of a shack at the northwest corner of Griswold and Larned Streets.[11] Her place of business was adjacent to the Old Washington Market at Larned and Wayne Streets. According to Silas Farmer, this market, opened in 1836, was never popular, and lasted only a half-dozen years. Eventually, the site was turned over to the Fire Department which occupied it continuously thereafter. It currently houses the headquarters and main offices of the Detroit Board of Fire Commissioners.[12]

In 1843, a new and more conveniently located public market was built in Cadillac Square. This was a rather elaborate building, the ground floor being divided into stalls, the upper floors being occupied as the city hall and municipal courts.[13] There, Nancy Martin became proprietor of a stall where she sold garden vegetables and poultry. Because this was the center of commercial as well as political activity, Nancy had the opportunity to know and be known by virtually everybody in Detroit. That she and her business became civic institutions is shown by the fact that until 1865 both her residence address and her business address were regularly listed in the city directories. Listed as "huckster" or "market grocer," living on "Woodward Avenue near Brady," or "near Toll Gate," her stall was given as "5CH Market" (City Hall Market). Not until she was established in the house built for her and Harper on Fremont Street, by which time she apparently had retired, did the directory cease to give her occupation. Then, she was listed simply as "Mrs. Nancy Martin, widow."

That she was a good businesswoman is unquestioned. She prospered and saved her money. Not only did she own, unencumbered, the Woodward Avenue lot, but she also purchased the additional fifteen acres farther out on the Pontiac Road, which became part of the Hospital's original endowment. She also is known to have speculated in other real estate. Nancy cultivated her clientele as carefully as she did her garden. She specialized in choice items, such as fancy game. One writer pictures her displaying "quail, partridge, woodcock, ducks and venison to these epicurean loafers—for though Detroit was a frontier village, it had people who knew how to live well and insisted on doing it." [14]

The "loafers" were the people who congregated around the market, and found particular enjoyment in haggling with Nancy, or baiting her with practical jokes. The attraction was Nancy's reaction. She had a sharp and salty tongue, and with her colorful—and not always polite— language she could hold her own with anyone. Her coarseness is often referred to. "The idlers of the town and rough element," said George Catlin, "tended also to hang about the market and discovering that Nancy Martin had a keen wit, a bitter tongue and a Rabelaisan vocabulary took . . . delight in stirring up her powers of repartee and she seemed to enjoy the Billingsgate exchanges as much as her would-be tormentors." [15] A newspaper account referred to her as possessing "a jovial nature, always ready to crack a joke upon any subject." She was remembered for having at her command "a large vocabulary of plain Saxon words, more expressive than elegant." [16]

While she prided herself on her honesty and honorable dealings with everyone, she could be a terror to rival dealers, or to anyone who angered her or gave her real or supposed offense. She had, one might surmise, few inhibitions. One of her habits was to greet the quality folks and distinguished patrons of her stall "with the utmost familiarity —a resounding slap on the back, and an inquiry as to the state of their mind and body." [17] Such characteristics caused her long to be remembered as "a local landmark." [18]

Her appearance, if her picture is any criterion, was formidable. She is shown wearing a Quaker-type bonnet, apron, and sort of pinafore —and a very grim and foreboding expression. This picture, the only one of her that is known and which was ordered by the Hospital trustees, shows her in the late period of her life. The artist made no effort to flatter her by adding touches of feminine charm or beauty. On the contrary, he showed a firm, set jaw and a lack of teeth which gave her a pugnacious look.

Nancy Martin, alas, was not always a model of lady-like propriety. She was addicted, on occasion, to strong spirits which, sometimes taken in too copious quantities, led her into error—and the lockup.[19] The old police court records show she was occasionally arrested for being drunk and disorderly, and she even served a term or two in the Detroit House of Correction for these offenses. The *Detroit Free Press* on May 14, 1859, only a short time after she had given her property to the Hospital, carried a report which was headed "Police Court: An Old Vagrant," and said:

Ann Martin, as on innumerable previous occasions, having just been released from bondage, paid her respects to her old friend, the corner grocer, and tried his stock of red eye. Having refrained from indulgence in this beverage, her palate was not so quick to distinguish the quality, thereby occasioning the imbibition of a large quantity before she was able to decide whether it was equal to what she was accustomed in former days to procure at the establishment. The result of this large consumption of course soon manifested itself in a loosening of the tongue and an inclination to be quarrelsome. She was interrupted in the midst of a profuse string of quite hard words, which were being aimed at the community generally and the grocer in particular, by the entrance of a police officer, who marched her off to her old quarters. She got another term of 90 days.[20]

Yet, there was another side to the picture—a much more attractive one. As recently as 1934, Mrs. Elizabeth Anne Ash McFadden wrote her childhood recollections of Nancy who, she said, was a frequent caller at the home of her parents who lived on upper Griswold Street. Mrs. McFadden, about eight or nine years old at the time, remembered Nancy's Sunday afternoon calls. She mentioned a "forceful and distinctive personality" and described the visitor's "flashing and penetrating black eyes, the smooth dark hair and beautiful pink cheeks." [21] Mrs. McFadden also described Nancy's appearance at the market:

. . . spotless in fresh gingham apron of huge proportions, brown and white checked material, always with sunbonnet to match. She wore big, comfortable shoes on the market which contrasted strongly with the elegant footgear which she invariably wore on Sundays. I always noticed her pretty Sunday shoes and her elegant dress of black velvet with fine lace neck ruching . . . I never saw her wear anything but black when she came for an afternoon visit.

Nancy, according to Mrs. McFadden's recollection, frequently attended the First Presbyterian Church. Like Walter Harper, however, she was not a member. Her charities were not limited to her big gift to the Hospital; her small ones were frequently mentioned, too. Apparently, she was as big-hearted as she was at times obstreperous. "She was," said one account of her, "a woman of generous and benevolent qualities, and ever ready to render assistance to persons in want or distress." [22]

She must have been patriotic as well as public-spirited. When the Civil War broke out and John Owen, the Michigan state treasurer, was desperately trying to raise money to equip the first troops, Nancy unobtrusively gave him two hundred dollars with an injunction to say nothing about it. She could not keep her money lying by when her country needed it, she told him.[23] She proved her patriotism again at the end of the Civil War. Having given the bulk of her property to the Hospital, she made a will dated February 12, 1864 in which she named Divie Bethune Duffield her executor. He was instructed to apply the remainder of her estate "toward the expense of constructing the Hospital building to be erected thereon." However, buildings were put up by the government soon after she made that provision, so she added a codicil on May 8, 1865, leaving her estate "for the benefit of the Orphan Children of the Soldiers of Wayne County, Michigan, as they may be found in needy circumstances and condition." This will and codicil were admitted to probate April 29, 1875. Unfortunately, no appraisal accompanies the will, so it is not known of what her estate consisted, or to what extent the orphans of Civil War soldiers benefited. All that it revealed was her love of country, her charitable impulses, and, above all, her true concern for the well-being of unfortunate children. Both will and codicil were signed   X , indicating her inability to write, even her own name.[24]

The exact relationship between Walter Harper and Nancy Martin has long stirred speculation. A medical history of Michigan refers to Harper Hospital's beginnings as having "a surprising tinge of eccentric romance." [25] But weighing all the known facts, one concludes that, while their association may have been one of mutual convenience, there was very little romance involved. What facts that can be uncovered are few and so inconclusive that it becomes extremely difficult to fan the fires of scandal.

Nancy Martin's first association with Harper, in Philadelphia, was definitely as a servant in the household of a respectable family of middle-class status. Having come to Detroit, they certainly did live together. Nancy herself is said to have stated that she had lived with Harper "since she came to Detroit," [26] but she did not elaborate. Her statement was made when she was an old woman, and it is highly probable that she was referring, in a general way, to having been a member of his household. A search of early city directories fails to reveal any evidence that they lived together prior to 1857. Before that time, Harper's name seldom appears. Nancy, the better known, was regularly listed. In 1857, and subsequently, Harper is shown as a "boarder" with Nancy, suggesting that, as he grew older, she cared for him. At that time, Harper was approaching seventy years of age.

Catlin refers to them as a "strange couple"; [27] a Harper Hospital report, reviewing the institution's first fifty years, tells of Nancy's friendship with the students of the Detroit Medical College who "would not care what kind of reputation she had." [28] Detroit, it should be remembered, was a relatively small place when Harper was a resident. Everyone knew something about his neighbors, and scandal could not have been hushed up. Neither would an open flaunting of the strict Victorian mores of the time have been overlooked by the gossips. Yet, no word was written and preserved to indicate that, in the eyes of the townspeople, there was anything irregular about their relationship. Had the tongues wagged, certainly someone would have taken note of it.

It has been suggested that each of them donated his property to the Hospital in order to soothe his conscience, that they were persuaded to do this by the Rev. Dr. Duffield. But he was too good a theologian to believe, or try to convince anyone else, that a sinner could purchase his way into Heaven. Duffield was their friend; it is not very likely that he would have been had he thought they were violating the stern moral laws of the day. Neither would Nancy, with or without her Sunday finery, have been welcomed into respectable homes if she was believed to have been, in the euphemism of the day, a Scarlet Woman. That phase of their lives, then, may be charitably forgotten, and their relationship accepted for what it almost certainly was—master and maid, and in the later years of Harper's life, aged patient and nurse, or ward and guardian.

Both Harper and Nancy lived to see the Hospital which they endowed become reality, and in their old age their lives were closely tied to it. After Harper's death in 1867, the cottage on Fremont Street became too lonely for the old woman to occupy and keep up by herself. On September 7, a few days after Harper's funeral, she moved into the Hospital where she was given a comfortable room and where she could be looked after.[29] Apparently, the years remaining to her were as happy as any she had ever known. She felt a sense of proprietorship in the Hospital which, at times, was embarrassing to the administrators. She had an inclination to give orders, to interfere in matters which were none of her concern. Yet, she had to be handled patiently and diplomatically.

It is related that she used to sit in the corridor in front of her door, engaging in loud and salty conversation with anyone who had time or inclination to stop and chat with her. She missed, it was said, "the companionship, the badinage and the bartering of the old market place, and was very lonely." When she could corner a listener, she would be apt to tell the story of her life in great detail, stressing all the hard luck she had experienced. She dwelt more and more upon the loss of her long-dead child, and the baby's high chair, which she had taken with her to Detroit, was a prominent fixture in her hospital apartment.[30]

During the later period of the Civil War, when sick and wounded federal soldiers were sent back to Detroit for treatment or convalescence in the Hospital, Nancy adopted them, and stories were often told how she spent most of her annuity purchasing small gifts and comforts for them.[31] The medical students were her particular favorites. They always had an impertinent word for the old woman, and she enjoyed it. They teased her, mostly to get her picturesque language flowing. One writer suggests that "the combination of anatomical jokes of the boys and Nancy's uninhibited replies must have been something to hear." [32]

As time went on, unfortunately, Nancy's intellect began to fail and she became somewhat childish.[33] She became even more of a problem to the Hospital authorities and trustees. On April 2, 1872, the board devoted a good part of its meeting to the subject of Nancy and what to do about her, and later that year it became necessary to appoint a guardian for her. That assignment went to Dr. George A. Foster, the house physician. Mrs. L. A. Sanborn and Mrs. D. M. Freeman were matrons who looked after her, and they had their hands full.[34]

But Nancy did not give up easily. She continued to be her lusty self, right to the end. On February 9, 1875, apparently in good health, she ate what was described as a hearty dinner. Shortly afterward, she suffered a stroke, and at two o'clock in the afternoon she died. "Apoplexy" was the medical diagnosis.[35]

In death, Nancy received all the honor that a grateful community could bestow upon her. Lengthy obituaries appeared in the Detroit and even the outstate newspapers. The casket containing her body was placed in the Hospital's reception room, and there, on February 11, the funeral service was held. The room was full to capacity, and the mourners included "the young woman who had been her nurse and constant companion for two or three years past. She had loved her eccentric charge. . . ."[36]

The Rev. George Baker, who had succeeded Dr. Duffield as pastor of the First Presbyterian Church, officiated, aided by the Rev. Dr. Aikman who read from the Scriptures. In his eulogy of Nancy, Mr. Baker did not entirely gloss over what he felt to have been irregularities in her life. Rather, he said, it was Divine Purpose that brought her to Detroit and gave her a successful business. "Although devoid of culture," he declared, "she had a very decided character that with proper cultivation would have made her in any sphere a remarkable, a noted woman."[37] A funeral procession accompanied her on the last journey to Elmwood Cemetery. The pallbearers were Jacob S. Farrand, Dr. George B. Russel, A. C. McGraw, R. W. King, Divie Bethune Duffield, and Frederick Buhl. Few Detroiters of much higher station could claim so distinguished a group of mourners.

Detroit never forgot Nancy Martin or ceased to honor her. Her portrait for years hung in the Hospital beside Harper's. The lying-in or maternity wing of the Hospital was named for her. When a street was opened from Woodward Avenue leading to the present Hospital, it was named Martin Place. Her likeness appeared along with other distinguished persons in a mural in Detroit's beautiful public library. In 1941, she was remembered by the planting of a tree, dedicated to her memory, in the Pioneer Memorial Walk on the library's spacious grounds. "It seems," it was said of her, "that she wisely concluded to see in her own day, the fruits of a charity which would not otherwise have matured until after her death."[38] And another obituary held her up as an example to other and more favorably circumstanced Detroiters, chiding them for not making philanthropic use of their wealth as Nancy Martin had done.[39]

Chapter 4

"FOR THE WIDER WELFARE"

Had the Harper Hospital
Board of Trustees been able to hold the lands originally deeded to them
by Walter Harper and Nancy Martin, the institution might today easily
be one of the wealthiest in the United States. Unfortunately, that was
not possible. The property involved was that which most benefited by
Detroit's expansion. Today, this land is high-priced real estate.

The history of the property, or that portion of it which since
the time of the bequest was incorporated within the boundaries of
Detroit, may have as a convenient starting point June 11, 1805, when
a fire all but obliterated the original town. Prior to that calamity, Detroit
was a small place of narrow streets and crowded timber houses, many
of them dating back to the city's French era. Enclosed by a stockade, the
half-fortified village was squeezed into a space between the Detroit
River and what is now Congress Street, bounded by Cass Avenue on the
west and Brush Street on the east. No one knows quite how the fire
started. Some say it began in the hayloft of a baker's barn. But whatever the cause, the flames, driven by a brisk breeze, ate through the old
wooden buildings, and in a matter of a couple of hours, Detroit was
reduced to a smoldering heap of ashes. Not a dwelling house inside the
stockade remained. The people scattered to find shelter with friends or
relatives in the farmhouses on both the American and Canadian shores
of the Detroit River. Others, having no place to go, put up tents or
erected "bowers" on the public common.[1]

The situation called for immediate remedy. A few days after the fire,
on July 1, a new governing board for Michigan Territory began to
function. The Governor and Judges, for so they were known, had

broad powers. They were empowered to constitute themselves into a land board with extensive jurisdiction over land titles. The Governor and Judges were faced immediately with rebuilding the city. They determined, however, that with hundreds of thousands of acres of virgin land at their disposal, the old errors of town planning would not be repeated. The city would be spread out, and everyone would be given breathing room. After some delay and much controversy, a new Detroit was laid out, with wide streets radiating from parks and "circuses." Each resident, whether or not a property owner at the time of the fire, was given a new lot, the location being decided by drawing numbers. This new city, primarily the concept of Augustus Brevoort Woodward, Chief Justice of the new Michigan Territory and a member of the land board, lay between the Cass and Brush farms, and extended north to Adams Avenue.[2]

A new city under a new regime required public improvements— starting with a courthouse and a jail. To provide these facilities, the Governor and Judges persuaded Congress to make a public land grant of 10,000 acres. This would be divided into farm lots of various sizes and sold to settlers at nominal cost, and the proceeds would finance construction of necessary public buildings. The 10,000 acres, which became known as the Ten Thousand Acre Tract, were located north of the newly planned city. It was in the shape of a huge T. The shank was a narrow strip on each side of what is now Woodward Avenue, but what was then known as the Pontiac Road. The east and west boundaries of this strip were approximately Cass Avenue and Brush Street. It extended north to about the point where the railroad crosses Woodward Avenue, two and one-half miles north of Adams Avenue. Above this strip, forming the top of the T, was the much greater part of the Ten Thousand Acre Tract. This occupied a good part of what later became Greenfield Township and today includes roughly almost all of that part of Detroit from Grand Boulevard to Eight Mile Road and from Brush Street west to the city limits.

On December 14, 1808, the land board met and entered the following upon its official records:

Ordered, that Mr. McCroskey [James McCloskey, as his name should have been spelled, was the public surveyor] be requested to survey the lands granted by Congress to this Territory, for the purpose of building a jail and court house, and that he commence his survey northwest of the street which runs thro' the Grand Circus [Adams Avenue] parallel with the main street [Jefferson Avenue]; that he shall there begin with lots of five acres, and increase the size of the lots as he proceeds . . .[3]

Colonel McCloskey went to work immediately, and by early spring of 1809, he had completed work on the shank of the T, dividing the strip into lots of approximately five acres, each with a frontage on Woodward, or the Pontiac Road, of about 160 feet. These became known as the Park lots; thereafter only the remaining larger area to the north was popularly known as the Ten Thousand Acre Tract. The survey of this latter area was not completed until 1816, partly because it was so far out in Indian-infested country that no one wanted it, and partly because the intervening War of 1812 made the work impossible as well as unnecessary.

On March 6, 1809, the Park lots were put up for sale at public auction and found ready buyers. They sold, generally, from $50.00 to $70.00 apiece, or approximately $10.00 to $12.00 per acre.[4] While most public land could then, and for a long time thereafter, be had for as little as $1.25 per acre, some idea can be gained from the prices paid of the early citizens' optimism about their city's future; they saw the Park lots as the natural direction future growth and expansion would take. The city officials, quickly recognizing north Woodward Avenue as an area for growth, in 1815 extended the city limits from Adams to what is now Alexandrine, taking in the future site of Harper Hospital. In 1824, still full of enthusiasm about the town's growth, the northern boundary was again advanced, this time to Piquette Avenue, leaving a small strip between the northern city limits and the southern edge of the Ten Thousand Acre Tract.[5]

About halfway up the stem of the T, on the right-hand or east side of Woodward Avenue, surveyor McCloskey designated one of the Park lots as Number 24. At the public auction, it and that adjoining it to the north were bid for by Benjamin Woodworth, the proprietor of the Steamboat Hotel, Detroit's most famous early hostelry.[6] "Uncle Ben," as he was familiarly known, had lived in Detroit since 1806, and had built his tavern at Randolph and Woodbridge Streets, close to the Detroit River. This was a choice location inasmuch as virtually all travelers arrived by boat, and Woodworth's was most convenient to the wharves. Besides being the brother of Samuel Woodworth, who wrote "The Old Oaken Bucket," Uncle Ben had several claims to fame, including springing the trap at the last legal public execution in Michigan. Like most men of substance of his period, he collected land like a modern philatelist collects rare stamps. A firm belief in Detroit's future undoubtedly prompted him to purchase Park lots Numbers 24 and 25. The terms were easy. He paid twenty-five per cent down, another twenty-five per cent in six months, and the remaining fifty per cent within a year.[7] As a speculative venture, it didn't make Woodworth rich. As late as 1817, the upper Park lots were valued at only fifteen dollars per acre, only five dollars more than Woodworth paid.[8]

By 1823, all of the Park lots had been sold, and many of them had changed owners several times. Lot Number 24 was ultimately acquired by Thomas Palmer, and in due time title passed to another early Detroiter and his wife, Thomas and Catherine Rowland. It was from them that Nancy Martin bought it, apparently by pieces, because there are three transactions listed: April 19, 1844; May 9, 1844; and January 30, 1845.[9] By the last date, Nancy owned all five acres, and it was there she built her first home and cultivated her vegetable patch. This site was usually referred to in the Harper records as the Grove lot, so called because of the stand of beautiful trees at its eastern end.[10] It was there that Harper Hospital was first located.

Prompted by pure speculation, Nancy also purchased, at a later time, an additional fifteen acres in the large part of the Ten Thousand Acre Tract from a Samuel Barrett. This, too, was located on the Pontiac Road, a couple of miles north of her Park lot. The site now includes the land at Leicester Court between Woodward and Oakland Avenues. It is not known how much she paid for it, but in all likelihood it was not much. In those days there was little demand for farm lots—that's what her acreage was—so far from town, and so inaccessible.

Nancy must have been stricken by the land fever. She was perpetually on the alert for a good real estate bargain. This had its troublesome aspects. Several years after she had given her property to the Hospital, and was comfortably established in the cottage on Fremont Street which the trustees provided her, it was discovered that she was purchasing another lot comprising ten acres. This land which she bought from J. Mott Williams also fronted on Woodward at Medbury Avenue. It was impossible for her to meet her obligations out of her $600 pension. As a result, and much to their annoyance, the trustees in 1864 had to take over the land contract or mortgage. As yet, the endowment was not producing enough income to meet the payments, so the trustees, in some cases, had to pay for the land, which they certainly did not want, out of their own pockets. McGraw and Farrand each put up some of the money; apparently McGraw, in time, took title to part of it. Ultimately, it was sold at considerable profit. Nancy gave her deed for her interest to the trustees on the same terms that applied in her original trust agreement.[11] She also owned and deeded to the Hospital two-and-one-half acres on Woodward Avenue between today's E. Canfield and Willis Avenues. This was the site for the house which the trustees built for her and which she shared with Harper. The house originally stood on Park lot Number 24, but during the Civil War, when her five-acre lot was needed for military purposes, it was moved at the trustees' expense to Fremont (now E. Canfield) Street.

Harper's property offered fewer complications. His Oakland County land, obtained by patent from the federal government about 1831, was a few miles north of Pontiac in Orion Township, on the east side of Lapeer Road (M 24). The eighty acres which it comprised were purchased for a farm homestead. Land at that time could be bought from the government for $1.25 to $2.50 an acre, and obviously Harper's investment was not great. That he did not choose to live long on it is understandable. It was, even in 1831, far out in the country and difficult to get to. The Pontiac Road offered a challenge which few travelers cared to accept. It was quite common for settlers of the Pontiac region to load their household and farm goods on scows and float them up the Detroit River to Mount Clemens, and then up the Clinton River which was navigable as far as Pontiac. Inasmuch as there is evidence that Harper lived for at least a year on these eighty acres, he must have had some kind of dwelling on them. There is, however, no recorded description of his house or cabin.

The biggest block of Harper property was the 864 $^{44}/_{100}$ acres which he bought, again by patent, in the Ten Thousand Acre Tract. This became known as the Harper Greenfield property. It was an irregularly shaped piece, easily located within the present city of Detroit boundaries.[12] Generally, it might be described as consisting of two principal parcels. One of them was a rectangle, of two quarter-sections, bounded on the north by Puritan Avenue, on the east by Fourteenth, south by Fenkell and west by Livernois. The other, larger, parcel was made up of two fractional sections, south of Fenkell and west of Livernois. The southern limit was Schoolcraft Avenue, and the westerly line lay at Wyoming Avenue. Today, this entire area forms part of one of Detroit's most populous and developed residential districts. Its value in present-day terms would be in the hundreds of millions of dollars. The Ten Thousand Acre Tract, after being surveyed in 1816 for farm development purposes, was divided into 12 lots of 80 acres each, and 48 lots of 160 acres each. It was several years before buyers were found for all of it.[13]

Quite obviously, Walter Harper knew what he was doing when he gave his Philadelphia property to the Hospital. Although located in what was then, and still is, the central part of the city, its value was greatly lessened as far as he was concerned because it was heavily encumbered and had deteriorated into the condition of a slum. It consisted of three parcels on the northeast corner of Locust and Thirteenth Streets. Two lots fronted on Locust; the third was in the rear, facing what was described as an alley extending from Twelfth to Thirteenth Streets. Each of the lots had buildings on it: that on the corner of Locust and Thirteenth was brick; the other two, frame. The corner building, three stories high, housed a grocery store on the ground floor and, like the others, was divided into rooms or apartments up above. These were rented out to tenants. It was this building, in all probability, in which Harper operated his own store, although he did not obtain title to the ground and building until 1830. He bought the building next door in 1816, and that in the rear in 1828. He purchased the latter from "Jacob Streinbeck, high sheriff of the city and county of Philadelphia." [14] Within a few short blocks of the Harper property were, or are, such landmarks as the Jefferson Medical College, the Pennsylvania Hospital, the old Walnut Theater, and, not far away, Independence Hall. Today, the area is rather on the seedy side, and a somewhat garish night club, of which there are a number in the neighborhood, occupies the Harper site.

The Philadelphia property was an unknown quantity to the trustees when they took it over, and one of their first acts, on February 7, 1859, was to send Divie Bethune Duffield to Philadelphia:

. . . with a view of examining into the business and affairs of the trust in that City, and ascertaining the condition and value of the property there situated, and the possibility of effecting a sale thereof, and that he be furnished with all necessary evidence of authority to carry out the object of this resolution.[15]

Duffield made the trip to Philadelphia and reported back to the trustees on March 7. His story was a melancholy one, and whatever hopes the board had of building up an endowment on the Quaker city lots and houses went glimmering.[16] The brick house, said Duffield, was used as a grocery store on the ground floor and was occupied above "by various tenants of rather poor character." The other two buildings "are low and poor frames, occupied by a shoemaker, sign painter, candy shop." The upper floors were rented by Negro families, "and the entire property is in poor and shattered condition." While some of the neighboring homes on Locust Street were handsomely finished and valued at $10,000.00, the Harper buildings "are in a dilapidated state, needing repair badly, and are in every way unattractive in character and will probably never increase." Eleven tenants paid rents totaling $1,071.00 a year. After subtracting mortgage payments, taxes, insurance, and repairs, the property netted a profit of only $210.10 a year. "My opinion," Duffield stated, "is that the property should be sold by the trustees as soon as possible. Nothing is gained by holding on." He added that the mortgages were in arrears, and if the trustees did not sell, the mortgagees would probably offer the property at auction.

Duffield reported that he had asked a Philadelphia real estate firm, Bullett & Fairthorne, to see if a buyer could be found. On April 5, a special meeting was hastily summoned after a letter arrived from Bullett & Fairthorne, stating that they had an offer of $10,500.00, subject to encumbrances. This, they felt, was a good offer and should be accepted. They recommended that the acceptance be by telegraph, in case the prospect changed his mind.[17] Dr. Russel suggested that they not rush into this deal. He had a friend in Philadelphia, he said, who might take the property "in exchange for iron stocks which might be sold later at a profit." The rest of the board was not inclined to speculate; Russel's idea was rejected, and a wire of acceptance was rushed off to Bullett & Fairthorne.* [18] The deal netted Harper Hospital exactly $1,472.95 which, under the circumstances, the trustees were only too willing to get. The purchaser, it turned out, was the Philadelphia Polyclinic and College for Graduates in Medicine, which on the site erected a new building which it occupied until 1886. In 1916, the Polyclinic and College was absorbed by the University of Pennsylvania, becoming its Graduate Hospital. Thus, even before it was itself a hospital, Harper had established an affinity with another great medical institution.[19]

The Michigan property proved more valuable and less of a problem for the trustees. In March, 1859, after the Nancy Martin deed had been signed, the trustees voted to pay an early visit to the lot "for the purpose of defining a site for the Harper Hospital." [20] They were impressed by what they saw. They determined they would abide by Nancy's instructions to build the Hospital on the Grove lot. In fact, they decided not to rush into a sale of any part of the Grove lot, according to Dr. E. L. Shurly, who stated that this property would "if properly managed, so increase in value that they would ultimately realize sufficient to establish such an institution as they contemplated on a permanent basis." [21] In June, Trustees McGraw and Farrand, who kept a watchful eye on the Grove lot, reported that it had been fenced along its rear line and "was safe from encroachment of cattle." They discussed putting a fence around the entire five acres, but concluded that it would not be worth the cost of $300. Instead, a fence was added along the division line, the posts being cut from trees on the upper part of the lot. It was cheaper, they decided, to retain Constable Benjamin Sparling "to keep a watch on the Grove Lot so as to protect same from trespassers." What really needed protection was the choice timber and the hay. They offered to sell the latter "for such sums as they deem it worth when ready for harvesting." [22]

The rest of the endowment lands were soon put on the market. Harper's Oakland County farm and Nancy's fifteen acres on the Pontiac Road were quickly disposed of. The former was sold for $587; Nancy's brought $1,800.[23] The trustees' attention was centered on the Harper holdings in the Ten Thousand Acre Tract. In June, 1859, the board voted to visit and examine the Greenfield Township property "next Tuesday, provided the weather was favorable for the spending of a day in the woods." The September 5 minutes note that the trustees had made the trip "once or twice since their last meeting." [24] Those must have been adventurous journeyings, possibly requiring overnight camping trips because of the distance. The trustees can be pictured on these outings— grave and full of dignity, with hampers of food packed, jolting over corduroy roads, or no roads at all, in a carry-all behind a strong team, penetrating the wilderness—all in the line of duty.

As a result of these expeditions, they resolved to sell the lands as quickly as possible. A surveyor named E. Jerome was hired to survey the tract and prepare a plan for subdividing the 864 acres into different sized lots "so as to suit that class of purchasers who would be likely to invest in said lands." A road was opened on the east side of Section 21 (about Livernois Avenue), timber was cut off, and the roadway was ditched. The plat provided for lots of 40 and 32 acres.[25] No lots were to be sold consisting of less than 40 acres (except odd-sized parcels). They were put on the market at $40 per acre on 8-year, 7-per-cent contracts. Down payments of one-eighth were required, and the penalty for delinquency was 10 per cent. One of the first purchasers of a 40-acre lot was Trustee Russel.[26] Naturally, with all the real estate available around Detroit, the sale of Harper's Ten Thousand Acre lands took several years to complete. In 1864, only about 400 acres had been sold. Ultimately, though, this property netted the Hospital $32,590.[27]

The total yield, then, of the combined Harper-Martin donation, including the Philadelphia property, but not including the Grove lot, finally came to $36,449.95.[28] In 1882, another $100.00 was picked up by the sale of "the old Nancy Martin House" on Fremont Street.[29]

And how did the principal benefactors fare under the arrangement by which they would receive annuities? Very well, it must be concluded. On March 4, 1864, after the obligations on his Philadelphia property had been cleared, Walter Harper's pension was reduced from $2,000 a year to $1,000. In 1864, he voluntarily reduced it again, to $600, matching Nancy Martin's.[30] Under this arrangement, the elderly couple received a minimum combined income of $1,200 a year, or $100 a month— a fairly generous arrangement for that period. Not many Detroit families had that much. It was a pretty good middle-class income upon which, with no other obligations, they could live, if not in luxury, certainly in comfort. Added to that was a home which cost them nothing. A garden plot went with the house, and it must be assumed that it was cultivated, putting vegetables and perhaps fruit in season on their table. Certainly neither Harper nor Nancy Martin knew want in old age.

Just how well they fared under the trust agreement can be seen from an item posted in the trustees' minute book after the deaths of the principals. From 1859, when he deeded his property to the Hospital, until his death in 1867, Harper's annuities totaled $7,666.66. Nancy Martin, under the deed, was paid $9,550.00. To this may be added the $200.00 given to Harper's daughter, Mrs. Latham.[31] This makes a grand total of $17,416.66 in annuities. Put the value of the house, $400.00, on top of that, and their financial arrangement with the trustees netted them close to $18,000.00. Deduct that from the money realized from the sale of the various tracts, and it will be seen that the two benefactors realized almost as much as the Hospital did.

This recapitulation, however, was made too early to give a really clear picture of how well the Hospital benefited from the trust. The proceeds on Harper's Oakland and Greenfield tracts, and the Martin tract on the Pontiac Road are only part of the story. It does not take into account the value of Park lot 24, the site of the Hospital. In the long run, that alone was worth as much, if not more, than all the other original trust property combined. Then, too, Nancy's little real estate "flyer" of 1864, from which the trustees had to rescue her, proved to be a sound investment. Those ten acres, as now located, had a frontage on Woodward Avenue, between Medbury and Harper Avenues, extending back east to the Brush farm line. This was platted in 1882 and put up for sale at auction on September 19. Most of the lots sold immediately and the rest was purchased in a year. "The net amount realized from this sale," according to the trustees' records, "was $54,325.74." [32] All together, then, the financial arrangement between donors and trustees turned out quite satisfactorily for all parties concerned.

There is one question still unanswered in connection with the Harper Hospital trust: Who first planted in the minds of Walter Harper and Nancy Martin the idea of giving all they possessed for the purpose of establishing a hospital? The credit, given to almost everybody except the two principal donors, primarily has been awarded to the Duffield family for determining Harper and Nancy to endow a Protestant hospital.* George B. Catlin is almost alone in conceding that the first philanthropic impulse was felt by Harper and Mrs. Martin. He states:

> In 1859, Mr. Harper and Mrs. Martin felt that they were growing old and that they were virtually strangers in Detroit despite their long residence. They wanted to devote their property to charitable uses and at the same time provide for care of themselves in their old age. Mr. Harper offered all of his Michigan property to the City of Detroit to be utilized for the founding of a hospital and a school for poor boys. [33]

Essentially, of course, that was the end result of the Harper deed, but this interpretation is not quite accurate if other—and more probable—versions are correct.

According to various others, including Silas Farmer and members of the Duffield family, Harper's first inclination was to give everything he possessed to the First Presbyterian Church. But Farmer takes too much for granted when he says that Harper turned for guidance to "his old friend and pastor, George Duffield." [34] Duffield may have been an old friend; he was not Harper's pastor, in the strict sense, because Harper was not really a member of the church. The First Presbyterian Church was, in 1859, the largest and most influential Protestant church in Detroit. It would have been natural for anyone thinking of making a large endowment for Protestants to seek Dr. Duffield's counsel. And, in all likelihood, that is what Harper did, although his first conversations on the matter with Duffield came some time before 1859.[35] According to Duffield's son-in-law, Dr. Morse Stewart, a prominent Detroit physician who had married Miss Isabella Duffield, the Presbyterian pastor did not approve of a church having control of a large amount of wealth. Duffield replied to Harper's offer, said Stewart, in these words:

The First Presbyterian Church is able and rich enough to care for all interests connected with its sphere of work.[36]

As an alternative, Dr. Stewart went on, Dr. Duffield suggested there was a great need for a Protestant hospital in Detroit, and the suggestion met with favor. Harper wanted it to be a Presbyterian hospital, but again Dr. Duffield dissuaded him from a "narrow use" which would have resulted if the institution had been made strictly denominational. Duffield, declared his son-in-law, was interested in "the wider welfare of the entire city." [37]

But even this version should not be accepted too literally. Divie B. Duffield stated that he had discussed the matter of a will with Harper in July or August, 1858.[38] Dr. Duffield, at the suggestion of his attorney son, was present at that meeting. A hospital was mentioned, but, to Divie Duffield, it did not seem to be a practical use of Harper's money because he wrote his father a note saying:

Dear Father, I have given some thought to Mr. Harper's matter, and have concluded in view of the limited sum likely to come from the land, that a hospital is rather too large an undertaking. It would require nearly all of its value to put up the building.

Then follows a most revealing statement:

That which appears to my mind as likely to be the most useful and easiest of speedy organization is one of those schools such as we have often talked about (such as the Racy [?] Haas near Hamburg) in which the pupils are instructed in letters and in some useful trade or employment. The City, it strikes me, needs this as much if not more than anything else and its sphere might be enlarged as the means increased so as to assume a very imposing and useful character.

With this in view and remembering that you have long been interested in this form of school, I thought perhaps this would be one of the best paths into which Mr. Harper's charity could be directed. I have accordingly drawn a partial will for him in which I have made this devise. . . .[39]

This letter raises the suspicion that Walter Harper had never heard of the "Fellenberg School" which was designated in his will, but that such an educational establishment was really a pet project of Dr. Duffield. It is even possible that Divie B. may have inserted provision for it in the deed as a hedge against the possibility that, if plans for a hospital did not work out, there would still be a school.

No doubt there was considerable discussion around the Duffield dinner table about Walter Harper's charitable intentions, and there must have been some family argument about how the old recluse's money could best be used. Dr. Stewart, it was reported, was present at one of these family discussions. "He suggested that 'what Detroit needed was a Protestant hospital. Mr. Duffield at once approved this idea, and said he would use his influence to persuade Mr. Harper.' " [40] Certainly Dr. Stewart would have been listened to by the family, and his suggestion would have been carefully weighed. He was as civic-minded as any of the Duffield family, and it is easy to believe that his wife, Isabella, reinforced his argument. Farmer even suggests that it was actually Mrs. Stewart who planted the hospital idea in her husband's mind.[41]

Up to this time, no mention had been made of Nancy Martin. But Farmer also says that Isabella Duffield Stewart had befriended the sharp-tongued huckster and market-stall mistress, and he implies strongly that she discussed the hospital proposal with Nancy and even persuaded her to follow Harper's example.[42] It is only a guess, but perhaps the promise of the Martin property allayed the fears of Divie B. that there wouldn't be enough Harper property alone to build and support a hospital.

Regardless of the role played by the Duffields, they made no effort to claim any credit. Years after the deed had been signed, Divie B. openly stated that the deed represented Harper's wishes in all respects. He quoted Harper as saying that:

Detroit had been too long without charitable public institutions and it was high time steps were taken to establish them—that he [Harper] had long wished to contribute by his means to the promotion of some charitable object of this sort and he thought he had hit on the best plan of doing what good he could with his property.[43]

But if the Duffields preferred to remain in the background, content with inspiring others to noble deeds, the benign shadow of the First Presbyterian Church is ever present. It assumed, through its authority to nominate the trustees, a perpetual, permanent trusteeship itself. But let it also be remembered that Harper Hospital was never under denominational or sectarian control. It became and continued to be, as Dr. Duffield hoped it would, dedicated to "the wider welfare of the entire city."

Chapter 5

A CITY IN SEARCH OF A HOSPITAL

It was a coincidence
that the same Detroit newspaper which, on February 9, 1859, announced Walter Harper's donation of property for a hospital also carried an article headed "The Sore Throat Epidemic." It told about a wave of diphtheria, a disease which at that time was endemic in Michigan. There was mention of the high death rate and the absence of a cure. "Its onset," said the news story ominously, "is sudden and insidious."[1] This news report pointed up, about as clearly as anything could, the need for better medical and hospital facilities in mid-nineteenth century Detroit. The shortage of hospital beds was something of which thoughtful citizens were becoming acutely aware. It was this awareness which enabled the Duffields and possibly others to impress upon Walter Harper and Nancy Martin that, among charitable needs, a hospital claimed high priority.

Detroit was fast growing up. It no longer was a rough-edged, pioneer riverfront settlement, crouching in the shadow of a citadel or fort for protection and survival, its economy symbolized by a trap for fur-bearing animals. The old French influence and culture had all but disappeared; it persisted only in street names and in the use of the French patois in the homes of some of the older families. "By 1820," said C. M. Burton, "practically all of the Detroit trade was in the hands of Americans,"[2] and, it might be appended, almost forty years had passed since 1820. Like most of the United States, and particularly that part north of the Ohio River, agriculture and the exploitation of natural resources were of primary economic importance to Michigan. But like so many other northern cities, Detroit was gradually discovering that manufacturing and industrialization offered glowing prospects. Added to the city's solid commercial base, new enterprise made it a growing, thriving town. In 1860, a year after the financial foundation for the Hospital was established, Detroit was the nation's nineteenth city in size, with a population of 45,619. In 1830, the federal census gave Detroit 2,222 citizens; in 1840, it had 9,192; and in 1850, only 21,019. Thus, in the 1851–60 decade, the city more than doubled in population, and was still on the threshold of expansion which would continue for the better part of a century.[3]

Detroit had plenty of room in which to grow, thanks to the foresight of the early city fathers, who combined optimism with available free land, and established municipal boundaries that could accommodate a tenfold population increase. At the time the Harper-Martin trusts were set up, the city limits on the east were at Mt. Elliott Avenue, on the west at Porter Road (now Twenty-third Street), and on the north at the railroad crossing just below today's Grand Boulevard. Most business and residential districts in 1859 were concentrated within the one-mile circle, which meant that beyond Adams on the north, Hastings on the east, and Third on the west, Detroit was a city of wide open spaces. A few main streets were open, and in distant clusters stood a few isolated houses. Farms continued to take up most of the vast perimeter areas, but not for long.

About the time of the Civil War, industry began to spread out east and west, generally staying close to the Detroit River or to the four major railroad lines which served the city. These were the Michigan Central; the Grand Trunk; the Detroit, Monroe and Toledo; and the Detroit & Milwaukee. Well-to-do families also discovered the "suburbs" and began to build fine new homes on East Jefferson or out Woodward. By 1863, Woodward Avenue, as far north as Adelaide, was lined with palatial houses, the showplace homes of such business and professional leaders as the Duffields, E. S. Heineman, L. R. Medbury, the Whitneys, Jacob S. Farrand, R. W. King, Thomas W. Palmer, and many others equally well known. Almost as far north as the Hospital property, Woodward Avenue was shaded by a magnificent arch of great elms and maples, long remembered after the character of Woodward had changed. As the people moved out from what was then the center of town, they took their churches with them. The Central Methodist, St. John's Episcopal, and St. Patrick's Roman Catholic were soon joined by the First Presbyterian, Westminster Presbyterian, and Emmanuel Episcopal. These were all, in due time, neighbors of the Hospital. So was the fairgrounds on Woodward at Canfield, which became a training camp for Civil War regiments, and which still later provided the site for a rambling frame clubhouse and sports field for the old Detroit Athletic Club.

The early "North Woodward" settlers at first had to have carriages to get "downtown"—either that or rely on "shank's mare," as many of them did. Then George Hendrie established an omnibus line which served for a while. But progress would not be denied. In 1863, the first streetcar lines began operation, that on Woodward running to Adams Avenue. In 1867, the line of horse-drawn cars was extended to Erskine. Visitors to Harper Hospital, using the cars, still had a long four-block walk from the end of the line.[4]

This gradual expansion and the accumulation of wealth which made expansion possible were related largely to Detroit's growing industrialization. Burton points out that "it was in the decade before the Civil War that the foundation of modern industries was laid."[5] There was a booming shipbuilding industry, with its handmaidens, marine engines and boiler works. Dr. George B. Russel was prospering more from his railroad car and wheel foundry than from doctoring. Eber Brock Ward had a good thing in his blast furnaces and iron mills downriver. By 1864, he would be using the Bessemer process there for the first time in America. Pharmaceutical companies were prospering. Such firms as Jacob Farrand's,* and Dr. Samuel P. Duffield's, which evolved into Parke, Davis and Company, made Detroit a leader in that business. Many of the town's new industrialists, as well as its other business and professional men who came to the fore at this particular time, ultimately were to be closely associated with Harper Hospital, as generous patrons and benefactors.

While industry helped make available the money which, in time, would build and operate hospitals, it also created a need for such institutions. Working with heavy machinery was hazardous, and factory accidents, as well as occupational diseases, became common. The need for hospitals became acute. The influx of a laboring class, without home or family roots, made shelter for the sick, poor, and homeless a social requisite. The need for what today would be called a medical center extended beyond Detroit to the farms of Michigan and lower Ontario, especially as the use of farm machinery became more common. "The whirring knives of the new reapers did not stop when fingers and toes got in their way," said Helen Clapsattle in her story of the Drs. Mayo, "and the revolving knuckles of the tumbling rod in the threshing machine took twisting hold of any loose garment that ballooned near them." [6] Few small towns had the medical or surgical talent to treat such accidents. Outstate communities began to look to Harper as soon as its facilities were available. Thus, from the beginning, the Hospital serviced not only Detroit, but also a large part of Michigan.

Detroit had its fair share of aches and pains, despite the glowing accounts of its mild and health-inducing climate, which were generously supplied by the early gazetteers, travel book writers, and land speculators. They were more interested in luring immigrants to Michigan than with strict observance of the truth. An early French visitor, M. de Bougainville, set the tone in 1757 when he described the Detroit region.

The atmosphere is of great beauty and serenity. It is a magnificent climate, having almost no cold weather, and only a little snow.[7]

Others favorably mentioned the lack of heavy, prolonged rains, the fine drainage, the clear, crisp air, the sparkling waters which were the essence of purity.[8] All of which, in the beginning, may have been true. But to quote the hymnologist, only man is vile, and when he arrived in substantial numbers, he brought with him an assortment of germs which provided an interesting, often painful, and frequently lethal collection of diseases. Early Michiganders coughed, shook, sweated, had pains and fevers, and wasted away from malignancies. Regarding many of their diseases as peculiar to the area, they were not mentioned in the brochures which sought to lure settlers.

Perhaps the most general affliction was what was commonly known as the ague, and it was a fortunate and rare citizen of Michigan who escaped it. It has been accurately described as "the bane of the pioneer." [9] It was a familiar visitor in almost every household, proud or humble. It reoccurred with dependable regularity, and the sufferer could almost mark on the calendar in advance when he would be laid up. "The minister made his appointments to preach so as to accommodate his 'shakes.' The Justice of the Peace entered suit on his docket to avoid the sick day of the party or his own." [10] That was the account of one medical authority. To the pioneers and their doctors, the mosquito was nothing more than an annoying insect, rather than a carrier of disease.

The ague was attributed to miasmic gases, released from the earth when it was broken by the plow. These gases also were thought to lurk in damp and swampy places—the breeding grounds of mosquitoes—and it was often called "swamp fever." Sometimes, it was referred to as "Michigan fever." Not until the land was drained and the many Michigan swamps dried up did the affliction begin to disappear. But that took a long time. Meanwhile, there was a popular ditty that went around, warning:

> Don't go to Michigan, that land of ills;
> The word means ague, fever and chills.[11]

Another source says that "early settlers have suffered from fever or ague, or, as we know it, malaria, which persisted until the early forties of the last [nineteenth] century. Whiskey was at first widely used as an antidote. . . ." [12] (Probably on the interesting theory that, even if it didn't cure the sickness, it made it more tolerable.) Although malaria became less troublesome as time went on, it did not entirely disappear, and Harper Hospital reported treating twenty cases as late as 1899.[13]

At the time the Hospital was established, the prevailing diseases, besides malaria, were listed as rheumatism, pneumonia, croup, and pleurisy.[14] Cholera was an occasional and devastating visitor to Detroit, the first recorded epidemic occurring in 1813. Another followed in 1832, and it came again in 1834. The last epidemic of cholera was in 1854, resulting in 259 known deaths.[15] Diphtheria was not only prevalent but caused "an appalling loss of life" among pioneers, and it was not until the development of effective vaccines that this disease ceased to be a scourge. For many years Michigan had the highest death rate from diphtheria in the world.[16]

Of course, these few maladies mentioned were not the only ones which afflicted the people of Detroit and Michigan. This region shared just about every known ailment that visited other American communities. Smallpox was perhaps not as common here as in some places, although Detroit had its share. Scarlet fever was always troublesome, as were the other common "children's" diseases—measles, mumps, and whooping cough. Typhoid fever was a serious community problem until recent years. In 1900, Harper Hospital had eighty-one cases, resulting in seven deaths. In 1911, thirty-five cases were received, but there were three deaths so the mortality was proportionate.* After Detroit became an industrial city, tuberculosis became, and continued to be, a serious problem.[17]

To combat its catalog of ills, Detroit had 54 doctors listed in the city directory in 1856. However, some of those whose names appeared no longer were in actual practice. Dr. Uriah M. Gregory, for example, who had studied medicine under his father-in-law, Dr. John Ely of Connecticut, a Revolutionary surgeon, went to Detroit in 1831, but soon established the city's first commercial college to which he devoted his time. There may also have been a few practitioners whom the directory missed. An estimated maximum of 60 doctors, or about one for each 750 of population, served the city.[18] Among the doctors listed, a few—a very few—gained lasting reputations as leaders of the profession. Among these were E. P. Christian, Richard Inglis, Moses Gunn, Morse Stewart, and Charles S. Tripler. These men would have an enduring impact upon medicine and surgery in Detroit; they would be closely affiliated with Harper Hospital.

The more successful practitioners in the 1859 era were for the most part located in the Griswold-Jefferson area. Within a few years, as the city spread out, many doctors opened offices on West Lafayette, near Griswold. This tendency to congregate there caused Lafayette to be known as "pill alley." [19] In spite of what appeared to be an adequate supply of doctors, Detroit suffered seriously from an "appalling lack" of hospital facilities.[20] Because of the high incidence of disease, both the medical profession and the public felt the need as early as 1827 for one or more hospitals.[21] Even during the British regime, progressive citizens had a hospital in mind. On December 26, 1785, John Askin told William Edgar that "We hope also to raise a contribution sufficient to make a small hospital for the reception of those only who have not the means of having themselves taken care of." [22]

It has been said that the hospital "has not been a feature of the American frontier." [23] Naturally, where the military played a prominent part in community life, as it did in Detroit, there were crude hospitals or infirmaries to take care of sick soldiers. In 1785, when Askin was talking about a civilian charity hospital, there was a garrison hospital to which His Majesty's soldiers and seamen were sent, and a similar facility existed when the Detroit fort became an American post.[24] But if civilians were ever admitted to either, there is no record to prove it.

1. WALTER HARPER — It was Harper's gift in 1859 of nearly one thousand acres of land that provided the initial endowment for the great Hospital which today bears his name. A Philadelphia merchant, he moved to Detroit in the 1830's, accumulating vast tracts of property which now comprise a substantial part of the city's northwest section.

courtesy Harper Hospital

2. Nancy Martin — The market woman whose gift of a five-acre lot provided the site of Harper Hospital was also a Philadelphian. She accompanied Harper to Detroit as servant and companion and became keeper of a market stall, where she accumulated a modest fortune. She was a colorful figure in early Detroit. She died in 1875 in the Hospital which, during her later years, was her home.

courtesy Harper Hospital

The first known Detroit hospitals were erected to meet the specific needs resulting from the cholera epidemic of 1832. A pest house was opened in a barn on the Leib Farm on Gratiot Road, about two miles from the center of the city.[25] Victims of the disease who had no one to look after them, and who were considered doomed anyway, were taken there to die. They were cared for after a fashion while they lived, and were buried at public expense when they succumbed. They received no real medical attention or nursing. The pest house was too far away to receive visits from badly overworked physicians. During the epidemic of 1834, Holy Trinity Church was turned into an emergency hospital, and the patients were laid on the pews, the floor, or wherever there was a place for them. Father Martin Kundig, the pastor, used such volunteers as he could assemble, mostly women, to help in the nursing and provide comforts. "They were joined," said Father Kundig, "by the Sisters of St. Clare, and day and night, through all the horrors of that direful dispensation, they lent their aid to the sick and dying." [26] It is worth noting that this Trinity Church building had recently been purchased by the Catholic Diocese of Detroit and moved from lower Woodward Avenue to Cadillac Square. It had been used on its former site by the First Presbyterian Church.[27]

The temporary use of a church, regardless of how valuable it was in an unusual situation, still did not fill the need for a real hospital. Father Kundig and the Poor Clares demonstrated that something more permanent was required, and they worked toward that end. Much of the organized charity in Detroit in the 1840's and 1850's was under supervision of the Catholic church, and on June 9, 1845, after both Father Kundig and the Poor Clares had left the city, another order, the Sisters of Charity, opened a hospital which they called St. Vincent's.[28]

St. Vincent's was a two-story log building located on the southwest corner of Larned and Randolph Streets, a site now occupied by the bus terminal, opposite Detroit's City-County Building. Formerly used as a parochial school, it provided room for twelve beds, only a fraction of what Detroit needed. Although operated by a Catholic order, it was non-sectarian in that patients were accepted regardless of religious affiliation or lack of it. Like most hospitals of that period, it was primarily devoted to the care of the poor and aged sick. It had no trouble whatever in keeping its twelve beds filled.[29]

As a Detroit experiment, St. Vincent's was so successful in filling a community need that within two years a fund-raising drive was undertaken to enlarge its facilities.[30] Mrs. Antoine Beaubien, member of an early French family, donated a lot which fronted on Clinton Street, near St. Antoine, and ran back to Mullett Street. Its frontage was 87 feet, and its depth 54. With cash which others had donated, a four-story building was erected on the Beaubien lot at a cost of $10,000, with beds for 150 patients. It was opened for use November 6, 1850, at which time its name was changed to St. Mary's. On November 21, 1879, 29 years later, a new St. Mary's was built on the same block, but fronting on St. Antoine Street. The old building was retained for clinical purposes.[31] St. Mary's continued to be one of Detroit's major hospitals; in fact, it still is, although ownership passed in 1948 to a group of doctors who now operate it as a private institution under the name of Detroit Memorial Hospital.

For several years, St. Mary's performed a unique medical function in Detroit, and its value to the city cannot be exaggerated. It was largely the success of this institution's efforts to provide Detroit with public hospital beds that aroused other citizens to the need which resulted in the founding of Harper Hospital. Early St. Mary's accepted contagious cases, although in time it opened a so-called pest house, mainly for smallpox cases, far out in the fields near what is now Kirby Avenue and St. Aubin Street.[32] Acceptance of contagious patients resulted in the death and martyrdom of the hospital's first superior, Sister Loyola, and another nursing nun who apparently contracted one of the diseases they were treating.[33] St. Mary's also gave humane shelter to the mentally sick and to unwed mothers. Out of these charitable enterprises eventually grew two other area hospitals—St. Joseph's Retreat, in Dearborn, and Providence Hospital, which had its origin on Fourteenth Street at Dalzell, but was long a landmark on West Grand Boulevard. Among other useful and pioneering efforts, St. Mary's in 1851 opened a free clinic, supported by public donations. Because it received general public support, and because it was open to those of all sectarian persuasions, it was not, as Catlin points out, regarded as a Catholic institution.[34]

Of more limited service to the community at large was Detroit's second hospital—the United States Marine Hospital. As early as 1829, the Michigan Legislative Council, precursor of the state legislature, became concerned about the care of sick and injured Great Lakes mariners who frequently became public charges. Congress was petitioned for the grant of a township, its sale to provide funds to build a hospital for seamen. Congress took no action as far as Detroit was concerned, although it soon began to establish hospitals for sailors in other ports.[35]

In 1854, however, Detroit's turn came, and acquisition of 8 acres at the southwest corner of East Jefferson and Mt. Elliott was authorized. This land, with a frontage of 274 feet on Jefferson, cost the government $23,000. An additional $80,000 was appropriated for a building which opened November 30, 1857,[36] with the transfer of 20 patients from St. Mary's. The original capacity of the Marine Hospital was about 75 patients, although over the years the facilities were expanded. Its operation was financed by a form of compulsory insurance; each Great Lakes sailor had 40 cents deducted from his wages each month. This was collected and paid over to the authorities by the captains. Any sailor with 3 months service was eligible for admittance. In addition to the hospital, a dispensary was operated at the office of the surgeon. At the time of the opening, the respected Dr. Zina Pitcher, regarded by many as the dean of Detroit's medical profession, was appointed surgeon. His office was in the Campau Building, Griswold and Larned.[37]

At the time it was built, Marine Hospital represented a great advance in hospital construction. "Its appointments," says the *Medical History of Michigan,* "which included hot air heating, supplemented with fireplaces, and hot and cold water on each of its three floors, were something luxurious." [38] But of vastly greater significance is the fact that St. Mary's and Marine, and in a little while Harper, benefited from interlocking staffs comprised of some of the outstanding members of the medical profession in Detroit. Thus, a thread of continuity was provided for the city's early hospital developments.

The modern hospital, of which Harper may be regarded as typical, has four chief functions, according to Dr. Malcolm T. MacEachern, author of the massive and authoritative *Hospital Organization and Management:*

In the light of the broad social responsibility for maintaining and restoring the health of all members of the community, the functions of the modern hospital are essentially four: (a) care of the sick and injured; (b) education of physicians, nurses, and other personnel; (c) public health-prevention of disease and promotion of health; and (d) advancement of research in scientific medicine.[39]

It took many, many millenniums before this ideal evolved. Not until the dawn of the modern scientific age did medical science and its handmaiden, the modern hospital concept, emerge from the dark jungles of ignorance and superstition. Nevertheless, it must be said, to the everlasting credit of the human race, that whenever and wherever in history a need arose a place was set aside to shelter the homeless or care for the sick. "The story of the birth and evolution of the hospital," says Mac-Eachern, "portrays the triumph of civilization over barbarism, and of altruism over egoism, the slow but certain upward struggle against individualism, and the progress toward an ideal characterized by interest in the welfare of the entire community." [40]

The hospital is the mark of a civilized and usually highly-cultured people. The savage and barbarian, while they may have been hospitable under some circumstances to the stranger, the traveler, or even the unfortunate, did not recognize the need for the hospital. Far back in the annals of time, long before the Christian Era, the Egyptians and the peoples of India had hospitals. The Greeks and Romans used their temples on occasion for hospital purposes; hence, historians have observed that the earliest hospitals were associated more with religion than medicine. This relationship carried over into the Christian Era, when a "hospitalum" was opened in connection with the residence of each bishop. It consisted of a room or two, set aside for poor and sick travelers. In time, care of sick and poor wayfarers was taken over by the monastic orders. At first, the hospital was simply a place of refuge or rest. Not until later was medical care added. [41] Generally, this was a development of the Renaissance when man began to investigate nature, rather than to take it for granted, and the first gropings toward medical science began. It was in the Italian hospitals of the Renaissance that the practice is said to have originated of permitting apprentices to walk the floors with experienced surgeons for the purpose of clinical teaching. [42]

Despite these forward strides, there was an unfortunate period of retrogression when both medical science and the hospital slipped so far backward that they did not measure up to the standards of ancient Greece. This period, which persisted, with a few notable exceptions, into the first part of the nineteenth century, was characterized by ignorance, callousness, and even brutal treatment of the sick. Hospitals, if they could properly be called that, passed in many instances from religious hands and fell under the direction of civil authorities. Often they were little more than alms houses; usually they had the characteristics of prisons. The patients were mistreated by doctors who had little knowledge at their command, and by nurses, or more accurately attendants, who were generally described as a drunken, thieving, brutal lot, often recruited from the criminal classes. As a result, hospitals were places where unfortunate people went to die, not to get well. The idea that they were "vestibules of death" persisted until modern times, despite vast and remarkable improvement. It was not long ago that the patient entered a hospital only because he was regarded as a terminal case, or because he had no friends or relatives to care for him. Respectable women bore their children at home, not in a maternity hospital or department which was usually reserved for unwed mothers.[43] The rare exception was the religious hospital where a few men and women, members of religious orders, provided dedicated and disciplined service. The average hospital in the United States did not really begin to emerge from its own kind of Dark Age until the middle years of the 1800's. The melancholy conditions in the first half of that century are vividly described by Dr. MacEachern:

Although institutions for the care of the sick were numerous, the first half of the nineteenth century stands as a dark period in hospital history. Surgeons of the day had sufficient knowledge of anatomy to lead them to perform many ordinary operations, and as a result more surgery was probably undertaken than during any previous era. But there was one important difference: Whereas the medieval and ancient surgeons had sought to keep wounds clean, even using wine in an attempt to accomplish their purpose, nineteenth century surgeons believed suppuration to be desirable and they encouraged it. Hospital wards were filled with discharging wounds which made the atmosphere so offensive that use of perfume was required. Nurses of that period were said to have used snuff to make conditions tolerable. Surgeons wore their operating coats for months without having them washed; the same bed linen served several patients. Pain, hemorrhage, infection and gangrene were rife in the wards. Mortality from surgical instruments was as high as ninety and even one hundred per cent.[44]

Many a story was told of the surgeon who stropped his knife on the sole of his boot before performing an operation. Had the word "sterilization" been spoken, it would have been met with a blank, uncomprehending stare.

The change came suddenly and spectacularly. It was the result of

several scientific discoveries or advances which occurred roughly between 1842 and 1867, producing radical changes in medicine, or more
specifically, in surgery. The first of these scientific landmarks was Crawford Long's use of ether as an anesthetic to remove a tumor from a
patient's neck. Four years later, William Thomas Green Morton became the first to use ether in the performance of a regular hospital
operation.[45] After that, pain and its disastrous aftereffects were materially
reduced, permitting more general use of surgery and raising that branch
of medical practice from butchery to a splendid science.

But even in the day of Morton and Long, anesthesia was by no
means the whole answer. Just because a patient could be rendered
safely and comfortably unconscious did not mean his immunity to infection was increased. Although some inquiring minds had doubts and
reservations, the majority believed that bacteria, floating freely in the
air, carried disease and infection. In fact, the idea was generally accepted that a certain amount of infection was a good thing. Surgeons
spoke knowingly and favorably of "laudable pus," holding to the opinion
that wounds were supposed to be lined with dead tissue which had to
be thrown out of the body in the form of pus.[46] Direct bacterial contact
as the chief cause of infection occurred first to a Viennese surgeon
named Semmelweiss, in 1847. His theory was proved by Louis Pasteur
who demonstrated that bacteria multiplied by reproduction rather than
by spontaneous generation. In 1867, Joseph Lister went a step further,
showing that disease-bearing or infection-spreading organisms could
be destroyed by the use of antiseptics. He demonstrated his point by
performing operations under what became known as the Lister spray,
a fine mist of carbolic acid injected into the operating room.[47] Lister's
phenomenal success, marked by an almost complete absence of postoperative infection with a sharp drop in mortality, attracted widespread
attention, first in Europe and eventually in the United States.

New ideas, regardless of how beneficial they may be, are sometimes
resisted; they are frequently accepted only after much delay. That was
true of Listerism. It was rejected on a variety of grounds. The elder
Dr. William Mayo, father of the famous Mayo brothers, and himself a
notable surgeon, was "defiantly anti-Listerism in opinion and practice."[48]

On the other hand, Dr. Donald Maclean, of the University of
Michigan Medical School faculty and later a distinguished member of

the Harper Hospital staff, worked with Dr. Lister and was one of the early advocates of Listerism in the United States.[49] As late as 1878, the merits of Lister spray were being hotly debated by the Ann Arbor Medical and Surgical Society.[50] Yet, while others talked about it, Dr. Theodore A. McGraw * performed the first Lister spray operation at Harper Hospital, assisted by Dr. Howard Longyear. That, too, was in 1878. The outcome of that operation is not known. Dr. H. O. Walker, a Harper house physician, probably observed the operation. Yet Walker had doubts about antisepsis, declaring in 1887 that it "is not always 'cock sure.' "[51] Others, refusing to see any value to antisepsis, carried more than mere doubt into the early years of the twentieth century. Fortunately, they were a small minority, although, in behalf of some doubters, it must be admitted that methods more satisfactory and effective than Listerism soon evolved. Still, the worth of asepsis was enthusiastically recognized by most of the profession, and for the time being, so it was said, "Let us spray" became the surgeon's invocation.[52] More important than bad punning was the solid fact, stated by the medical historian, Thomas N. Bonner, that "with the advent of asepsis, hospitals changed."[53] And, it might be added, for the better.

Even the Civil War, which came a few years too early for asepsis, made a contribution to medical and hospital advancement. What was learned under the most adverse conditions about army hygiene was carried over into civilian life in an enlarged interest in public health. The great mass of statistical information gathered by the Union army medical department was of incalculable value once the war was over. A large-scale program for the building and operating of general army hospitals taught valuable lessons for postwar hospitals. The same can be said of nursing which, during the war and under army supervision, first began to emerge in the United States as a profession.[54]

Thus, this period of about twenty-five years, beginning with Long's first application of ether, marked an era of great medical progress. It was just about at the climax of this quarter-century of progress that Harper Hospital came into being. It was a most propitious moment, then, that Walter Harper and Nancy Martin chose to establish a hospital in Detroit.

Chapter 6

THE MILITARY HOSPITAL

The Harper Hospital
Board of Trustees must have experienced a feeling of frustration during most of the three-year period, 1861–63. They had a mandate to build a hospital. The Harper-Martin lands had been put up for sale. There was some cash in the treasury, and the amount was growing each month as purchasers met the payments on their land contracts. But, unfortunately, the money on hand was not yet sufficient to permit construction of a hospital on the scale desired. Other matters, too, were interfering. On April 19, 1861, the thunder of guns over the harbor at Charleston, South Carolina, announced the beginning of civil war. As in all of the North, the people of Detroit and Michigan were directing their minds and energies into other channels. Nevertheless, the trustees felt a moral obligation to carry out the terms of the trust. There were a few querulous public comments, guardedly questioning whether the trustees were actually meeting their responsibility. To men of integrity, such remarks smarted, even though they were not a general, or even a fair, reflection of public opinion. But the trustees were uneasy; no one wanted to get started more than they.

In 1862, they went so far as to confer with an architect.[1] An offer to help came from the Rev. William A. Passavant, of Pittsburgh, who was regarded as the leading American authority on hospital planning and administration.[2] According to the minutes of May 4, 1863:

It was stated by Mr. Buhl that Mr. Passavant of Pittsburgh had expressed a willingness to come out to Detroit and give his counsel and aid in organizing the hospital, suggesting at the same time as the most economical as well as the most beneficial mode of commencing the charity contemplated, the immediate opening of the hospital in some temporary building to be procured for this purpose.[3]

Passavant's suggestion had appeal and each trustee was asked to investigate "as to the practicability of some house to be procured for the use of the Board and the terms of its occupancy."[4] Nothing came of this immediately, and Passavant's offer to go to Detroit was not accepted.

Consideration was given to a proposal made by faculty members of the University of Michigan Medical School that a medical school clinical department might be combined with Harper. A meeting of the trustees was held in the mayor's office to explore the possibility. The University was represented by Dr. Samuel G. Armor and Dr. Alonzo Palmer. "The whole subject was fully and fairly discussed with the utmost unanimity on both sides," reported the *Detroit Free Press*. "The meeting was merely to discuss the matter, and of course no action was taken on any subject."[5] That the discussion was held in the office of the mayor could have been interpreted as a sign of official public concern about the trustees' delay in getting started. The trustees evidently chose to interpret it in that light. Association with the University of Michigan, or any other public body or institution, had little appeal, because it carried, in the trustees' minds, the implied danger that their control might be lessened.

At a board meeting on March 3, 1864, the chief topic of discussion was a "speedy procurement of a suitable place for the opening of the Hospital on a moderate scale." Obviously, the trustees were back to Passavant's idea of using temporary quarters. Trustee David Cooper, the treasurer, "offered the building owned by him and now occupied by the Industrial School at the rent of $400 per annum."[6]

Opened in 1857 as a charitable enterprise, the Industrial School was intended to provide a useful occupation for children who were currently being sent begging from door to door. The sponsors of the school were about sixty public-minded women. Teachers were hired, and free schooling, together with clothing, was offered boys and girls under the age of fourteen. It is no surprise to learn that Mrs. Divie B. Duffield was one of the school's founders and until 1862 its recording secretary.[7] First opened in rented rooms on Monroe Street, the school grew, and in 1858 it moved into larger quarters—a two-story building owned by Cooper at the northwest corner of Washington Boulevard and Grand River. Shortly before Cooper offered it to his fellow trustees for hospital purposes, the school had 180 pupils. The building was reported to be badly in need of repair.[8]

The trustees weighed Cooper's offer carefully, but took no steps beyond agreeing to examine the property "and reflect upon the proposition so as to be prepared for action on the subject at an early day." [9] The "early day" never arrived. Other forces were at work which soon were to resolve the dilemma of the trustees and result in construction of a hospital before another year went by.

Those other forces were the Civil War battles, the mounting casualties, and sickness in the Union army, and, more particularly, in the regiments from Michigan. When the Civil War began, the Union armies were as woefully lacking in adequate medical services as they were in most other tools of war. The sudden increase in the armed force of the federal government, from a few prewar thousands widely scattered in coastal forts and western frontier posts to divisions, corps, and armies numbering in the hundreds of thousands, created entirely new problems for the handful of regular surgeons. Although there were a few hospitals or infirmaries attached to some of the larger posts, in 1861 there was not a single general hospital.

Fortunately, though, there were some able men in key positions in the army medical service, and more were brought in. Not only were they skillful surgeons, but they also proved to be capable organizers and administrators. They were assisted by a semiofficial organization, known as the United States Sanitary Commission. This was composed of civilian doctors, clergymen, and prominent civic leaders who undertook to provide funds and know-how, and to act as a goad when Congress or the military needed to be prodded into action. The Sanitary Commission operated in the field, in the Capitol at Washington, and on the home front, performing a wartime service comparable in many ways to that furnished in later wars by the American Red Cross.

It was not long after hostilities started that the casualties began to pile up in such numbers that regimental, brigade, and division hospitals simply could not care for them, particularly for protracted periods of convalescence. Then, too, there were the sick. It took the army a long time to understand the importance of sanitary camp conditions. While those lessons were being learned and typhoid and other camp diseases were being brought at least partially under control, the doctors had to cope with the "children's diseases"—measles, mumps, chickenpox, and scarlet fever—which the young recruits brought with them from home. Disease incapacitated three or four times more men than the war did, but the sick and wounded alike required treatment.

In 1862, the federal government began to establish large general hospitals to which the sick and injured could be evacuated after field station treatment. At first, these hospitals were in the general area in which the armies were operating. Thus, in the East, they were concentrated in Washington, Alexandria, Annapolis, and Philadelphia. In the West, they were at Louisville, Memphis, St. Louis, Columbus, Ohio, and Jeffersonville, Indiana. As these filled up after such devastating battles as Gettysburg, Chickamauga, and still later, Grant's sledge hammer campaigns around Richmond, more general hospitals were added. They were called "general" hospitals because men were sent to them without regard for their military units. Patients from various armies, corps, and divisions were mingled at these hospitals. As more were built, they were located in or near the communities from which the men originally came. It was believed that a wounded soldier would recuperate more quickly in a hospital in his home state, near his family and friends.[10]

As the war progressed, a wounded soldier might be given emergency treatment on the battlefield by his own regimental surgeon. He would then be moved a short distance behind the line to a brigade or corps hospital where more advanced treatment could be given, including the common and dreaded amputation. After a few days in this hospital, or as soon as he could be safely moved, he was shipped off to a general hospital.

In the early part of the war, the general hospitals were pretty bad, being mere improvisations. One, in Washington, had been a jail; in Philadelphia, a railroad station, a coach factory, and a silk mill were converted into general hospitals. In time, however, conditions improved, and as new hospitals were built, they incorporated the best known features of hospital design and construction. Much of this improvement was the result of unremitting pressure from the Sanitary Commission and other agencies.

Constructed especially for the purpose they were to serve, the general hospitals were of the so-called pavilion type, in which the wards were separate, barracks-like buildings. The wards were ordinarily 150 feet long, 25 feet wide, with a row of beds along each wall. The ceilings were from 12 to 14 feet high. Plenty of ventilation was provided, the prevailing belief being that infected air had to find escape. It was also the opinion that in time the buildings would themselves become contaminated. Accordingly, they were of somewhat flimsy construction so that, after a few years service, they could be torn or burned down. By the end of the war, there were 204 general hospitals throughout the North, with a total bed capacity of 136,894.[11]

For the time being, Michigan was bypassed when general hospitals were built in the North. Michigan contributed its share of the wounded, and hospital beds elsewhere were occupied by a fair quota of Wolverines who had been picked up on scores of battlefields—in Tennessee, Mississippi, Virginia, Maryland, and Pennsylvania. Bullets found their marks in Michigan flesh at Shiloh, Stones River, Chickamauga, the Peninsula, Antietam, Fredericksburg, Chancellorsville, and Gettysburg. The Michigan victims of these battles were sent to established general hospitals in a dozen or more cities and states—everywhere except in Michigan.

At the outset of the war, the Detroit Barracks had been constructed on Clinton Street, just west of Elmwood Avenue. The Barracks was used to house the provost guard, serve as a recruiting and induction center, and be the general center of the district's military administration. The Barracks had infirmary facilities which were expanded so that by 1862 a few wounded men were being accepted. Not designed for or intended to be a general hospital, the Barracks infirmary left much to be desired as a place for the sick and wounded. It was described in a July 22, 1862 article in the *Detroit Advertiser and Tribune:*

We would not recommend the Barracks as a pleasure resort, or a retreat for invalids, but under the management of the present efficient officers, they are well suited for the purposes for which they were intended. At present there are but few invalids, and they are convalescent in an encouraging degree, so much so that, with a few exceptions, they are all able to navigate.

The different expedients to which they resort to drive away the monotony are ingenious and novel in the extreme. Here a crowd may be seen swallowing "salt junk" on a wager and it is said (though we are inclined to think they meant to "stuff" us) that individuals are frequently known to secrete thirty-pound chunks at one swallow. At another place a detachment may be seen stretched at full length on the ground, with bare feet, while one of the number tickles the others with a straw between his toes, and the one that first permits his risibilities to overpower him has the last chance at mess. Various other innocent and interesting methods of amusement are resorted to, but we refrain.[12]

One of the "efficient officers" of whom the *Advertiser and Tribune* referred was Surgeon Charles Stuart Tripler, United States Army.* On August 1, 1862, he reported for duty at Detroit headquarters where, according to the order of Lieutenant Colonel J. R. Smith, he "will have charge of sick and convalescents at the Hospital of Detroit Barracks. He will be obeyed and respected accordingly." [13]

In addition to the Barracks, sick and wounded were cared for in St. Mary's Hospital, the Marine Hospital, and at the post infirmary at Fort Wayne. St. Mary's, while given over largely to the care of soldiers, never became a military general hospital. It continued as a private institution, taking soldiers on a contract basis.[14]

The existing local hospitals could handle only a few of Michigan's sick and wounded. The vast majority was bedded elsewhere. As late as October, 1864, James Edmunds, president of the Michigan Soldiers Relief Association, reported 586 Michiganders in Washington hospitals, "although the usual number was 1,000." At St. Louis, in 1864, 226 Michigan men were admitted to the general hospital between March 1 and November 15, 1864. Of these, 20 died. Michigan's wounded also were in hospitals in Kentucky, Ohio, and Indiana, as well as in a dozen institutions in the East.[15] These men were not forgotten by the home folks. They were regularly visited by members of Michigan relief and aid agencies who reported conditions to the Michigan adjutant general. What disturbed these visitors was the number of deaths that occurred. This was not attributed to lack of care—the feeling seemed to be that the recovery rate would be higher if these men could recuperate in the beneficial climate of their native state.

Tripler shared this opinion, although his feelings were based on more practical considerations than climate. Early in May, 1863, he received notification that 200 sick soldiers were being sent to Detroit from the general hospital in Louisville. Having no accommodations for them, Tripler cancelled the order and sent off an indignant letter to General R. C. Wood, assistant surgeon general at Washington.

There is a good deal of feeling in this state [Michigan], that while provision has been made in Indiana and Ohio and perhaps other states for hospitals for the sick of these states, none has been made in Michigan. Without in any way intimating that this feeling is in my opinion formulated, or that the public service would be promoted by the establishment of extra . . . hospitals . . . I take this occasion to urge the construction of the single hospital I recommended last autumn, plans of which, by command of the Surgeon General, I prepared and forwarded to that office. I have received during the month of April 100 or more Michigan invalids from the Department of the Ohio and have accommodated them in St. Mary's Hospital in this city, most of these men were hopeless cases—some from here have recovered and have been returned to duty, others have been already discharged —more will be as soon as they can be paid. Judging from these men, I think if from time to time the volunteers from this state who have been inmates of Hospitals more than three months would be sent to me, these cases would be more promptly discharged than they are. For that purpose, the Hospital I have projected, of 200 beds, would be sufficient.[16]

General Wood endorsed this proposal, and so did a lot of Michiganders. Tripler, perhaps without realizing it, had started a ground swell of public opinion that before long would all but engulf Washington. Others quickly added their voices. In his message to the legislature on January 7, 1863, Governor Austin Blair sounded the keynote of the campaign for a Michigan hospital, pointing out that the invalid soldier should be sent home where "the bracing air of his native clime, and the cheerful voices of sympathizing friends, will restore him to manhood again like magic." [17] More important, Blair instructed his military agent stationed in Washington, Dr. Joseph Tunnicliff, to get busy. Today, Tunnicliff would be called a lobbyist. But by whatever term he was known, he was indefatigable in behalf of the interests of Michigan and her soldiers. In the days that followed, he wore a groove in the pavement between his quarters at Ninth and G Streets and the War Department. The formidable and irascible Secretary Henry M. Stanton could hardly open his office door without finding Tunnicliff lying in wait for him in the anteroom.

Others were equally busy, in their own way, working through channels available to them. Dr. David O. Farrand, an army surgeon and brother of Jacob S. Farrand, the Harper Hospital trustee, supported the idea, although at the time he was the surgeon in charge of military cases at St. Mary's. The *Detroit Free Press* got behind the move. So did the Michigan senators, Zachariah Chandler and Jacob Howard. Civilian members of the Sanitary Commission and the Soldiers Relief

Association pulled strings. Luther Willard, state military agent at Nashville, wrote home that Michigan soldiers in the hospital in that Tennessee city were "shabbily treated by incompetent surgeons" who were guilty of "a shameful and criminal neglect of their patients." [18] James M. Edmunds of the Relief Association declared that "we must look after our own men, or neglect and suffering will be sure to follow." [19]

However, Tunnicliff * questioned the motives of the civilian agencies and thought they were doing the cause more harm than good. He accused them of magnifying the suffering of Michigan soldiers for the purpose of keeping "the people harassed and alarmed so that they would lavish funds and supplies on them for disposal." [20] He thought Dr. Tripler and other medical leaders in Detroit were prejudicing the case.

Before being sent to Detroit, Tripler had been surgeon-in-chief for the Army of the Potomac. He was relieved of that duty, and this action, which amounted to a demotion, left him embittered. Apparently, he was a difficult man at best. He was referred to as "old, bald headed, nobody liked him. He was pompous, overbearing, the soldiers disliked him." [21] Some of his associates questioned whether he was even a good doctor. The *Detroit Advertiser and Tribune* astringently called him the man "through whose official stupidity and inhumanity Michigan soldiers were kept on the battlefield after the fight at Chickamauga, writhing in pain for want of medical stores, which he refused to permit distributed until overruled by a superior. . . ." [22] Obviously, he was not the hospital's most effective advocate.

In the long run, it was pretty much Tunnicliff who got results by the direct pressure he brought to bear on the War Department and Secretary Stanton. In a letter dated August 3, 1863, he told Governor Blair that he was making headway with the War Department and that he had completely won over a subordinate who promised to bring the matter to the attention of the surgeon general. [23] The latter's assistant told the Michigan agent that "this is an excellent time for your people to move for a general hospital as we are about breaking up some of the hospitals at New York." [24] Tunnicliff then stated that if the federal government lacked funds for a Michigan hospital, but would agree to the transfer of the state's invalids, he was positive a hospital could be built by local subscription. This proposal interested War Department officials, who assured Tunnicliff they were positive the surgeon general would "cheerfully acquiesce." [25]

At the same time Tunnicliff told Blair that the surgeon general's office had promised him that, in the event a hospital were built by the people of Michigan, the federal government "will supply all the hospital's furniture. . . . I see nothing now in the way but the approval of Secretary Stanton." [26] Tunnicliff wrote:

I understand that a large building, erected for a machine shop and now not in use, stands on high ground at the south-eastern limits of the city [Detroit]. A few additional wooden buildings of cheap construction might be needed built with special adaptation to their intended use. I think if you secure the consent of the Secretary of War, the people of Detroit could fit up the building in two weeks. [27]

Tunnicliff also wrote Benjamin Vernor, who participated in soldiers' relief activities in Detroit, to present the idea to patriotic and influential citizens of Detroit and the state. Apparently, the response was not what Tunnicliff anticipated, and the idea was not further pursued. [28] In October 1863, Tunnicliff assured Blair that he "had secured a positive arrangement with Surgeon General Hammond," that the hospital would be established "within a very short time." [29]

Up to this point, little had been said about a location. Tunnicliff, who was from Jackson, Governor Blair's home town, personally favored Ann Arbor, where the Board of Regents had offered the use of a couple of professors' quarters. Proximity to the University of Michigan Medical School would provide clinical facilities which that institution badly needed, he pointed out. [30] Senator Chandler believed the old arsenal at Dearborn could be converted into a hospital. This site was rejected because Dearborn was "one of the most malarious localities in the state." [31] Governor Blair apparently had no preference as long as the hospital was on the main line of the Michigan Central, thus providing easy access for both the patients and their families. The surgeon general's people looked with favor on taking over and converting the Detroit Barracks, estimating the additional facilities needed could be built for no more than $1,000. But army authorities rejected that plan, flatly declaring the Barracks was needed for military purposes. [32] The upshot was that the War Department agreed to send an inspector out to Michigan to look over the ground. After visiting several possible sites, he recommended Detroit. At the same time, the Department again promised that Michigan should have its hospital "regardless of expense." [33]

Then the Harper Hospital trustees resolved the whole matter. At their meeting on March 5, 1864, Jacob Farrand made a motion to the effect that:

> . . . the President was authorized and directed to communicate with Dr. Tripler, Medical Director, and offer thro' him to the U.S. a lease of the five acres belonging to the Harper's Hospital for the erection thereon by the Govt. of a Hospital building upon such terms as may be agreed upon between the parties, a nominal amt. only being asked for the use of the ground to consist of the payment of taxes and the maintenance of suitable & sufficient enclosures around the premises.[34]

The genesis of this proposal is not difficult to find. Farrand's brother, Surgeon David Osburn Farrand, who was closely associated with Tripler and under his command, was quite aware of all the maneuvering going on to get a Michigan hospital, and it was only natural that he would keep his brother informed. Then, too, all the trustees would know of Tunnicliff's suggestion about raising money for a hospital through local subscription. There was no need to tell the trustees about the need for a hospital, either. Several of them and their wives were active in soldiers' relief activities. Obviously, there must have been some prior discussions between members of the Board of Trustees and Tripler and, perhaps, other military authorities. When, where, and how often they took place, there is no way of telling. That there was at least an understanding that the Harper offer would be favorably considered before Farrand made his motion appears certain. Also, it is highly probable that some such proposition prompted the trustees to move toward formal incorporation and adoption of a seal on May 4, 1863, in order to give them a more secure legal position in contracting with the government.

Dr. Duffield, as directed by the trustees, began negotiations with the government, which was represented by Captain George W. Lee,* chief quartermaster for the Michigan district. A native of Howell, where he had been a farmer before joining the army, Lee was as anxious as anyone to get the hospital started. He proved to be most co-operative. Still, it was with a somewhat heavy heart that Dr. Duffield saw his cherished dream of a hospital for the sick and poor of the city shunted aside for the time being. To his diary, he confided his disappointment, pointing out that if he had had his way the hospital would have been built long since. He had been frustrated, he said, by others, and while he mentioned no names, he certainly referred to some members of the board as well as to members of his church.

It has been no little grief to me that plans and measures which I devised and suggested for good and not for my own glory or advantage have almost always met with opposition and that chiefly from people of religion and of my own church. . . . So many are so proudly tenacious of their own opinions and really know so little, that it is scarcely practicable to lift them up to great ideas and plans. . . . Oh how much might have been done for the cause of Christ and the good of this city by the Presbyterian church. . . .[35]

Even though his heart was heavy at having to abandon his hopes, Duffield went along with the board. On April 7, he conferred with Tripler and Lee, "who let me know that the U.S. Govt. had accepted the offer I made of a lease as directed by the trustees of the Harper Hospital of their lot, and would proceed to erect a hospital building, forthwith upon it." [36] Two days later, April 9, the trustees met with Captain Lee, and formally approved the lease of Park lot 24—Nancy Martin's five acres.[37] There was a most important clause in the lease. It stipulated that at the end of the war, when the government no longer needed the Hospital, the trustees would be given "preferred opportunities for purchasing whatever improvements the United States might, during its term, have placed on the premises." This, of course, included the buildings used for hospital purposes.[38]

There was, however, an immediate, unforeseen problem. Captain Lee and other military officials, prior to April 9, had inspected the property and reported that five acres was not sufficient for a hospital of the size the government contemplated building. It was suggested that Harper acquire an additional adjoining five acres and include it in the lease. Park lot 25, north of the Nancy Martin property, was examined, and, as it corresponded in size with lot 24, it seemed logical to purchase it. Park lot 25 is that land now on the north side of Martin Place, extending nearly to East Alexandrine Avenue. It fronts on Woodward while its east boundary is between John R and Brush. In 1864, this lot had been divided into two parcels. One was owned by J. S. Dudgeon, the other by a Mrs. Mauch. At the April 9 meeting, the board approved the appointment of a special committee "to inquire into the probability of a purchase" of lot 25.[39] It was learned that Dudgeon would sell his piece, the north half, for $5,000.00, and Mrs. Mauch would part with hers for $5,587.50.[40] The trustees, although holding some assets realized from the sale of the Harper-Martin properties, felt the military hospital was sufficiently in the public interest to warrant soliciting for the funds required. They organized a campaign to raise the purchase price, meanwhile contracting with Dudgeon and Mrs. Mauch and in turn executing a lease to the government for Park lot 25 on the same terms as lot 24.[41]

Except for raising the money, the project now was in government hands. Captain Lee was assigned the job of overseeing the construction. An able, industrious officer, he went to work immediately. The *Detroit Free Press,* on June 9, 1864, announced that Lee had received his orders "to proceed at once with erection of the Military Hospital on Woodward Avenue." The work of sewering and grading had already been started by that date. There was, in fact, a main sewer extending along the line of Woodward Avenue to a point north of the Hospital. All that was required was to connect a lateral sewer to it, no great undertaking.[42] The *Free Press* stated that J. W. Ingersoll had been picked as the contractor. He was described as "the well known builder," and the paper added "workmen are now advertised for. . . . A large amount of money will be expended on the grounds and in the erection of the buildings, and when completed they will be alike an ornament to the city and an honor to the government."

While matters moved ahead satisfactorily with regard to construction, the money raisers were having their troubles. Most of the burden of solicitation, for some reason, fell on Dr. Duffield. Buckminster Wight, on whose assistance the minister counted, was sick and could be of little help. As early as May 26, Duffield made the rounds, wrote circulars, and solicited subscriptions. The results made him most unhappy. His fellow trustees quickly subscribed their share; they and their immediate friends and relatives pledged about $5,000. Then the campaign bogged down. Said Duffield:

> The Episcopalians generally have refused and so have the principal monied men in the Fort Street and others in the Jefferson Avenue Pres'n churches. I am reminded very often of the jealousy and envy which for years from both quarters have opposed my influence and refused with any

and every public and benevolent object that I may have initiated or taken active interest in. It is not for personal injury done anyone of them but I have by my preaching stripped the pretensions of many pharisaic formalists to a piety which they claim to be Christianity but which they reconcile with very many things I teach and believe to be inconsistent with true faith in Christ and the holiness Christ required in all his followers.[43]

Envy and other bad feelings were blamed by Duffield for his difficulties. "Lord keep me," he prayed, "from harboring un-Christian feelings or rendering evil for evil." [44]

Captain Lee told Duffield he had talked to Henry P. Baldwin, leading Episcopalian layman and future governor of Michigan, about some financial aid, but Baldwin "at first rather snappishly and angrily refused to give anything to us and the hospital, alleging it was a Presbyterian sectarian affair" controlled by Duffield. "Mr. B. knew better," Duffield replied. Baldwin had been invited to serve on the Board of Trustees at the very beginning, but had declined. He had indicated an interest in establishing an Episcopalian hospital.[45]

In order to lure dollars from prospective subscribers, the trustees adopted a bylaw, setting up a schedule of hospital benefits for contributors. Three classes of subscribers were provided for:

1. Life Patrons—those who gave $1,000 or more would be entitled to have one patient free of charge on the books at all times.
2. Donors—contributors of less than $1,000 could have one patient on the books free of charge at the rate of one month per year for each $100 contributed.
3. Annual Subscribers—those giving $100 per year could have one patient for eight months of each year for which the contribution was made; $75 allowed one patient for six months; $50 for four months; and $25 for two months. Those giving less than $25 were "entitled to a patient on the books for a time equal to double the amount of his or her subscription at the established rates for pay patients." [46]

Altogether, the canvass brought in $6,490.00 from 58 contributors, including not only the trustees, but also such distinguished individuals as Mayor Duncan Stewart, Senator Chandler, Hiram Walker, Philo Parsons, and Eber B. Ward. Even Baldwin finally relented and gave $100.00. Several firms were among the contributors, such as, G. & R. McMillan and the Detroit City Railroad Company. Amos Chaffee, who later would make the first endowment for Grace Hospital, was down for $25.00.[47] George W. Bissell, a leading shipper and lumberman, donated $50.00, little realizing when he did so that he would die in Harper Hospital in 1902, the victim of Detroit's first fatal automobile accident.[48] Still short of the necessary $10,587.50 by more than $4,000.00, the trustees voted, on October 7, 1864, to make up that difference by the sale of bonds and from other assets in the hands of the treasurer.[49]

Harper Hospital, 1865

Chapter 7

HAVEN FOR THE WOUNDED

Harper Hospital,
no longer a dream wrapped up in a trust agreement, was officially
opened Wednesday, October 12, 1864.[1] As a military hospital, reserved
for the casualties of Civil War battlefields, it was something quite different from the place envisaged by its founders for the care of the indigent sick and poor of Detroit. Nevertheless, it existed, and that, for the
time being, was progress that could not be discounted.

Announcing the opening, the *Detroit Advertiser and Tribune* said it
was "gratified." At the moment, that, no doubt, fairly reflected the
sentiments of most people. There was unquestionably more interest in
a military general hospital located in Michigan than there would have
been in an exclusively civilian hospital. The war had put its mark of
personal tragedy on hundreds of Michigan homes, and there was more
to come. Scores of Michigan boys, crippled and disabled by wounds and
disease, filled hospital beds in a dozen other states. Among the wounded
still remained many who had been struck down in the bloody en-
counters at Gettysburg and Chickamauga. Now a new flow of wounded
was pouring into the military hospitals as Grant unleashed his hammer
blows against Lee in Virginia, and as Sherman fought his way into
Atlanta and then began his push across Georgia to the sea. The Wilderness and Spotsylvania were names indelibly imprinted in letters of
horror in the minds of northerners as Grant, without regard to casualties, threw the full weight of the Union armies in Virginia into a campaign which was to crush the South. But the cost in human suffering
was terrible. Those in Michigan who could afford to, or who could
contrive to obtain official permission, traveled east or south to visit

their stricken sons and husbands. But for most of the boys, well-treated as they were, loneliness and homesickness in distant hospitals slowed their recovery and added to their misery.

Now, however, they could come home—or at least some of them could. Dr. Tunnicliff summed it up well, even if his language was on the flowery side, when he stated: "The sick soldier, whether slowly recovering from a wound, or convalescing from a lingering fever, longs for his 'native air' and the endearments of home and kindred."[2] By the same token, his loved ones were comforted by the knowledge that their son was close to home, within comparatively easy visiting distance. That was why the Hospital's opening was a cause for general rejoicing. The *Advertiser and Tribune* said:

> The buildings will not be entirely finished, but the work is being prosecuted with energy, and will soon be completed, when the capacity of the institution will be sufficient for the accommodation of 500 patients. . . . The institution will be in charge of Dr. John H. Rauch, the chief medical officer of Michigan.
>
> The Hospital is located on the east side of Woodward Avenue, a little over one mile north of the City Hall, and a few feet beyond the present terminus of the street railway.
>
> It is divided into eight wards, each comprising a separate building, the better to insure airiness and general comfort, with the main, or "administration building," in the center. The wards are frame structures, of one story, 180 feet in length by 24 feet in width, admirably lighted. The ceiling is uniformly 14 feet in height, and the buildings are provided with a modern system of ventilation, by means of exhausting shafts in the center. . . . There is room for 68 beds in each ward. There are two small rooms in front, for the use of attendants, and bathroom, etc., in the rear. The wards are 22 feet apart. . . . Each of them will have a verandah in front. . . . At the rear of the range of buildings, there is a covered walk uniting the whole, and thus extending the distance of 420 feet. . . .[3]

From this description, Harper Hospital conformed to the pavilion construction which at that time met standard government specifications.[4] The buildings were raised a foot or two off the ground to keep out insects and dampness. Each of the separate pavilions had windows along each side, 3 feet apart. The beds were placed in pairs, close to each window. With only 500 beds (later increased to 578), Harper was a small hospital. Some had as many as 3,000 beds.[5]

As the *Advertiser and Tribune* indicated, the front of the buildings, which were erected in a row, faced on Woodward Avenue and extended back to about the present line of John R. That street had not been opened north of Adelaide Street in 1864. The administration building stood in the center. It was flanked on each side by four ward buildings. Before long, the Woodward Avenue front was landscaped, and a picket fence was erected across the entire front which occupied most of the space between today's Alexandrine Street and Orchestra Place. In the rear of the entire installation was the "grove" which made a delightful park in which the patients could sit or stroll in good weather. Altogether there were eleven buildings. Besides the administration building and the eight wards, there were a guardhouse and a barracks or dormitory for the hospital personnel. There is some evidence that a twelfth building, a tool house, was later added.

The administration building, like all the others, was frame, but had two stories. Its dimensions were 307 by 32 feet, with about 20 rooms on the first floor. These were used for general offices, examining rooms, and steward's department, with the kitchen and dining room at the rear. All patients who were ambulatory had their meals in the common dining hall. The kitchen, a room of 32 by 40 feet, was equipped with a large iron range. The second floor provided living quarters for the doctors and other officers attached to the Hospital. From the *Advertiser and Tribune* came this description:

Near the northeast corner of the cleared portion of the grounds is located a fine and commodious building for guards, the dimensions of which are 24 by 124 feet. It is two stories in height, with a verandah in front. . . . Opposite this structure, near the southeast corner, and uniform in size and appearance with it, is another building, to be used as quarters for nurses and attendants, and for store rooms.[6]

The cost of all of these buildings was estimated to be between $30,000.00 and $40,000.00, which did not include the interior fittings and equipment.[7] The beds were iron cots, considered comfortable and luxurious by men who had slept mostly on the ground in camp or in field hospitals. A typical bill, submitted by J. W. Tillman, a furniture retailer, for equipment furnished in November and December, 1864, was for $32.12. It covered the cost of twenty-five "rush cottage" chairs, one office chair, one office stool, one looking glass, and one and one-half yards of cloth.[8]

Once the new hospital was completed, surgeon Rauch stepped aside and Dr. David Osburn Farrand, who carried the army rank of acting assistant surgeon, took over as surgeon-in-charge. Farrand had been in charge of military patients at St. Mary's, but, by the end of October, 1864, his name no longer appeared on the St. Mary's register. He was succeeded there by Dr. W. H. Gominger.[9]

The pungent smell of fresh paint and raw pine was still strong, and the hammers of the carpenters were still ringing when the first patients began to move into Harper. The record books show that the honor of being the first patient went to Private Henry Larkin of Detroit, a member of Company H, Fifth Michigan Cavalry. He was admitted in September, a month before the Hospital was officially opened. How and under what circumstances he got there at that early date are not disclosed.[10] The next man listed came in on October 13, the day after the official opening. He was Private Robert Gladstone, Company 1, Twenty-seventh Michigan Infantry. He brought with him a painful gunshot wound in the right shoulder, a battlefield souvenir from Spotsylvania.[11] The following day, October 14, Larkin and Gladstone were joined by Michael Schmouder, Company H, Twenty-seventh Michigan. Also a Spotsylvania casualty, Schmouder was wounded in the hand.[12]

After that, the Hospital began to fill up very rapidly. Almost immediately after the opening, Farrand transferred surgical patients to Harper from St. Mary's and Marine Hospitals. That seems to have been the pattern. Wounded men went to Harper; the sick, for the most part, went to St. Mary's or were cared for in other hospitals.[13] By October 24, Dr. Farrand had his hands so full looking after new arrivals that he confessed he had not had time to make a detailed report on his patients. He had 140 of them. By the next day, he was still too busy to take care of his paper work, although he noted that 38 of the men counted on the twenty-fourth had been furloughed, and one was in the guardhouse.[14] After that, organization must have been perfected and operation of Harper settled down to a routine, because nothing more was said about inability to keep up to date.

The transfers to Harper were made, at first, almost entirely from other general hospitals. It does not appear, as a matter of fact, that many cases were ever received direct from the front line field hospitals, although, of course, there may have been some. The earlier records of transfers show that Harper patients came from about twenty different general hospitals, including those in Nashville and Knoxville, Tennessee. The majority, however, came from institutions in and around Washington. There is only one early record of a transfer from a division hospital.[15] No officers were among the Harper patients. As a usual practice, sick and wounded officers were cared for either in special officer hospitals, or they went by choice to private hospitals.

How satisfactorily Harper was working out is indicated by the 1864 report of the Michigan adjutant general. It states:

> Transfers to hospitals in our state were necessarily infrequent, for the want of hospital accommodation. This difficulty is now somewhat remedied, and transfers of those of our gallant boys as have lost an arm, or a leg, or have been otherwise so seriously wounded that many months will elapse before restoration to health can be reasonably expected, are now being made.[16]

Furthermore, that Harper was fulfilling its intended mission of providing near-home care for the state's wounded, is shown by the records of admission of members of the Twenty-fourth Michigan Infantry between October and December, 1864. The Twenty-fourth was as gallant a regiment as any which went to the front from any state. Recruited as an all Detroit-Wayne County outfit in 1862 and attached to the Army of the Potomac, it was made part of the famous Iron Brigade. It tasted its first blood at Fredericksburg but achieved great distinction at Gettysburg. It was one of the Union regiments which opened the battle on July 1, 1863. By helping to hold up the Confederate advance until General Meade could get his entire army into position, the Twenty-fourth won imperishable glory. It also nearly won extinction. At the end of the day's fight, it had lost eighty-eight per cent of its men. That was the highest casualty rate suffered by any regiment on either side in a single engagement.[17] Its ranks included Chaplain Edwin Wight, brother of Buckminster, Gurdon L. Wight, a nephew of the Harper trustee, and Lieutenant Frederick Buhl, son of another trustee. Quite understandably, a special effort would have been made to bring wounded members of the Twenty-fourth home. During the three-month period, there were about twenty or twenty-five who were transferred to Harper. Most of them had gunshot wounds; a few had been wounded by shells. Several, including Gurdon Wight, had been hurt at Gettysburg, although Akin Holloway of Company C had been shot through the right lung in the Battle of the Wilderness in May, 1864.[18] Unfortunately, there was a good deal of red tape involved in obtaining a transfer to Harper. It was not an automatic procedure for a wounded Michigan soldier. Michigan military agents or members of the Sanitary Commission would discover a Wolverine in some other hospital. The agent would make out the papers and file the application for transfer. Often there would be a considerable time lag before it was approved. Also, it was not uncommon for a wounded man to lose his identification papers, or perhaps his commanding officer had not gotten around to filling them out. In that case, the wounded man not only had trouble getting a transfer, but his pay also would be held up. Again, there was something for the sympathetic state military agent to straighten out.[19]

The number of Harper patients fluctuated widely from day to day, partly as a result of transfer delays, partly because men were furloughed or discharged as fast as their health permitted. While there were 140 patients on October 24, 1864, there were only 56 on the twenty-eighth. By October 31, the bed count was 78, and on December 31, 1864, it had risen to 314.[20] Up to that time, the transfers had been made either as individuals or in small groups. The Medical Director of Transportation, a branch of the Army Medical Department, had headquarters in Philadelphia. It was his duty to keep informed of the number of available beds in the various general hospitals. In 1865, he was endeavoring to clear out, as fast as possible, those hospitals near the front, the ones in and around Washington. On July 2, 1865, when the shooting war was over and demobilization had begun, the Harper staff was notified that it would receive, in a single draft, 137 patients.[21] That was the largest single consignment. Nevertheless, through most of 1865, the Hospital was well filled. The peak was reached May 1, when 645 beds were filled. After that, with no new battle casualties, the Hospital's population began a steady decline, until on December 31, 1865 not a patient remained.[22]

When Dr. Farrand took over as surgeon-in-charge at Harper, he was only twenty-seven years old, and not long out of medical school. He joined the army as a surgeon in 1862 without having very much medical practice or experience. He served for a short time in a general hospital in St. Louis before he was ordered back to Detroit and assigned to St. Mary's. Both his commission and his hospital assignments, including that at Harper, were apparently due, in part, to the influence of Dr. Tripler. Farrand, one might judge, was a Tripler protégé. Nevertheless, despite his youth and lack of experience, David Farrand proved to be an excellent surgeon and administrator, fully justifying Tripler's confidence in him.[23]

Early in 1865, Farrand was relieved, replaced by Dr. Byron Stanton, a surgeon of volunteers. Stanton remained only a short time at Harper before resigning to accept a position as head of a mental institution in Ohio. Farrand had remained in Detroit, practicing under Dr. Zina Pitcher. He was recalled and again placed in charge at Harper. Once more his tenure was brief. For reasons not explained, he requested a transfer to command of the post hospital at Fort Wayne. He was succeeded this time by a Dr. Wynkoop, of Pennsylvania, who remained in charge as long as Harper was under military jurisdiction.[24]

Associated with Farrand and comprising his surgical staff were Drs. W. A. Chandler, William C. Catlin, E. W. Jenks, and G. W. Fitzpatrick. These men had all worked with him previously at St. Mary's. In addition, there were others who apparently assisted at Harper, either on a contract basis or simply as volunteer consultants. Among them was Dr. George P. Andrews, who had been on the St. Mary's staff, as well as Drs. Theodore McGraw, A. F. Jennings, and Samuel Duffield. These men, including Dr. Farrand, ultimately were key members of the staff of Harper when it became a civilian hospital.[25] Dr. Don Campbell, a later member of the Hospital staff, recalled that when Harper filled up with soldiers, "the very best of the medical men of Detroit were on the staff." Mentioning McGraw, Jennings, Duffield, and Andrews, Dr. Campbell stated:

> These men were great men, they were leaders. . . . Under their care was this large number of people coming from the war, and they thought to themselves, now we must make some use of this, we must have some teaching done here, so they started a clinic in this hospital, and from that clinic grew what now is the Wayne [State] University School of Medicine.[26]

By any set of standards, it would appear that the Michigan wounded, hospitalized at Harper, were in the best hands the medical profession had to offer. It is no wonder that Harper, while one of the smaller general hospitals, was considered by many to be among the best.

In addition to the medical or surgical staff, there was a complement of contract nurses, all of whom were men, several women nurses, matrons, and stewards. The number of these attendants varied according to the load at any particular time. For example, on July 31, 1865, there were

19 contract nurses, 14 female nurses, 2 matrons, and 2 stewards. The normal complement of attendants and guards was 120 to 200, depending on the size of the hospital.[27] This latter number included the guards of a detachment of the Veterans Reserve Corps, under the command of a line officer. Actually, the Veterans Reserve Corps was attached to the Detroit Barracks under the provost marshal. These men were veterans, who were either wounded or in some way physically or mentally unfit for front line duty. Nationally, they were organized into two battalions with a total enrollment of 60,000, although all that number was never serving at the same time.[28] Besides being used at the hospitals, they also guarded military installations, helped preserve civil order, aided in the conscription, and generally made themselves useful on a local level.

Quite frequently, hospital patients, including some at Harper, instead of being discharged for disability, were transferred into the Veterans Reserve, as they were considered able to perform light duty. Because of this, and because as guards and sentries they were responsible for preventing patients from slipping out of the hospital for a night on the town or from going A.W.O.L., they were not too popular with the convalescent soldiers. Some patients, when ready for duty, preferred to return to their regiments in the field rather than be assigned to the Veterans Reserve.[29] It was the feeling that the Veterans Reserve Corps did not offer the most honorable and patriotic type of military service. One report describes it as composed mostly of men "who are always taken a little lame just before the fight, and drift back from the rear of the army to the hospitals." [30] But regardless of their warring capabilities, or the lack of esteem in which they were held by real fighting men, they were a boon to the Medical Department, giving that branch "what it had long wanted—organized military companies, controlled by line officers, to guard the hospitals and care for the clothing and effects of the patients." [31]

Michigan soldiers, while they were patients in hospitals in Knoxville, Jeffersonville, or Alexandria, griped loud enough to be heard back home. Griping is a prerogative of soldiers—an honorable practice known to all warriors in all the wars of history. When taken to Michigan to recuperate in the beneficial climate of their native state, close to friends and relatives, and far from the fields of battle, they still griped. Their complaints were shrill. Nothing suited them. The food was bad; the surgeons were heartless butchers; the restraint imposed by military disciplines was intolerable. Nothing pleased them, or would have pleased them, short of full discharges, or at least indefinite furloughs. The abuse of which they considered themselves the unfortunate victims allowed no credit to the fact that they received medical and surgical care at the hands of some of the best practitioners to be found and that their treatment in the Harper military hospital compared favorably with what could have been obtained in the best civilian hospitals in either Europe or the United States at that time. There was an ambulance that met the trains and boats and took them to the new hospital out on Woodward with a minimum of discomfort. They had comfortable iron beds and clean linens. The food was far superior to anything they had eaten for a long time in the field. The citizens of Detroit could not do enough for them in the way of providing entertainment and small luxuries.[32]

Of course there were irritations and annoyances in the hospitals as well as in the field. Red tape was not shot away by Confederate minié balls that found their mark. Delay in getting their pay was a common and justifiable complaint. When a soldier became detached from his regiment because of illness or wounds, his company commander was expected to report the reason for his absence on the soldier's "descriptive list," on which were noted his condition, whether his pay was in arrears, and how much. If the commanding officer was too busy fighting battles to keep his paper work up to date, if records were lost or destroyed as they frequently were, the wounded man could neither draw pay nor clothing until he had threaded his way laboriously through a maze of bureaucracy, a process that often took months. There were thousands of such cases reported after the Battles of Spotsylvania and the Wilderness.[33]

Men were furloughed from the hospital as fast as their conditions warranted. This enabled convalescents to go home where recovery was often speedier and also provided space for new arrivals. The soldiers abused the privilege thus extended them at every opportunity. Without too much hard persuasion, they would prevail upon their home town physicians to give them sworn statements that they were unfit to travel and needed additional days or weeks at home after their furloughs were up. If a man failed to return, the provost marshal was notified, and he was classed as a deserter. Frequently, the local doctor's statement was not acceptable to the hospital authorities, even if issued, as sometimes was the case, in good faith. When that happened, the wounded man felt more persecuted than ever.[34] Yet, in spite of such annoyances, real or imagined, the Harper patients received excellent care.

. REV. DR. GEORGE DUFFIELD —
interested in establishing a hospital in Detroit for the care of the
indigent sick, Dr. Duffield, min-
ster of the First Presbyterian
Church, persuaded Walter Harper
o endow the institution which be-
ame Harper Hospital. Dr. Duf-
eld served as first president of
he Harper Board of Trustees
rom 1859 until his death in 1868.

ourtesy Burton Historical Collection

. DR. CHARLES S. TRIPLER — A
Civil War Surgeon, Dr. Tripler
ampaigned for the establishment
f a general military hospital in
Iichigan. The result of his efforts
was the building of Harper in
863 by the government for the
are of convalescent troops. After
he war, the Hospital filled a dual
ole as a soldiers' home and civil-
n hospital.

ourtesy Burton Historical Collection

5. The Detroit Medical College — Established in 1868 by Harper doctors, the college occupied two of the original army hospital buildings on Woodward Avenue. A high wooden fence surrounded the Hospital and the grove of trees, which is seen in the rear, bordered on Recreation Park.

The college subsequently became Wayne State University College of Medicine. When the buildings were torn down in 1884, the two-story center connecting section of the college erected in 1868 was moved to Beaubien Street near Eliot, and was still standing in 1963.

Courtesy Wayne State University Archives

Chapter 8

THE TRAVAIL OF PRIVATE GROSS

Hippocrates said that
"war is the only proper school for the surgeon," a thesis upon which was based the corollary that "the Civil War paved the way for modern surgery." [1] To the extent that each observation is true, Harper patients received the most up-to-date surgical attention. Most of the men entering the Hospital were surgical cases, suffering from gunshot wounds, usually in the extremities. There were few shell wounds, and virtually none from bayonets.[2]

When the men arrived, Harper was ready for them, even if the facilities, by modern standards, were primitive. No operating rooms had been provided. Patients were readied for surgery by placing them on tables, made of doors resting on sawhorses. Generally this rough and ready arrangement was set up in the wards. Sometimes operations were performed on the counter of the dispensary in the administration building. Wherever it took place, the patient was stretched out and given a whiff of chloroform. Then Dr. Farrand, or Andrews, or one of the other surgeons, would take over. Without anything resembling antisepsis and working against imperfect anesthetic, a limb would be amputated, a stray fragment of metal would be extracted, or the rush work performed in a field hospital would be corrected. Although crude, these methods were the best that medical knowledge had to offer at the time. Every possible attention was given the patients; every known safeguard was employed.

Being primarily a surgical center, care was taken to prevent the spread of contagious diseases. For example, in December, 1864, a private in the Thirtieth Michigan Infantry came down with measles. Realizing what the consequences might be to other patients, Dr. Farrand promptly arranged for his transfer. Pointing out that the man could not remain at Harper without exposing the entire Hospital, Farrand called upon the authorities at St. Mary's. "If you can admit him," he said, "please send your ambulance for him." [3]

There were many Civil War amputees, and Harper had its share of them. But the government saw to it, whenever possible, that artificial arms or legs were provided at government expense, and many of these limbs were fitted at Harper. Unfortunately, this program also was bound up in a certain amount of red tape. A directive from Dr. Tripler called attention to the fact that the patient waiting to be fitted was required to furnish proof that he was an enlisted man; he had to submit an affidavit, endorsed by his commanding officer, showing that his limb was lost while in service, and describing the details. In addition, full and complete measurements were required for the guidance of the manufacturer. [4] There was reason for all of this paper work. Because amputees had to wait for complete healing and full recovery before getting their artificial limbs many were discharged, and when they returned at a later date, it was often to a hospital other than the one in which the operation had been performed. The government wanted to protect itself against providing limbs which might have been lost in non-service accidents occurring after discharge.

The quality of the care and treatment given the wounded at Harper and other general hospitals is shown in the mortality records. For all of these institutions, for the entire period of the war, the mortality rate was eight per cent, "the lowest ever recorded for military hospitals and lower than in many civil institutions." [5] The exact mortality rate for Harper during 1864–65 is not known, but at one period it was slightly above four per cent. Considering that some patients arrived in moribund condition after major battles, that is an extraordinarily low rate. In 1895, after medical science had made great advances and the Hospital was completely equipped, the Harper mortality rate was 7.5 per cent. [6]

This fact was not lost upon the patients, despite their natural and normal complaints. The skill of Farrand and his associates made a favorable impression that carried over when Harper Hospital became a civilian institution. The Wolverine patients came from all over Michigan —from the Upper Peninsula mining and lumber regions, from Lansing, Kalamazoo, Port Huron, and hundreds of other towns and farm districts. After the war, the former patients recalled with a sense of gratitude what had been done for them; their friends, neighbors, and local physicians saw the results of their treatment at Harper, and the reputation of the Detroit institution spread across the state and beyond.

The good people of Detroit looked upon the soldiers who were patients at Harper as their own charges, and organized efforts were made to entertain them and provide them with small comforts and luxuries. A bowling green was installed for their entertainment, with proceeds from the sale of instruments after the Harper band was discontinued. Books, newspapers, and magazines, including the inevitable religious tracts, were furnished in abundance. The Rev. Dr. Duffield noted in his diary on May 23, 1865, that "in the afternoon with Rev. Harwood, Mr. Kuilts, Mrs. Thurstone, Mrs. Andrews and other ladies, who sing, visited the Harper Hospital praying with and exhorting the sick in 7 out of the 8 wards, there being a surgical operation going on in one which prevented our entering there. There were [illegible] patients in the Hospital. We distributed tracts in each and I occasionally stopped to converse with the sick confined to their beds." [7] Groups of women, usually representing church organizations, emptied their fruit closet shelves of jellies and jams, and baskets of delicacies from the kitchens of scores of households were regularly taken to the Hospital for distribution. The patients, when short furloughs or passes were handed out, were welcomed in the homes of the citizens. There was never a lack of visitors. Band concerts were given, and choruses of young ladies staged concerts. The grove at the east end of the Hospital grounds was an ideal place in good weather, and it is likely that more than once it provided the spot for a romantic interlude for a wounded soldier and a pretty young lady who came to the Hospital to sing and remained afterward to be courted.

The *Detroit Free Press* of December 28, 1864, reported that the "patriotic ladies" of the city provided "another splendid dinner for the soldiers at Harper's Hospital which was given on Monday. Everything was provided in abundance. After dinner, tables were cleared, music provided, and the festivities shaped themselves into a social dancing party." [8] The ladies, particularly those engaged in the good work of the Michigan Branch of the United States Sanitary Commission made one contribution which consisted of 108 towels, 7 pounds of rags, 5 books, 3 pamphlets, and 150 newspapers.[9]

That the patients were well fed can be established by the Harper record of food purchases. The menus were prescribed by army regulations and were the same in all hospitals as far as local conditions permitted. The government allowed a commutation of eighteen cents per day per patient.[10] While that does not seem like an excessive amount, the stewards of a well-run hospital were able to save enough on that budget to provide for special diets. The standard government "full diet" consisted of breakfast: coffee, cold meat, bread; dinner: pork and beans, bread pudding; supper: tea with milk, bread, and butter. Although this was perhaps nourishing, being confronted with the same bill of fare, meal after meal, day after day, was one of the patients' chief complaints.[11]

Still, at Harper, there must have been considerable variation from this regulation diet. The grocery bills, or at least many of them, have been preserved. John F. Clegg appears to have been the principal contractor, and one of his bills, dated January 21, 186[5?], shows that he delivered butter, 109 pounds; squashes, 2 dozen; oysters, 10 cans; fish; turnips, 1 bushel; beets, 1 bushel; currants, one-half bushel; lemon peel, 2 ounces; as well as various quantities of eggs, cranberries, and raisins. Other invoices show purchases of fairly substantial amounts of pork, beef, flour, beans, coffee, sugar, vinegar, soap, salt, pepper, apples, potatoes, butter, and cooking oil.[12] One two-month bill for milk amounted to $150.40.[13] Certainly in 1864 and 1865, a good deal of milk could have been bought for that much money. That not all of the fancier items represented on the grocery lists went on the tables of the doctors and staff is fairly well established by the ration returns signed, at times, by Dr. Farrand. The conclusion is that, while the regulation daily menus were monotonous, they were augmented by delicacies, furnished not only by the Hospital, but also in generous amounts by the ladies of Detroit. Then, too, there was nothing to prevent patients who could afford to do so from eating in restaurants when they had passes, or from buying snacks, either at the city stores or from the sutler or exchange, which was probably somewhere on the Hospital grounds.

Civil War soldiers were dedicated letter-writers and diarists, and when they were hospitalized, their pens were busier than ever, helping to relieve the monotony of convalescence. Fortunately, one patient who kept a diary while at Harper recorded a running account of his experiences, providing a vivid—and, we may believe, typical—picture of life in the wards.[14] The soldier was Frank Gross of Algoma, a village of six hundred souls in Kent County, a few miles from Grand Rapids. He was eighteen years old when he enlisted in Company B, Sixth Michigan Cavalry on September 8, 1862, at Grand Rapids. The Sixth was one of the regiments in General Custer's famed Michigan Cavalry Brigade, and as a member, Frank Gross saw a good deal of campaigning, including participation in the Battle of Gettysburg. In 1864, along with the rest of the Army of the Potomac, his regiment was in northern Virginia in the vicinity of Fredericksburg. General Grant had taken charge; command of the Cavalry Corps was given to Philip Sheridan; and the campaign which began with the battles of the Wilderness and Spotsylvania would culminate in the investiture of Richmond and Lee's final surrender, a year later, at Appomattox.

For most of March and April, 1864, Gross's entries were largely concerned with the abominable weather in Virginia, and the fact that "I have not had much to do today. I guess business ain't very pressing just now." But "business" picked up when the weather got better in May. On the sixth of that month, the regiment was near the old battleground of Chancellorsville in the Wilderness, that tangle of forest and undergrowth which was a nightmare for an infantryman and sheer hell for a horse soldier. It was there that Frank Gross's active military career came to an abrupt end. He wrote:

> This morning we were on the march by daylight. About 10 o'clock, as we were dismounted in some small pines by the roadside, a company of rebel cavalry charged us, yelling like so many demons, but they did not catch a "weasel asleep," as they supposed. A spirited action commenced in which I was severely wounded.

Gross was struck in the hip by a musket ball, and from his later description, it would appear that the bullet penetrated deeply and struck the bone, either being deflected by it or lodging against it, but in either case, chipping it. Although not a fatal injury or one which called for amputation, it made walking and riding impossible for the time being. It put Frank out of action and, after some delay, into the hospital.

> As it was no place for the wounded, several others like myself were put in ambulances and carried to the rear. It was *then* I began to realize the horrors of war. All the other hardships I had seen were as mite cast into a whale's mouth, by the side of the intense suffering that I now endured,

with no fair prospect of its being alleviated very soon. The wounded began to come in very fast and to hear the groans of the wounded and dying men was most discouraging indeed . . .

The field hospital to which I was carried was some two miles as near as I could judge. Here our wounds were examined and a great many of us put into six mule wagons and started back to the Rapidan with the intention of taking the cars for Washington, but upon reaching the ford, it was ascertained that the rebels had got there and destroyed the depot. Of course we could not go that way, so we turned about and made for Fredericksburg, which place [we] reached after a severe ride of two days and three nights over roads that would be a disgrace to the *poor* roads of Michigan.

At Fredericksburg, Gross and his companions were put in a building, formerly a warehouse, and bedded on the floor which "seemed to have uncommon hard feelings towards us." They remained there several days. On May 23, they were moved across the Rappahannock, taken the next day by rail to Aquia Creek, put aboard a ship, and carried to Alexandria. Gross finally arrived in the King Street Hospital and was later transferred to the Mansion House Hospital, where he remained until February, 1865.

The surgeons at first were unable to locate and extract the ball in Frank's hip. Later, after a large abscess had formed, he was operated on, and a small piece of the bullet, which had broken up in his flesh, was removed. After that, he began to improve and was able to get around on crutches. He had a setback, however, when attempting to go downstairs "one of my crutches caught and threw me down with great force on my wounded hip." By the end of February, he had recovered from that mishap. He had no complaints about his treatment, stating that "we have good quarters here. I am waiting now for a transfer to Michigan." He was looking forward to going home, and the time passed slowly until his transfer orders were received and he left Alexandria on March 30, 1865. On the way home, he took some "Dutch leave," stopping over in Ohio to visit relatives near Akron. He arrived in Detroit "at this Hospital Apr. 6th."

He was not impressed at all with Harper Hospital or the surgical staff which looked after him. He probably thought that being back in his native state and close to home would be like living in the Elysian fields compared to what he had gone through. He soon learned differently, however, and the remainder of his diary is mostly one long complaint. He said, disapprovingly, of his hospitalization at Harper:

Was very much disappointed with the way this is carried out. A private soldier is but little better than a dog. I was uncommon homesick for the first in a long time. I expected to get a furlough when I got here but found myself mistaken. A person can hardly get away after he is there. The food is not as good as one might suppose. The hospital quarters are excellent, but I do think the doctors are very incompetent for hospital surgeons, especially the one in this ward. I guess they come in the service to keep from starving. It is a disgrace to the state of Michigan to employ such doctors. Men here are put in the guard-house for the least thing out of the way; one consolation is that shoulder-straps cannot domineer always.

April, 1865 came and with it the end of the war. Rumors circulated through Harper that now everyone would be going home. But Gross was not ready for a discharge, and therefore was not too disappointed when the rumor proved false.

My wound is a very bad one and must be taken care of for a long time yet. I did have some idea of having an operation performed on my hip to search for the ball or dead bone, but I have so little confidence in the surgeons here that I have given up the notion. . . . I've got so out of humor with the way men are treated here, that I would not let them have the privilege of hacking me to pieces for a fortune.

Part of Gross's hesitancy to have an operation performed was based apparently on fear and from having observed the effects of surgery on other soldiers.

Two patients from this ward went to the operating room and took chloroform. Both wounds were in the feet, but on one case, nothing was made out. Considerable dead bone was found in the other wound. They both looked pale. It put me in mind of old times last summer. Chloroform had a bad effect, taking two or three days to get over it and sometimes making the patient very sick.

Gross was set on a furlough. He applied for leave to go back to Algoma over July 4, and he grumbled because it was not immediately granted. Boredom and disappointment affected his disposition, causing him to write late in June:

Grub miserable this evening. I never ate a mouthful. If this is the way wounded men are treated, I'm sorry I ever was a soldier. I shall never get well as long as I am here. There is not enough substance in the food to keep a well man, much less one that had a running wound.

On June 29, he noted that the guards were removed and the patients were permitted to leave the Hospital for short periods without passes. Later, the privilege was revoked.

It's the men's own fault. They began to carry off hospital clothing as fast as they were discharged.

Gross did get his July 4 furlough after all, and went home in good spirits. "My wound," he said on his departure, "is doing very well."

The folks on the farm at Algoma were busy haying while Frank was there, and to a country boy the weather was a matter of prime concern then, as well as after his return. His health and spirits, in fact, seemed to rise and fall with the barometer. "Today was fine," he reported on one occasion. The next day "it rained a good share of the time. . . . Plenty of musty hay through the country this season." Again, "the weather still cold and rainy. The times dull and most awful lonesome." On a bright, sunny day, "my wound seems to be getting along slowly." On another, "my wound is not as well as usual. Rather cloudy weather for wounds."

He returned to Harper July 9, having overstayed his leave by a day, but nothing was said about it. He found the Hospital full. "A man was put in the guard house just before I came or I would have to sleep on the floor for a few days." Men were being discharged rapidly from July on, and from time to time Gross had to help out with the paper work in the office. But that occupation didn't take his mind off his troubles. He would get well and be discharged too, he thought, if only "the rations were fit for a dog." He heartily disapproved of the diet, describing his supper on July 11, as "steamed water, called *tea,* melted grease, called *butter,* and bread passable here, but would not be at home." He expressed the opinion that the only reason bread was given the patients was to keep it from becoming moldy.

To occupy himself when he was not writing out discharges for other men, Gross made picture frames. Once he made a ring which he sold. He also stood fire watch from time to time. Once he went to the theater; again he visited the Detroit reservoir but didn't see much, as it was too early for visitors. On another occasion he went to town to help a comrade apply for a disability pension. Any little diversion was welcome, although he was not too enthusiastic about visitors. He remarked somewhat bitterly:

The people who come in to visit us occasionally think this is a great benefit for wounded soldiers, but they are greatly in error, for they will not find one in a hundred that can say with truth that he is contented. We like liberty too well. The war is over and we all want to be free.

Apparently he didn't make use of the bowling green; perhaps his injury prevented him from doing so. But the other boys, he observed, kept it "running all the time when it don't rain."

He was thinking again about having an operation, "and run the risk. It can't make me much worse off than I am at present." The doctors talked to him about it, but he still couldn't decide what to do, although he added that "it will cost me considerable to have it done after I'm discharged." He took note of Dr. Farrand's leaving and the arrival of a new surgeon-in-charge, who must have been Dr. Wynkoop. Gross must have respected Farrand because he expressed doubt about whether the new man could measure up to him.

Early in August, 1865, Gross applied for a discharge and immediately his wound began to feel better. But he had a relapse when his application failed to clear the red tape immediately. "I am in hopes my papers will get around soon, so I can get out of this 'prison' as it should be called," he said. With each day that he had to wait, his hip was more painful—"my hip has ached outrageous today." The next day "my wound does not feel very well." The third day "my wound feels miserable." But on the fourth day he received mail from home and "my wound feels better."

He began to worry about the delay in getting his discharge and blamed it on the

. . . miserable surgeon in charge. This morning he had a quarrel with Col. Smith, the mustering out officer, because he discharged the men too fast to suit him. If the Dr. could have his way, the men would not get out of here very soon. He did not make much out of the Colonel.

On the afternoon of August 18, Gross went to see a cricket match between Detroit and Toronto. "The Detroiters got the little end of the horn." But when he got back to the Hospital, he found that he had won, if the Detroit cricketeers hadn't. His discharge had come through, but it was too late to pick it up that day, Saturday. He had to wait until Monday—during which time "my wound aches bad by spells, and runs worse than usual." But by Monday noon things had improved. He got his " 'Spread Eagle' as it is called," visited the paymaster, and drew $164.75. In the afternoon he went to Canada and purchased a pair of boots, and that evening—August 21, 1865—he "left Detroit on the everlasting accommodation train."

That ended the Harper Hospital saga of Frank Gross. Despite his constant complaining, which unquestionably grew out of physical discomfort and boredom, he was, by his own evidence, humanely treated, and in all probability his life was saved. He may have thought himself badly abused while he was in Harper Hospital; his feelings undoubtedly mellowed once he was released. He would not have been discharged in August unless it was reasonably certain that he was sufficiently recovered to go home.

His experience was typical of hundreds of Michigan soldiers, brought back to health in Harper Hospital.*

Chapter 9

THE SOLDIERS' HOME

Harper Hospital was
empty of patients on December 31, 1865, all the Civil War soldiers
having been discharged or transferred. The hiatus was a short one. On
January 1, 1866, Harper became a civilian hospital. Control passed
overnight from the government of the United States to the Board of
Trustees. To transform the Hospital from an emergency measure arising
out of a national need to its original purpose took months of negotiation
between federal authorities and the Board of Trustees. It had been
stipulated in 1864 in the lease to the government that, when the need
for a military hospital no longer existed, the property would be returned
to the association represented by the trustees. It also was agreed that the
Hospital would have the opportunity to acquire, also through negotiation, such improvements as the government might have made, including
buildings and equipment.

With the war over, and with the number of patients gradually de-
creasing, the trustees began to move toward recovery of the premises.
Meeting at the office of Secretary Divie B. Duffield on September 28,
1865, the trustees considered and approved a motion by Jacob Farrand
that a committee be named to confer with Major General Orlando B.
Willcox "in respect to an application by the association for the acquisition
of the buildings on the lot or hospital grounds from the U.S. Govt. &
the proper persons to apply to in respect thereto." [1] The committee, which
consisted of the Rev. Dr. Duffield, Frederick Buhl, and Buckminster
Wight, wasted no time in calling upon General Willcox and getting the
necessary transfer machinery in motion.

General Willcox was one of Michigan's foremost Civil War heroes.

A graduate of West Point, he saw service in the Mexican War. He resigned from the army after that conflict and became associated in the practice of law with his brother, Eben Willcox. When the Civil War broke out, Willcox was given command of the First Michigan Infantry and led the first contingent of Michigan troops to the front. Wounded and captured at First Bull Run, he was exchanged and was soon back in action. Before the war ended, he commanded a brigade and then a division in the Army of the Potomac, and on occasion he served as a temporary corps commander. A winner of the Congressional Medal of Honor, Willcox had the respect of the people of Michigan, and his influence extended to the War Department in Washington. He was a logical choice for the trustees' intermediary. Willcox apparently was successful in opening the door of Major General Edward O. C. Ord, the quartermaster general. Just prior to November 14, the board had a letter from General Ord. While its exact contents are not known, it must have been encouraging. The board authorized the committee "to act in the premises as circumstances may require, calling the Board together if necessary for further authority and direction in this matter." [2]

Another ally was found in Captain (by now a Colonel) George Lee, who had supervised the construction of the hospital buildings. Dr. Duffield noted in his diary:

> Was met today [November 30, 1865] by Col. Lee who spoke to me of the proposed sale of furniture of the Gov't in the Harper Hospital. I have urged Mr. Frisbee [not identified] to buy it all and prepare for a speedy opening of the hospital for city sick and others. Lord let this enterprise have thy blessing. Give us wisdom, fidelity and zeal to act so that we may be the means in thy hand of initiating and carrying forward our hospital that may be a blessing to this city. Provide for us and may we be thy servants.[3]

Preparing to sell the furnishings would indicate that the government was rapidly moving toward complete evacuation of the premises. This was proved to be the case when Dr. Duffield, on December 12, received a letter from Washington, stating that the association's request for the buildings had been approved. The terms were most favorable—all the trustees could have asked or hoped for. The hospital buildings were, in effect, to be a gift of the government, conditioned only on the agreement of the association that the Hospital:

> . . . will take care of invalid discharged soldiers from the State of Michigan without calling upon the government for further aid or material and that

such transfer shall be in full satisfaction of any claim against the U. States arising out of the occupation of the property of the association for hospital purposes.

This bore the approval of the Secretary of War and Brigadier General C. H. Hoyt, chief quartermaster of the Department of Ohio in which Michigan was included.[4]

"The Lord prospers His own enterprizes," Dr. Duffield proclaimed upon receiving that letter. "Blessed be His name. Oh grant us wisdom and ability to make it a great blessing!"[5] Dr. Duffield immediately called a meeting of the Board of Trustees and triumphantly read the letter. He estimated the value of the buildings at $30,000 to $40,000.[6] A resolution was promptly adopted, stating that the trustees:

. . . do very gratefully accept the proposition . . . and cheerfully pledge themselves to the faithful performance of the condition annexed thereto, which condition this Board recognize as both appropriate and just on the part of the United States, in connection with their release of the property thus generously made to the association; and they do hereby release the United States Government of and from all claims for the use of said property by the United States for hospital purposes.[7]

At the same time, another resolution was adopted, commending Colonel Lee and acknowledging his efforts and influence in effecting the transfer.

In the faithful and intelligent manner in which he has discharged the duties of his office in ordering and superintending the construction of the buildings devoted to hospital purposes, and the improvement of the grounds, he deserves the thanks of the soldiers of this state, of the people of Detroit, and also of the officers and friends of this institution.[8]

With the hospital buildings assured them, the trustees saw no reason why the furniture, equipment, and medical supplies should not also be transferred by the government. The proposition had been discussed by Dr. Duffield and General Hoyt, who was in Detroit on December 14, 1865. The general apparently had been in town for a few days previous to the fourteenth in order to arrange for the transfer of the property. Papers culminating the deal were held by the board "until information is received in respect to the furniture, supplies and medical stores on hand."[9] Duffield, on the advice of Hoyt, telegraphed the Secretary of War through "our Senator at Washington" (probably Zach Chandler) petitioning for the supplies.[10] The reply, received on December 16, was favorable. The government only asked for a complete inventory and appraisal, and to make the survey a committee was named, of which Jacob Farrand and his brother, Dr. David Osburn Farrand, were members. The appraisal required only a day's work. The furniture and supplies were then turned over to the hospital, and receipted for. At the same time that this transaction was completed, Colonel Lee informed the trustees that the quartermaster stores on hand, valued at $3,000, would also be given to the Hospital.[11]

Everything was in order by the last week of December. It then occurred to the trustees that they had assumed a responsibility, namely, caring for invalid Michigan veterans. To do that, more money was required than was on hand. It was decided to seek public help.[12] The trustees declared:

Immediate demands will be made for outlay of money to carry out the conditions assumed by the association with the U.S., and further, reliance must be had in a large measure upon the generous impulses and benevolence of our citizens both in Detroit and thro' out the state.[13]

It is interesting and significant that on the eve of Harper's becoming a civilian hospital, Dr. Duffield's original concept of service to Detroit had broadened. Because of the government's stipulation that Michigan soldiers must be provided for, the trustees, as indicated in this appeal for funds, were now thinking of serving the entire state. First as a military hospital and then as a civilian hospital, Harper was regarded as a state, rather than a purely local, institution. At midnight, December 31, 1865, the transition was made, and Harper Hospital passed from the jurisdiction of the United States to the Board of Trustees.

On the morning of January 2, 1866, Harper Hospital opened its doors as a private institution and received its first patients, twenty-four Michigan veterans, transferred from the Soldiers' Home.[14]

On January 3, 1866, the trustees held their first meeting of the year and faced problems of organization. They voted to advertise for private patients (as opposed to veterans) and to fit up rooms for their reception. There also was the matter of a staff. Medical, nursing, and administrative personnel were needed at once. Several applications for jobs had been received, but for the moment they were not acted upon. It was decided to delegate hiring to the provisional committee, "to appoint such persons, male and female in charge of the Hospital as they in their judgment may deem expedient and until the definite action of this Board in the premises." [15]

Mrs. L. A. Sanborn, who also had been connected with the military hospital, continued on as matron, assisted by Mrs. D. M. Freeman, while the superintendent and steward was R. R. Knapp. Doctor E. W. Jenks and George P. Andrews were named attending physicians, and Drs. Theodore A. McGraw and David O. Farrand were the attending surgeons. The consulting staff consisted of Drs. N. D. Stebbins and Morse Stewart, physicians, and Drs. Charles Tripler and Zina Pitcher, surgeons. Dr. Samuel P. Duffield, who then had a Ph.D., but not yet his medical degree, was added as chemist and microscopist.[16] These were among the most outstanding and successful practitioners in Detroit. Their names were familiar, all of them having been associated in some degree with the Hospital when it was under government operation. Thus, as far as the medical staff was concerned, the change from military to civilian status was not a sharp one.

On January 17, President Duffield reported a plan of organization and rules for the future operation of the Hospital. Drafted by Divie B. Duffield, it apparently stirred up some discussion and was not immediately adopted. Instead, it was referred to a special committee for revision and resubmission. When finally adopted, the proposal represented the combined thinking of the trustees and medical staff. The exact date on which it was approved is not known, but it was prior to November, 1866, when the plan was first presented in published form, although it was in effect long before that.[17]

The initial statement of policy was but little more than a reaffirmation of the terms of the original Harper-Martin trust. The Hospital was to receive and care for the "more extreme and dangerous" cases of indigent sick and to treat those able to pay a reasonable charge. In addition, the Hospital would maintain "an Hotel for invalids who may obtain the comforts of a home," together with medical care. This applied principally to "the brave invalids and disabled soldiers of the State of Michigan" under the terms of the property-transfer agreement with the United States government. A lying-in department was provided for, as was a surgical department, "for the treatment of patients that may be suffering from wounds or disease, or injuries requiring amputation of limb, and the use of instruments in the hands of a skillful surgeon." Provision was also made for the relief and care of that class of diseases "for which resort is too commonly had to inexperienced, uneducated quacks, and the imposition of empirics that rob their patients and effect no permanent cure." Finally, the trustees pledged the Hospital to work for "the elevation and advancement of medical science and practice with, and by means of, Clinical Lectures and Instruction." [18]

Although this last provision was somewhat remote from the original plan for a "Fellenberg School," it still was recognition of an educational obligation. Instead of teaching trade skills to boys, the Hospital would seek to raise the general level of skill and knowledge and advance the standards of the medical profession. This certainly fulfilled the spirit, if not the letter, of Walter Harper's bequest.

The rules and regulations designated the principal officers and employees and defined their duties and authority. The superintendent was to be, in general terms, a business manager. Responsible not only for the grounds and buildings, he also would keep the books, supervise the personnel, and discipline both the staff members and patients. He was responsible for the reception and discharge of patients and the compiling of all records and statistics pertaining to them.

He shall see that neither the attendants, patients, or their friends, or any convalescent or other boarder, bring into the Hospital clandestinely, any drugs, medicines, intoxicating liquors, or any newspapers, pamphlets, or books, other than shall be approved by the Superintendent and the Committee of Visitation of the Board. He shall also prevent all introduction of cards and other means of gambling, and see that no games of chance or gambling, or use of intoxicating liquors, be had in the wards or on the premises. He shall see that every ward is well provided with Bibles, and have charge of religious books, that may be, with his approbation, and that of the Committees of Visitors, donated for the library or for religious uses. He shall, as far as practical, see that there be daily reading of the Scriptures and prayer, morning and evening, in each ward.

It was the superintendent's further duty to make certain that no employee leave the buildings or grounds without permission, or indulge in any profanity, drunkenness or other gross misconduct. To see that these rules were obeyed, he was charged with visiting each ward at least once every day.[19]

Provision was made for a steward, but for the time being, the superintendent was to perform that officer's functions. The matron was both cook and housekeeper. There were to be ward attendants when needed, and the female nurses, "in part, at least, shall be of the class called 'Deaconesses,' or religious women of the Protestant faith, trained to and familiar with this work." [20]

The members of the medical staff, composed of attending and consulting physicians and surgeons, were to be "gentlemen of well established character and eminence in their profession and practice." The consulting staff "shall be considered as counsellors," to be called upon when their services or advice was required. The attending staff members were to arrange and schedule their time at the Hospital so that one would always be available when needed. Both a consultant and attendant were to visit the Hospital at noon each day and look at all cases in their respective wards.

The regulations adopted by the staff were, if anything, more detailed and comprehensive than those formulated by the trustees. One of the consulting medical men was to be president of the medical board, an office to be rotated on the basis of age. The staff was to arrange for clinical lectures when circumstances warranted, and they were entitled to bring medical students with them on their visits to the patients. A house physician and an apothecary were provided for, although these posts were not immediately filled. House pupils also were to be added to the staff when it was felt their presence was needed.[21]

For the first several months of operation by the association, Harper's change from a military to a civilian hospital was not easily discernible. The patients continued to be almost entirely Civil War soldiers, because the Hospital took over the care of sick, wounded, and homeless veterans, a responsibility which, during the war, had been assumed by various relief agencies. In Michigan, several of these agencies were operating, chief of which was the United States Sanitary Commission, financed with funds raised by local subscription. Because administration was on a state basis, the Sanitary Commission had its Michigan branch with its own officers. In order to make it effective, it was broken down into divisions with various functions, and local units were established, primarily for fund-raising purposes. There was a Michigan Soldiers' Relief Association, for instance, to look after the needs of men from the Wolverine state. This, in turn, had its own branch, the Detroit Soldiers' Aid Society, which was concerned with the comforts of men in uniform from Detroit. Each of these units raised money for its own specific purposes.

The Detroit Soldiers' Aid Society was organized in 1861, largely through the efforts of women's church groups. Among the leaders were Mrs. George Duffield and her daughter, Mrs. Morse Stewart, who began collecting money, items of clothing, and other necessities about May, 1861. The organization took formal shape November 6, 1861 and established a headquarters at 164 Jefferson Avenue. The officers were Dr. Zina Pitcher, consultant; Mrs. Duffield, president; and Miss Valeria Campbell, corresponding secretary. The sister of State Supreme Court Justice James V. Campbell, Valeria Campbell was the guiding spirit of the Society and has been referred to as its real chief administrative officer.[22] In the summer of 1863, the Detroit Soldiers' Aid Society became an official branch of the United States Sanitary Commission and so came under the supervision of such officers as John Owen and Benjamin Vernor.

One of the principal enterprises of the Detroit Soldiers' Aid Society was the operation of a home, or hostel, for men in uniform—a place where soldiers in transit could be fed and housed. It was not until January, 1864 that this establishment was opened. A two-story building at 81 Jefferson was rented and extensively remodeled. It had thirty beds, with emergency provision for thirty more, a kitchen, dining room, bathroom, and reading room. It was known as the Soldiers' Home.[23] Miss Campbell described it as a place where soldiers, passing through Detroit and having no resting place, could find protection. The transient men, she reported, were "preyed upon and led into trouble by the gang of designing and unprincipled sharks who are constantly lying in wait for soldiers whom they daily swindle out of what money they have." [24] Considering that the typical soldier was a youth of eighteen or nineteen, raised on a farm and unfamiliar with city life, it was a temptation, during a stopover or furlough in Detroit, to spend time and money in saloons or more notorious establishments.

That the home was popular and served a good purpose is indicated by the fact that in February, 1864 it had 639 guests, served 3,374 meals, and furnished 740 lodgings. At that, hundreds had to be turned away.[25] As the war went on, or rather as it drew to a close, the character of the Soldiers' Home underwent a gradual change. Instead of offering overnight accommodation to men passing through town on their way to or from the army, it found itself caring for an increasing number of homeless veterans, many of them disabled, some of them blind. There was no place else to send these unfortunate derelicts of war, and they were kept and looked after in the Home. It became a composite permanent soldiers' home and relief agency.[26]

With peace restored to the nation, the relief organizations, such as the Sanitary Commission, began to curtail their operations. In September, 1865, the Commission notified the Soldiers' Home that it was ending its financial assistance. This posed a problem of what to do with the men the Home was housing. Officials, principally Miss Campbell, began to think of using Harper whose days as a military hospital also were numbered. She talked to Dr. Tripler and the always-helpful Colonel Lee. Tripler thought one of the Harper ward buildings could be used, and, while he was in no position to make positive commitments, he thought that necessary kitchen and other facilities could be provided.[27] The Harper trustees were approached, and they reacted favorably. The discussions went on, according to Miss Campbell, for several months.[28] But they really came to a head on December 12, 1865, when the trustees directed their secretary, Divie B. Duffield, to "invite from such Society such a request or expression of their wishes in regard to the occupation of one of the Hospital buildings as will enable the Board to take definite action thereon." [29]

Two days later, on the fourteenth, Trustees McGraw and Buhl were delegated to confer with the officers of the Soldiers' Home and invite them to meet with the Board "in reference to a transfer of their association to the buildings of the Harper Hospital." [30] Several conferences then followed in which John Owen and perhaps other officials of the Sanitary Commission were present. These meetings were climaxed on December 29, by an agreement between the Hospital and the Commission whereby the latter, rapidly closing out its affairs, offered to turn over to Harper "such soldiers as may now be under their care, and such deserving cases as hereafter come upon their hands." Harper would take them in, and give them "all needful shelter, food and medical care." [31] In return, the Sanitary Commission agreed to pay to the Hospital $2,000 immediately, and such other money that it might have as soon as its assets could be liquidated. It was estimated that the Commission assets would have an eventual value of $6,000.[32] The Commission was granted the right to appoint a Board of Visitors who would have access to the Hospital at all times. Signing the agreement on behalf of the Commission were Benjamin Vernor and Valeria Campbell.[33] This arrangement having been completed, the trustees stipulated that all soldiers entering the Hospital would have to assign their pensions to the treasurer.[34] This opened the way for the transfer of the soldiers into the Hospital, where they were assigned to the "flank" or north ward building.[35] Of the twenty-four who entered, nine were sick, while the other fifteen were simply men who needed food and shelter.[36]

Observing this arrangement, the Masonic order inquired as to whether some similar arrangements might be made for invalid Masons. The matter was taken under advisement by the board, but nothing further was heard about it.[37]

Meanwhile, the Soldiers' Home had closed, and it, too, turned over its remaining assets to Harper. Thus, there were initial payments of $2,000.00 from the Sanitary Commission and $2,818.87 from the Detroit Soldiers' Aid Society.[38] From time to time, the Commission paid in more of its funds, until its 1866 total was $3,471.14.[39] In addition, paying patients, most of whom must have been soldiers, contributed $246.11.[40] All of the patients, following the January 2, 1866 opening, were soldiers.

In March, the trustees decided it was time to open the Hospital to private patients, although few, if any, were admitted until later in the year.[41] On May 3, 1866, the Hospital reported that since January 2, "there had been received and cared for 117 men, making a total of 3,733 days from January 2 to May 1, 1866, at a cost of $2,010.54." [42] During the entire year, the Hospital received "267 patients, chiefly soldiers," and provided 13,273 days board and attendance. The cost was $6,526.58. By the year's end, only 10 private patients had been admitted. During 1866, 12 patients died, and on January 1, 1867, the Hospital's population was 47.[43]

The arrangement between the Hospital, the Sanitary Commission, and the Soldiers' Home continued until April 7, 1868. By this time, each agency had completely exhausted its funds, and it was obvious that other arrangements would be necessary.[44] Other states had established soldiers' homes at public expense, and there was a rather general feeling that Michigan should move in the same direction. The Harper trustees, anticipating an end to private relief funds, approached the state legislature with an offer "to become the almoner of the State's bounty toward the invalid, disabled and honorably discharged soldiers of the State of Michigan, now or hereafter in the Soldiers' Home in charge of the Harper Hospital." [45] This proposition was made near the close of 1866, in the hope that the legislature, convening in January, 1867, would take action. The board was not disappointed. Urged on by public opinion and supported by the State Military Board, a Senate resolution was introduced February 12, calling for the establishment of a Soldiers' Home under contract with Harper Hospital.[46] The resolution was adopted and became law on April 11. It carried with it an appropriation of $20,000 to cover costs for 1867 and 1868. The law provided that the State Military Board would represent the state and make rules governing admissions and discharges. Those to be admitted might be any soldier, sailor, or marine "credited to this State during the late war; that he was honorably discharged, and at the time of making such application [for admission] is sick, infirm, maimed, or otherwise unable to maintain himself." The Military Board had the power to appoint a superintendent of the Soldiers' Home, and got around to that very neatly by naming the Hospital superintendent. The latter received a small stipend for his services to the state.[47] Upon the Military Board's recommendation, Dr. Ira Fletcher, the Harper house physician, was made superintendent of the Home. He and his successors served in both capacities for many years thereafter.[48]

Thus, in 1867, Harper served a dual role. It was a private hospital, and it also was the official Soldiers' Home of the state of Michigan. The Military Board was well pleased with the facilities which, by state action, it had obtained when Harper Hospital became the state Soldiers' Home. Before the contract was made, a committee inspected the premises, and its report was most complimentary to the Hospital.

We found the Hospital dining-rooms, kitchen, washrooms, etc., under the direct supervision of the present matron, Mrs. Sanborn, in excellent order. The most scrupulous neatness and cleanliness existed in every department, under her charge. There were some sixteen soldiers in the Hospital under treatment who are in rooms separate and distinct from the other patients and as far as your committee can judge were receiving the best of care. We counselled with many of them and found no complaints as to the attention they were receiving.[49]

The section reserved for convalescent patients was separate from the rooms occupied by the sick, and these "apartments" were "spacious and comfortable."

The men themselves did not measure up to the standards of their surroundings, the Military Board sadly commented. If they would only observe the same degree of neatness maintained in the Hospital generally, it "would reflect much credit upon its occupants."[50] Inasmuch as the inmates were ex-soldiers, the Board felt a little more military discipline would be in order.

At present the men are allowed to go and come at their own discretion. Oftentimes, they return late at night intoxicated and disorderly and create disturbances among their comrades. The superintendent should and must have some authority by which we can control the men in this particular. There is a good guard house attached to the premises and could be used to advantage on such occasions.[51]

The Board also concluded that some of the inmates were malingerers, who should be earning their living, and recommended medical examinations and discharge of those found fit. The Hospital trustees, it was added, concurred in this conclusion and were quite willing to cooperate. The Military Board stressed the point that Harper was a "temporary" home, and it was not intended to take care of chronic and permanently disabled cases. The members pointed out that federal homes had been provided for those who needed constant, long-term care. Whenever possible, Harper veterans in that category should be transferred to one of the national homes.

Harper's role, then, as a soldiers' home, was to receive and care for the sick or the indigent who needed only a chance to get back on his feet. That policy was followed, with the result that the Harper Soldiers' Home bed count fluctuated widely from week to week. This is reflected in a report by the Military Board covering the period from March 1, 1867 to December 1, 1868. In the 20 months, 228 men were admitted. Of this number, 76 were transferred to a national home; 129 were discharged, 10 died, and 13 remained in Harper. This represented a total of 15,214 days' board, or an average of about two months' stay per man. The cost of maintaining these patients and inmates was about 55 cents per day. These figures, both cost and attendance, remained fairly constant over a period of several years, permitting the Hospital to keep its Soldiers' Home costs within the annual $10,000 appropriated by the state.[52] These cost figures, however, do not tell the entire story. They covered only the bare necessities. What few luxuries the men received usually bore the label of public bounty. The women of Detroit, particularly, did not forget the men who, in earlier days, had gallantly fought to save the Union. Valeria Campbell and her friends collected food and clothing, along with other things which the Hospital needed. One list, for instance, shows gifts of 15 flannel shirts, 25 pairs of socks, along with night caps, dressing gowns, bandages, slings, writing paper, newspapers, and even 4 bottles of wine.[53] The Military Board expressly commended John G. Bagley, Detroit tobacco processor, for gifts of tobacco.[54]

When the men were transferred to other hospitals, or discharged, they took little with them. It is believed they were handed a small amount of cash, although this does not show on the records. They did, however, have to sign receipts for such articles of clothing as they took with them. Accounts which have been preserved show, for example, that on June 18, 1867, when James Harrold of Company I, First Michigan Infantry, was discharged, he receipted for one cap, one greatcoat, one flannel coat, one pair of "trowsers," two shirts, two pairs of drawers, one pair of boots, and two pairs of socks. William Blake, a Negro who had served in the One-hundred-and-second Infantry (Colored), left with only a pair of drawers and a pair of socks, making one hope that the weather in June, 1867 was mild.[55]

The contract between the state and Harper was renewed, year after year. As time passed, fewer old soldiers applied for admission; the number decreased materially after 1886 when the permanent Soldiers' Home was established at Grand Rapids. Yet, they were still coming as late as 1882, when the Michigan adjutant general referred to Harper as being "still deemed a necessity as a place of shelter for destitute Michigan soldiers while preparation is being made for their admission to the national homes." In 1887, after the Grand Rapids home was opened, Harper still cared for 26 men, and soldiers were occasionally listed as late as 1891.[56] The importance of the arrangement whereby Harper looked after the Civil War soldiers should not be underestimated. While this service was not a true hospital function, it served well in providing the income which helped to keep the institution operating, publicizing its facilities and establishing its reputation for humane and high quality medical service throughout the entire state.

Chapter 10

OLD HARPER—1866-84

For a period
of eighteen years after Harper became a civilian hospital, there was very
little outward change from the military institution of 1864-65. This was
true because the changes which occurred were changes in policy rather
than physical appearance. The same frame, barracks-type buildings were
used; no new structures were added, nor were there any extensive exterior alterations. The military appearance was preserved by the operation of the State Soldiers' Home, and for a while, the veterans in the
Home greatly outnumbered the civilian patients. The first, and really
the chief, task of the trustees after the Soldiers' Home had been established was to get private patients to use the facilities Harper had to offer.
In due time, Dr. Duffield's dream of a hospital devoted to "the wider
welfare of the city" was fulfilled.

In May, 1866, an enterprising reporter for the *Detroit Advertiser
and Tribune* paid a visit to discover how Harper was doing as a civilian
hospital. He came away, obviously impressed, because he told his readers
that "this is a hospital of which the city of Detroit and State of Michigan
may well feel proud. . . ." [1] He continued:

There are in all ten buildings [actually there were eleven] comprising
the Harper Hospital, located on Woodward Avenue about a mile from
Campus Martius, and being one of the most beautiful sites in the city. They
are all constructed of wood, and were erected in the winter of 1864-5 and
last spring and summer, for a great portion of the time every available space
was occupied by soldiers brought from the tents and battle-fields of the
South for medical and surgical treatment.

The lot is nearly 300 feet in width on Woodward Avenue, and extends
back several hundred feet. [2]

Like everyone who saw the site, the reporter was struck by the beauty of the grove behind the buildings. It never failed to draw comment and must surely be regarded as one of the Hospital's most valuable early assets. "The main building," continued the newspaper's description, "is in the centre of the lot, is two stories in height, 35 or 40 feet in width, by about 200 in length. This building was erected for offices, store rooms, medical dispensaries, etc., for the hospital."

The account continued with a picture of the arrangement of the ward buildings, three of which stood on each side of the center, or main administration building. Each of these ward houses was fitted to accommodate about sixty patients. The life of the Hospital centered around the administrative hall. In its rear was the soldiers' dining room. Some of the wards were closed; two were being used for storage of equipment and commissary material. The Soldiers' Home was housed in what was originally used for the Veterans Reserve Corps in the rear, or east end, of the north ward.

It is quite commodious, and is divided into sitting rooms and sleeping rooms. The building is divided into two apartments similarly arranged, and after the inmates have occupied one-half for three months, they remove to the other half while their vacated apartments undergo a thorough cleansing. There are at present in the Home about 20 soldiers, most of whom have either lost an arm or leg, while some are so broken down in health as to be incapacitated from work. There are also two blind soldiers who lost their sight while in the army. One young man, who has lost a leg, is attending the commercial college, and fitting himself for future usefulness and finds a home in this institution. Another, who is crippled, is engaged in an occupation by which he earns a few dollars a week . . . The soldiers of the Home pass their time in reading, playing checquers, dominos, etc.[3]

The Hospital proper, that is, the part devoted to the care and treatment of the sick, whether soldiers or civilians, charity or private patients, was confined to the main building and the old dining hall which occupied a separate part of the rear or east end of the main building. Each section had been divided into wards, with a bathroom attached to each ward, and such other rooms as were necessary. This remodeling had been done at a cost of about one thousand dollars.

At the right, upon entering the main building, is the reception room, the furniture of which was donated by Messrs. Marcus Stevens, Henry Webber, and several other gentlemen. Next to this room are the library, the dispensary, and two commodious wards, with a bath room between. On the left side, upon entering, are the surgeon's office, the baggage room, the linen room and ward and bath rooms. The linen room is very large and is well stocked with sufficient linen and bedding to furnish a daily change for a hundred beds, together with invalid dressing gowns for soldiers, blankets, etc. The second story of the hospital is also divided into wards with a bath room between every two, and also for the matron. The old dining room has been divided into three separate departments, the first comprising four wards and two bath rooms, the second the dining room and the kitchen. Besides the inmates of the Soldiers' Home, who take their meals at the hospital dining room, there are now but two patients in the hospital—both of them formerly soldiers—a less number than at any time since the institution was founded. Both of these have pulmonary consumption, and one is very low.[4]

Although the organizational plan which the trustees had adopted provided for a superintendent, the real direction of Harper Hospital was under the efficient supervision of the matron, Mrs. L. A. Sanborn, who, for her services, was paid a salary of thirty-two dollars a month, provided with quarters, and given her meals.[5] "Her efficiency as a matron is abundantly attested," said the *Advertiser and Tribune,* "not only by the hearty approval of her management by the association, by the neatness, cleanliness and orderly arrangement everywhere prevailing, but also by the economy exercised in all departments of the institution." [6]

In the winter, the frame buildings became very cold, and the stoves which were provided in each room and ward barely were able to take the chill out of the air. Both wood and coal were used as fuel, and patients who were able to do so looked after their own fires.[7] The wood was brought in and piled in convenient places by one of the employees. Some of the wood was cut on the Harper property, but most of it was purchased in lots of 100 cords or more.[8] Oil lamps were used for illumination. At the trustees' meeting on June 7, 1870, it was decided to "ascertain the probable cost of introducing gas pipes and fixtures into the Hospital buildings." The result of the investigation was favorable, and gas was installed during the summer and first lighted the institution in September. The Detroit City Gas Company submitted a bill for that month for $7.95. In October, the first full month of gas use, the bill was $29.33.[9]

Upkeep and maintenance of the Hospital property and equipment were always matters of concern to the trustees, and improvements were constantly being made, both inside and outside. The old iron cots and mattresses inherited from the army were sold, and new white-enameled beds were purchased along with new mattresses.[10] The white bedside tables, usual equipment in modern hospitals, were lacking, but each bed had a wooden stand beside it, or, if there were not enough of those to go around, a chair served the same purpose.[11] Bills were regularly presented to the trustees for painting, whitewashing, and plastering. Fences and gates were kept in repair, not only for the sake of appearance, but also for the "control of inmates and to keep out intruders." [12] As more patients entered the Hospital and additional facilities were required, the trustees opened and equipped new wards and rooms in buildings which previously had been closed. Thus, there appear in the proceedings instructions to the secretary "to draft plans for additional rooms and wards in the building adjoining the centre Hospital building on the south." [13] At the following meeting, the secretary was authorized to make the necessary contracts for the work of expansion.

The second annual report called attention to the fact that during the year 1868:

. . . the Board . . . has improved the grounds of the hospital by changing the walks and seeding down the lawn, and also by constructing a circular carriage drive around the grove which, though not very extensive, is perhaps one of the most attractive summer resorts to be found within the city limits. To convalescent patients it affords a delightful opportunity to secure the benefits of exercise, as well as rest in the open air during the oppressive heats of summer.[14]

Gratitude of the board was expressed to Eugene Robinson for gratuitously surveying and staking out the driveway, which was graded with fill dirt removed from some of the neighboring side streets which were being opened at that time. Trustee Farrand sought to obtain the fill free, but in the end, the board had to pay twelve and one-half cents a wagon load.[15] Alanson Sheley, a pillar of the First Presbyterian Church and a firm friend of the Hospital, planted at his own expense a row of shade trees along the entire front, on the Woodward Avenue side of the grounds.[16]

The inside was not neglected either. At one board meeting, the trustees were delighted to find the walls of the parlor in the administration building "beautifully decorated with eleven photographic views, handsomely framed of scenes in the vicinity of Gettysburg." They were donated by Major Edwin B. Wight, brother of Buckminster. Wight had served with the immortal Twenty-fourth Michigan and had been critically wounded at the Battle of Gettysburg.[17]

Easy access to the Hospital was of importance to the trustees. Hence, they were frequently petitioning the city of Detroit to widen and improve neighboring streets. Woodward Avenue, prior to 1876, was only a dirt road north of Brady, and the trustees were largely responsible for persuading the city to pave the street with cedar blocks to Alexandrine, cheerfully paying the special assessment which was levied against the Harper property.[18] Some years later, in 1882 to be exact, when the board had plans for a new hospital set farther back from Woodward, the minutes noted that Trustees McGraw and Farrand were appointed a committee "to confer with the city attorney in reference to the contemplated opening of John R Street."[19] The introduction of streetcars in 1863 and the extension of the line to Edmund Place caused the suburbs to build up rapidly. Although the horsecar line ended at least a quarter-mile south of the Hospital, it was much better than no transportation at all. It must have been a matter of considerable concern and inconvenience to all connected with Harper when, as Silas Farmer noted, all cars were compelled to stop running in the fall of 1872 "on account of the epizootic, or horse disease."[20]

The Hospital enjoyed what would today, perhaps, be called a "fringe benefit" from the operation of its own farm during the period 1866–84. Apparently this enterprise was never very extensive, but it did produce some revenue, as well as fruits, vegetables, milk, and, possibly, meat for the commissary. In 1870, the secretary reported that "one of the cows belonging to the Hospital had been sold for $60, and that a fresh cow had been purchased at a cost of $50."[21] Outside of earlier arrangements for cutting hay on Hospital property, this was the first reference to any agricultural activities sponsored or conducted by the institution. In July, 1870, a calf was sold for $2.00.[22] There is evidence that at one time pigs also were kept. Originally, there may have been some cultivating and pasturing on the unused grounds of the Hospital proper, although later this activity was confined to other lots, including the one on Fremont Street where Nancy Martin had her house. In 1881, that lot was rented to W. M. Howard for one year at $150.00, with the understanding that "the products of the orchard and all other fruits, not including vegetables, should be shared equally between the Hospital and tenant. The Hospital also was to retain the privilege of pasturing one cow in the orchard." The annual report, covering 1881, stated that "the products of the garden attached to the Hospital, less all expenses, were appraised at $337.67." [23] Possibly that report convinced the trustees that the results were not worth the effort. There were no further references to any farming activities, but that may be explained also by the fact that property under the Hospital's control was being sold, leased, and developed as the city grew northward. As early, in fact, as 1873, the board refused offers to rent the "upper 10 acre lot"—the one at Woodward and Medbury—for market garden purposes. The trustees much preferred to cultivate subdivisions instead of "garden sass." [24] Taking everything into consideration, the 1866–84 Harper Hospital presented an attractive, well-kept appearance, both inside and outside, prompting the publisher of the 1868 city directory to remark that "the buildings, which were erected expressly for Hospital purposes, have all the modern improvements." [25]

However, all the modern improvements the trustees were able to provide meant little without patients to benefit from them. From 1866 and for some time thereafter, the principal effort of the governing board was to fill those new white-enameled beds. While the Soldiers' Home served a useful and humane purpose and enabled the Hospital to meet a moral obligation to the government and the community, a temporary shelter for veterans did not fulfill the true purpose for which Harper Hospital was established. Yet, to get patients, to educate the medical profession of Detroit and Michigan to send its sick and injured to the institution for treatment and repair, to convince the people that Harper and its facilities were there to serve them, was largely an educational and public relations job.

One of the first acts of the board, following the Hospital's opening as a private institution in January, 1866, was to instruct its executive committee "to advertize for private patients and fit up rooms for their reception at once." [26] It has been seen how immediate steps were taken to provide a staff, renovate the buildings, and arrange for rooms and wards as they were needed. That the public might be made aware that Harper was ready to receive private patients, arrangements were made with a local printer, William Graham, to publish a pamphlet and to place notices of the opening in such newspapers as Dr. Duffield might decide on.[27] Authorization was also given to "procure a cut of the front view of the Hospital buildings and grounds." [28] This resulted in an illustration of Harper Hospital as seen from Woodward Avenue. Widely used and circulated, this engraving, while not the first picture of the Hospital, was the most familiar and offered the best idea of the pavilion arrangement of the buildings during the 1866-84 period. It shows the center, or main building, with its two stories, flanked on each side by four ward buildings, each with its small veranda or portico. The buildings are set back, perhaps one hundred feet or so from Woodward Avenue. Along the sidewalk is a picket fence. The main entrance has a decorative archway, either of iron or wood lattice. Between the fence and the buildings, the grounds appear to be well tended and landscaped, with small trees and shrubs and a spacious lawn. Near the main entrance stands a tall flagstaff. It is interesting to note that the Calvert Lithographing Company which printed the engraving, also continues to be a Detroit institution after one hundred years.

Also printed and widely distributed were cards, probably the work of William Graham. The cards carried the heading "Harper Hospital Woodward Avenue, Detroit, Mich.," under which appears "For the reception of all Diseases (not contagious) and Lying-in Women." It goes on to describe the buildings as having all the modern improvements, and a staff of physicians and surgeons who "are of the first rank in their profession." Furthermore, "Great care is taken in the selection of nurses and attendants, and everything that is necessary for the comfort of patients is provided." The names of the trustees and the medical and surgical staff members were listed, along with that of Mrs. Sanborn, the matron. Applications for admission, the public was told, could be made to the trustees, the staff, or the Hospital. Prices in the wards, including board and medical attention, were $3.50 per week. Private room charges were "according to accommodations." Michigan volunteer soldiers, honorably discharged, were admitted free, and "all pregnant females desiring skillful medical attendance, and experienced nurses, at a moderate cost, can be admitted to the general wards at the low price of $5.00 per week. . . . A deposit of the amount of four weeks' board will be required. Patients leaving before that time will be refunded any amount unexpended."

One way, of course, to fill hospital beds is to accept, through arrangement with municipal authorities, public patients, or those who

today would be considered "on welfare." At the time Harper opened as
a civilian hospital, most city and county charges were sent to St. Mary's.
The cost of their treatment and care was borne by the unit of government responsible for them on a fixed charge contract basis. The trustees
soon sought to have some of these cases sent to Harper. Toward the end
of 1867, a committee consisting of Trustees Buhl and Farrand was appointed to confer with the Wayne County Overseers of the Poor "to
see if any arrangement can be made with the county for the taking care
of the lying-in-patients." [29] Apparently no immediate agreement was
reached, because it was not until April, 1869 that the first record of public
patients is found.[30] For the entire year 1869, there were 110 city patients
cared for, according to the annual report.[31] The earliest record of county
patients was in 1870 when there were 2.[32] Regularly thereafter, Harper
had both city and county patients, but the numbers were never large,
suggesting that most of the public charges sent to the Hospital were
maternity, or lying-in cases. For example, in 1871, out of a total of 674
patients at Harper, 77 were charged to the county account and only 15
to the city. Thus, in that year, less than 14 per cent of Harper's cases
could be classed as the "welfare" type.[33] The average cost of maintaining
a patient, public or private, in 1872 was 73.3 cents per day. During 1872,
the Hospital received a total of $1,878.41 from the city of Detroit for
the care of its patients, and $1,348.50 from Wayne County.[34]

There is reason to suspect that there was some political jockeying
in the choice of the hospital to which these cases were assigned. There
was sometimes the feeling on the part of the Harper trustees that their
Hospital was not getting its fair share of the business. In 1871, the
trustees had a talk with members of the Detroit Common Council:

. . . for the purpose of ascertaining whether the arrangement existing previous to the city contract with St. Mary's Hospital for the care of the city sick
poor by which all such had the privilege of choosing the hospital they prefer
to be sent to, cannot be restored, and that the same rate per week for their
care be made the same as it was prior to the contract with St. Mary's.[35]

That St. Mary's had the contract in 1871 which gave that institution a
virtual monopoly of city business, almost to the complete exclusion of
Harper, is indicated by the fact that Harper, that year, averaged only a
little more than one city patient per month.

Another case which Harper accepted was the so-called boarder.

Dr. H. O. Walker — He became the first
house surgeon at Harper Hospital in 1868. Dr.
Walker had a distinguished medical career in
Detroit until his death in 1912.

Dr. David Osburn Farrand — A member
a family closely identified with Harper, Dr.
Farrand served as medical director while Harper was a military hospital. He continued on
the staff until his death in 1883. The Farrand
Training School for Nurses was named in his
honor. He was the brother of Jacob S. Farrand,
a member of the Hospital's original Board of
Trustees and its president from 1884 to 1891.

Dr. John Henry Carstens — A colorful
and beloved physician, Dr. Carstens was long
a fixture of the Harper Hospital staff. During
the late 1880's and early 1900's, when he was
chief of staff, Harper gained preeminence in
the field of abdominal surgery.

9. HARPER HOSPITAL AND THE SWAIN HOME — The Swain Home, named for its donor, Mrs. Eleanor Swain, and located on John R Street south of the Harper building, was opened in 1893 for nurses enrolled at the Farrand Training School for Nurses. It was later remodeled and used as the hospital director's residence.   *courtesy Burton Historical Collection*

10. HARPER AT THE TURN OF THE CENTURY — Built in 1883, the new Hospital on John R Street formally opened June 19, 1884. A 250-arc tower, seen in the right foreground, lighted the street. Notice the cedar-block pavement on Martin Place.   *courtesy Burton Historical Collection*

These were usually aged and infirm persons who agreed to turn over their property to the Hospital in return for a home there for the rest of their lives. Actually, there were very few of these, and they were admitted only after careful consideration on the part of the trustees. The minutes of July 11, 1871 record that a male patient, whose name was not stated, offered to transfer his property which was worth about $1,800 to the trustees in return for a permanent home. The board decided this proposition would be acceptable, provided that an investigation showed the value of the patient's property to be as he represented it.[36] Another man, a Mr. Melody, was given boarder status by assigning to the trustees a mortgage he held, which paid $150 a year.[37] James Mills, not otherwise identified, proposed to turn over the $2,000 which he possessed, the interest to accrue to the trustees:

. . . and be applied in the payment of his board and attendance at the Hospital as long as he, Mills, shall live, it being understood and agreed that the Board shall retain $1000 of the sum so deposited, when said Mills shall decease, the remainder of the $2000 to be subject to the disposal of Mills.

The board decided that the deposit by Mills should be $2,500 instead of $2,000. After discussing the matter for several months, Mills's original proposition was accepted.[38]

Frequently the help in the Hospital, the attendants and those who performed menial tasks, were either patients or former patients. Some were staying on for treatment and were able to engage in light work to assist in paying their fees. These duties included maid service on the part of the women, while the men looked after the fires and worked on the grounds, according to their physical capabilities.[39] In the early years of the Hospital, there was no intercommunication system, and messages were carried from one part of the institution to another by indigent people who had been patients and were working out their small bills. The drawback to this arrangement was that the messengers were often emergency cases, in the Hospital for only a few hours, or overnight at best, with the result that the service changed as frequently as the patients changed.[40]

Occasionally, the employment of patients had bothersome results. One man, assigned to light tasks, submitted a bill for his services, contending that the work he had done had a value in excess of the charges against him. Needless to say, his claim was disallowed by the trustees.

The board was quite upset at one time to learn that a patient named Turner had some cards printed and widely circulated, "setting forth that he was 'Dr. Turner' with his office in the Hospital." To what extent he was successful in attracting "patients" of his own or how extensive a practice he was able to build is not known. His medical career in the Hospital, however, came to an abrupt end when the secretary "was directed to notify the man Turner to quit the Hospital premises forthwith." [41]

Some of these aides performed useful services. Mention is made of one of them, Mary Murphy, better known as "Nurse Mary," who was a fixture around the Hospital for many years as a valuable helper. She was remembered as being "always on duty, night and day, doing her bit wherever she was most needed. . . . She lived the remainder of her days in the present Hospital." [42]

Another well-known character around Harper in the early years was a man known only as Charley. Originally a patient—probably a soldier—he eventually won a precarious place on the payroll. That he was at times a problem and a trial to the officials is indicated by his occasional appearance in the records of the trustees when it became necessary to apply disciplinary action. Just what caused Charley's fall from grace in the spring of 1869 is not known, but official recognition was given to his sins, whatever they were. The superintendent was authorized by the board:

. . . to discharge Charley, the Hospital nurse, unless he attended to his duties more faithfully than he has done for sometime past, and he [the superintendent] was also requested to notify Charley that his wages would be but $10 per month from the 1st instant.[43]

A possible clue to Charley's transgressions may be found in the very next entry in the records, which stated:

Resolved, That under no circumstances will any male visitor be admitted to the room of any female patient unless accompanied by either the matron, or resident physician except in cases of husbands visiting their wives or fathers their daughters, of which relationship the matron or physician shall be satisfied.[44]

Charley must have reformed, because two months after he was placed on probation, so to speak, his wage was increased to twenty dollars per month "on condition that his services prove as satisfactory to the Board as they have been during the past month. Otherwise, his pay is [to] be at the rate of ten dollars per month." [45]

In order to make life as attractive and pleasant as possible for the patients, different kinds of entertainment and other diversions, some of a serious nature, were arranged. A minister regularly visited the Hospital, acting as chaplain. The Rev. George Harwood won an official expression of the trustees' appreciation for "his Christian visits and religious services which . . . he has systematically and regularly conducted among the soldiers of the Home and the inmates of the Hospital." [46] Another expression of thanks was extended to:

> . . . the ladies of the First Presbyterian, Jefferson Avenue and Westminster Churches for their continued generous and liberal remembrance of Harper Hospital, and for the kindly interest they have for years past manifested for the comfort and well-being of its inmates.

These women collected clothing, put on Thanksgiving dinners, and provided "weekly gifts of fragrant flowers and baskets of luscious fruits." Mention also was made of individual gifts of "books, magazines and other publications for our hospital library." The activities of these churchwomen may properly be regarded as the origin of the auxiliary work which is and for long has been an important part of the Hospital's service to its patients. [47]

One of the early and important features of Harper Hospital's 1866–84 period was the stress placed upon obstetrics and its development. There was a twofold purpose in this. First of all, prior to 1866, there were no local hospital facilities for the care of lying-in cases. Because child deliveries too often were left to doctors without adequate training, or to incompetent midwives, both mother and child mortality rates were needlessly high. Second, there was the mandate for a lying-in department in Nancy Martin's trust. The trustees accepted that as one of their responsibilities. While maternity cases were admitted almost from the beginning of the civilian hospital, the trustees at their meetings frequently discussed the need for a more specialized service and a section of the Hospital devoted to obstetrics—a term which, incidentally, was but infrequently employed at the time. In 1867, seven babies were born at Harper. [48]

Leadership in this effort to supply what was needed came from the staff, and particularly from Dr. Theodore A. McGraw, son of the trustee. At the annual meeting of the board, March 4, 1868, McGraw presented a report which bore the endorsement of the other staff members, and which was favorably received by the trustees.

In order to make Harper more effective, particularly in meeting its obligations, Dr. McGraw stressed the importance of providing a lying-in hospital which would be available to patients desiring private rooms and seclusion as well as to charity cases. Lack of funds, he pointed out, had compelled the Hospital to refuse admission to many unwed women at a time "when their condition has demanded the most liberal and tender charity."

The multitudes of young women, who, in a large commercial city like Detroit, become the victims of licentious and heartless men, should not, we believe, be driven to a life of shame by the exposure of their misfortune, or to murder their unborn offspring to hide it. It would be well, indeed, to separate the virtuous poor from the erring; but at the same time, we feel convinced that a charity of this kind can never fulfill its proper mission as long as it rejects the very class of unfortunates whose sad lot most requires Christian sympathy and assistance.

We urge upon the trustees the importance of bringing to the notice of these people in our community, who manifest a willingness to aid suffering humanity, the facilities which Harper Hospital presents for the concentration of the various charitable projects now being canvassed. In connection with the Hospital there might be a Foundlings' Home and Children's Hospital and an asylum for erring women, where wanderers may be reclaimed from vice and their physical ills receive prompt attention. *Vice* and *disease* are indissolubly connected, and from necessity a home for the victims of iniquity must to all intents and purposes be a hospital.[49]

McGraw pointed to the facilities Harper already had and which could be furnished without a great financial outlay. He suggested immediate steps be taken to make:

. . . our lying-in department one whose doors shall be closed to none, so that the friendless and homeless, the rich and the poor, those who pay and those who do not, whether the wedded wife or the "unfortunate," may all here find an asylum in their hour of trial.

He emphasized the desperate need of unmarried girls, pointing out that "the virtuous but destitute poor, who are unable to procure proper nursing and medical attendance" were already welcome at Harper.

While the great size of the Hospital buildings would afford ample room for all these various charities, their peculiar arrangement would render it easy to keep them entirely separate, even when under the same general management; and it would seem to us a waste of means to erect buildings elsewhere for these purposes, when the wards of this Hospital, which now stand empty, and which can be used for no other purpose, offer all the necessary accommodations.

Behind Dr. McGraw's plea was, quite probably, a definite purpose. There existed in Detroit a church-sponsored organization known as the Ladies Christian Union. Organized in 1860, this group was interested in doing something about the problem Dr. McGraw discussed, and there was a movement afoot to establish a women's hospital and foundlings' home.[50] Obviously, McGraw and his associates felt that with the facilities which Harper had at its disposal it would be useless duplication to build another hospital. Dr. McGraw's eloquent statement received wide publicity in the Detroit newspapers, and without doubt influenced subsequent events.

To maintain the necessary discipline in the Hospital and to keep it a well-ordered and regulated place, the trustees finally got around to adopting and publishing a list of "Rules to be Observed in Harper Hospital." These, with occasional additions and amendments, remained in force until 1883. As an indication of what life in Harper Hospital was like at this period, these rules are worth examination. Besides the normal and expected requirements concerning payment of board in advance and regulation of visiting hours, the list included a warning that patients would be held responsible for furniture which they might damage or destroy and a prohibition against lounging about the main hall or entrance. "No profane or loud talking," the list warned, and "scandal talking is strictly prohibited." There was to be no smoking, and "patients must not spit on the floor or matting." Gaslights were to be turned down at 9:00 P.M., at which time all patients were expected to be in their rooms. Patients were not permitted in the kitchen or laundry without express permission of the matron. "Patients must not throw anything whatever on the ground below their windows." All alcoholic liquors were prohibited except those prescribed by the superintendent; patients were warned against lying on the beds with their clothing on; and, finally, probably the cruelest regulation of all, "patients are not allowed to talk with each other about their diseases."[51]

Chapter 11

DETROIT MEDICAL COLLEGE

If there had been
any thought that Harper Hospital would be an institution restricted to
the care and treatment of Detroit patients, that it would be exclusively
a Detroit hospital, that misconception was quickly corrected. Records
which have been preserved show that, as a civilian hospital, Harper's
area of service extended far beyond the Detroit city limits and into all of
Michigan. Many patients were attracted from Canada. Considering
Harper's proximity to the international border, the ease of access from
southern Ontario, and the lack of sophisticated hospital facilities west
of Toronto, it is not at all remarkable that it should have received many
Canadians.

It is true that as a civilian hospital Harper got away to a slow
start. During the first full year of operation, 1866, only 10 private patients were admitted. All others were sick and disabled soldiers. But it
was not long before there was a marked shift in the Hospital's population. During 1867, there were 56 private patients and boarders, in addition to 6 private soldier patients. In 1868, the private patients for the
first time outnumbered the state-supported veterans by 106 to 81. From
that time on, the private patient register grew rapidly. The 1869 count
was 426, which included 110 city welfare cases. Ten years later, 483
private patients entered the Hospital. In 1884, the year after the original
Hospital had been replaced, Harper cared for 655 private patients and
295 in other categories including public charges and charity cases.[1] The
increase in the number of private admissions in the 1870 decade may be
attributed in part to a policy which permitted patients "to employ, if
they so desire, any regular physician not connected with the regular

staff of the hospital." Exactly when this rule, which made Harper an "open hospital," first was adopted is not clear, but it was in effect in 1873.[2]

As Harper gradually gained wider renown for the capabilities of its staff and the quality of treatment given both medical and surgical cases, more patients began to come in from distant communities. An examination of the patients' register for 1874–78 reveals that at least thirty-five per cent of those admitted came from communities other than Detroit. The names of their home towns read like a gazetteer of southern Michigan, and it is difficult to find a town of any consequence that was not represented. Naturally, the majority came the shortest distance. Thus, St. Clair, Macomb, and Oakland counties sent the largest number. Port Huron probably led all other cities. But farther afield, there were patients from Lansing, Battle Creek, Jackson, and Ann Arbor, not to mention smaller communities like Auburn, Eaton Rapids, Orion, Salem, Frontier, and others which can barely be found on modern maps. Windsor and Ontario, generally, sent their quotas, and a surprising number came from Ohio and Indiana—although it must be recognized that some patients from more distant points may have been visiting in Detroit at the time they required hospitalization.[3] Wherever the patients came from, they reflected the continually widening circle of respect Harper was gaining. Its reputation grew until, within a few years, the claim would be made that "our territory is large—reaching north 1,200 miles and taking in western Ontario and the whole Lake Superior region as a great many of our patients come from outside the city."[4]

The esteem in which Harper was held was shown in a testimonial printed some years later in a Lapeer, Michigan newspaper. The publisher had been a patient, and his treatment and recovery were so satisfactory as to wring an editorial salute from an eloquent pen. Headed "A Great Surgeonry—Michigan's Excellent Provision for the Suffering," the writer went on to extol the skill of the staff, including several of its early members. Referring to Harper as "Michigan's great and philanthropic institution for the alleviation of the ills of suffering humanity," he went on to point out that "science has been making astounding strides, and nowhere is this more apparent than at Harper. All that skill, research and experience can bring to bear upon a case is available here." If, he concluded, anyone in the vicinity of Lapeer should ever face the ordeal—Heaven forbid—that the newspaper editor faced, "we would certainly commend them to Harper" where "every known comfort and all that is available in medical science are available." [5] It was from such encomiums, printed or passed by word of mouth, that Harper's reputation grew throughout Michigan and adjoining areas.

It took a couple of decades at least before compilation of hospital statistics became the fine art which it is now. In the early years of Harper, the trustees and even the medical staff were more concerned with financial records than with vital statistics. Sometimes the medical chief, in his annual report to the trustees, offered some detailed information about the patients, but not always. Even when this information was provided, it did not always follow a set pattern permitting accurate comparisons from year to year. Not until regular publication of the *Harper Hospital Bulletin* began in 1890 was there any real continuity to the available statistics. Prior to that time, they had to be found wherever they existed and, unfortunately, they did not always exist.

What statistics there were, however, were frequently revealing, both in reference to the Hospital and to the community. Originally, the statistical records included in the minutes, covering the medical chief's monthly and annual reports, mentioned only births and deaths. Often there was none to report. In the minutes of March 2, 1869, it is recorded "no deaths or births during the month [February, 1869]." [6] Despite the fact that such entries were not made regularly, it was still possible to compute a fairly accurate mortality rate which, even in the early days of the Hospital, was extraordinarily low. For example, in 1866, the first full year of operation under the trustees, there were 12 deaths among the 267 patients, a mortality rate of 4.5 per cent. The following year, 1867, the rate dropped to 3.8 per cent, and in 1868 and 1869 it was 5.3 and 6.6 per cent respectively. No compilations were made for the next few years, but when figures became available again, the rate fluctuated between 5 and 10 per cent. [7] In 1890, when Harper treated 1,268 patients during the year, it reported 77 deaths. [8] The mortality rate that year was 6 per cent. Considering the fact, as the medical or superintendent's report generally indicated, that many patients were admitted in a moribund condition, and considering also that medicine and surgery of that era had not reached their present level of sophistication, the early mortality rates indicate excellent professional skills.

The patients' register or record books which, unfortunately, were not preserved at Harper prior to 1870, contain a great deal of valuable information about the patients and the illnesses for which they were treated. The latter listings are of particular interest as they show the ills to which the people of Detroit were most frequently subjected 100 years ago. Among the typical and most frequent ailments were senility, insanity, childbirth, cancer, tuberculosis, blindness, burns, bruises, venereal diseases, delirium tremens and chronic alcoholism, paralysis, typhoid fever, and diphtheria. Despite the fact that from the beginning Harper Hospital emphasized that it accepted no contagious cases, diphtheria accounted for a substantial number of cases. Actually, those which Harper did take—diphtheria and scarlet fever—were accepted only after special isolation facilities had been provided. The prohibition against contagious cases applied chiefly to smallpox. Patients with that disease were cared for at home or sent to the public pesthouse.

During the first dozen or so years, the available statistics show that medical cases outnumbered surgical cases by a fairly wide margin. In 1874, for example, there were 217 medical and 168 surgical cases. This ratio did not materially change until about the mid-1890's when surgery became predominate at Harper. It is interesting that in the first couple of decades among the surgical cases, many of which could be classed as emergencies, a high percentage resulted from railroad accidents. These occurred in the yards. While some of the victims no doubt were drifters, the majority were railroad employees, unprotected by the safety laws and regulations which came along later. Railroading, it must be assumed from the early Harper records, was a hazardous occupation.

From time to time, progress reports were included, covering the patients discharged during the year. Thus, there appears the following breakdown for 1890: "Well—642; improved—391; not improved—62; died—77." [9] The nativity of patients was listed beginning about 1870, and a sampling of 80 cases in 1874 shows the following birthplaces: United States, 29; Canada and Ireland, 10 each; England, Scotland, and Germany, 7 each; France, 4; Finland, 2; and Mexico, 1.[10]

Starting in 1887, the occupation of the patient was listed. As might be expected in a hospital where the accent was on charity, most were laborers and artisans, although nearly every vocation was represented. In 1890, for example, 219 patients were classified as laborers; 225 were miners, showing how Harper's field of service reached as far as the copper and iron areas of Michigan's Upper Peninsula. Housewives—

many being maternity cases—numbered 174, while there were 143 domestics. Clerks and mechanics accounted for 247; 55 were farmers. Among the others were commercial travelers, merchants, students, teachers, firemen, seamstresses, artists, sailors, journalists, clergymen, and lawyers. Also admitted were 6 physicians and 9 nurses, who obviously knew where to go for treatment.[11]

There was no segregation or discrimination against race or religion at Harper. Among the wounded soldiers in the military hospital and the veterans in the Soldiers' Home, there were Indians and Negroes. Later, in the civilian hospital, Negro patients are often listed. In 1890, the 1,268 cases were divided as follows: "Males, 801. Females, 467." Three hundred and forty-eight patients were between the ages of five and twenty years; 547 between twenty and forty; 251 between forty and fifty; 78 between fifty and sixty; and 44 over sixty. The Protestants numbered 971; Catholics, 278; and Hebrews, 19.[12] Obviously, Harper Hospital served all groups and classes of people and fulfilled all of the requirements of a truly civic institution.

Of course, many patients entered Harper Hospital prior to 1874, but John O'Conner, who was admitted on October 8 (probably in 1873), is the first person for whom any record has been preserved—and even that is incomplete. A native of Ireland, O'Connor lived at 218 East Congress Street, Detroit. He was age seventy, 5 ft. 9 in., and married. Both his parents were dead of causes unknown to him. He was examined and his mental condition was described as good; his eyes were good; his tongue "well"; his respiration normal; stomach "in order." He was constipated, his bladder was "good," and he had a sore in his mouth. The diagnosis was "epithelioma of right side of mouth near last molars." To state it another way, John O'Conner had cancer of the mouth. He was treated, without surgery, until November 11 when the notations on his record cease. The result of the treatment remains unknown.[13]

The second patient whose medical record is available was a Mrs. McDonald, of Toronto, a white woman, age forty-three, and married. Her story is not a pretty one to read. Her previous medical record indicated she had once had syphilis. She entered the Hospital January 1, 1874. Her condition was described in these words: "Tongue dry and pulse fast and very weak. Gave immediate stimulants. Evening better, pulse full and slower." She was given medication, but did not sleep well that night. The following morning, her condition was about the same as when she was admitted. Despite that, she was "conveyed to her home, Jan. 2."

"This patient," said the résumé of her report, "was a woman of loose character and had contracted syphilis some years ago. At the present time she had all the symptoms of secondary syphilis, sore throat, ulcerations of the skin in different parts of the body. . . . Leaving Hosp. so soon, there was no opportunity to observe the result of treatment." The report concluded with a single word: "Prostitute."

By contrast, thirteen-year-old Charlie Ingle was admitted on or about the third of January. He had what was described as "congenital deformity of the face." Dr. David O. Farrand took his case, reporting that one side of Charlie's face was "denuded of skin along the side of nose from eye to lip, leaving the nasal fossa exposed." Dr. Farrand operated "by bringing the edges of the wound together and retaining them in place with silver pins." The final notation was "wound doing well."

C. O. Messenger, a farmer, was admitted on February 17, with frozen feet and hands and with the toes of the left foot gangrenous. "Dr. McGraw removed them on the 27 Feb. 74. Wound doing well." John Armstrong, a sailor, had his right arm mangled when he caught it between the shaft and the adjacent framework in the engine room of the U.S.S. "General Grant." He was taken to Harper on July 20, 1874, the broken bone was "set up in splints," and on September 24, Armstrong was discharged, his condition "all right."

Not all the case histories in this first patients' record book had happy endings. There was, for example, an Englishman, K. Thomas, who was admitted May 3, 1874. He had been a British soldier and had seen service on Malta, in the Crimea, and in British North America. Suffering from tuberculosis, he was in "a sinking condition." For four days, the Harper staff fought to save him, but to no avail. On May 7, according to the record, the patient was "delirious from yesterday noon till the time of his death which took place at 2 P.M."

Despite the quality of work being done by Farrand, McGraw, and a few others, the organization and evolution of the Harper Hospital staff were slow. When Harper opened as a civilian hospital, the staff consisted of four consultants—two physicians and two surgeons—and four attendants, two of whom also were physicians and two surgeons. Most of the work was done by the attending physicians and surgeons, although much of the load, both medical and administrative, was carried by the resident or house physician. There was no medical superintendent in the now-accepted sense. The superintendent in 1866 and for some time thereafter was no more than a bookkeeper and janitor. It has been said, in fact, that prior to 1875, "the administration of the Hospital had been part of the duties of the matron, aided by members of the staff." [14] It might be added that the Board of Trustees also played a prominent administrative role. As long as the Soldiers' Home played such an important part in the Harper scheme, it was customary for the Hospital's house physician to occupy the post of superintendent of the Home. The first to hold this dual post was Dr. Ira Fletcher. Gradually, he and his successors began to assume general administrative functions, and in time, the house physician evolved into the general superintendent.

Following Fletcher, Dr. A. T. Smith became house physician August 4, 1868, on the recommendation of Dr. McGraw. Dr. Smith served for about a year, until June 1, 1869, when he resigned to accept an appointment in the regular army as acting assistant surgeon. He was succeeded by Dr. George A. Foster. Both Smith and Foster were capable men, and they began to assume some of the authority and responsibility which later marked the office of superintendent.[15]

About the time of Smith's appointment, Dr. George B. Russel, the trustee, was given the title and position of medical chief of the Hospital, apparently to act as a buffer between the staff and the trustees and to settle questions and disputes which arose within the staff itself. Much occupied with his industrial enterprises, there is no record of Dr. Russel's ever having treated a patient in the Hospital. As chief, he appears to have been the board's own representative where medical questions arose.[16]

Foster continued as house physician until April 1, 1873, a tenure of almost four years. Like his predecessors, he served as superintendent of the Soldiers' Home, for which he received from the state the impressive wage of sixty cents a day. The Hospital paid him nothing beyond board and quarters until September 4, 1871, when the board, "in view of the valuable services rendered by Dr. G. A. Foster, and his fidelity in the discharge of his duties," voted to allow him the princely stipend of fifteen dollars a month.[17]

Following Foster's resignation, Dr. Theodore A. Felch became house physician with the same remuneration which Foster had received. It has often been stated and has appeared frequently in Harper records that the first real superintendent's office was created in 1875 with the appointment of Dr. Howard William Longyear.[18] But the trustees' minutes of April 7, 1874, on the occasion of Felch's resignation, express "regret that we are to lose his services as superintendent and resident physician, the duties of which position he has discharged to our entire satisfaction." [19] Felch enjoyed the services of an assistant, Dr. Frank Gamble, appointed April 1, 1873, "without pay, except his board." Gamble succeeded Felch, not only as resident but, it can be assumed, as superintendent also. When he resigned in November, 1875, Dr. Long-year was given a temporary appointment "on the same terms as existed with Dr. Gamble." [20]

Therefore, if Howard Longyear was not the first superintendent, as it has been claimed, he did fill the post of medical superintendent with great distinction for three years, and for another forty years he was a member of the staff, becoming one of the great figures in Harper history.[21] It was said that in his connection with the Hospital, he "did much to stimulate its progress and improvement." [22] Born in Lansing, July 24, 1852, Longyear was only twenty-three years old when he became administrative head of Harper. He had attended the University of Michigan and took his medical degree at the College of Physicians and Surgeons, of New York. Upon graduation, he studied abroad under the distinguished Dr. Lawson Tait of Birmingham, England. In private practice, he specialized in gynecology and abdominal surgery. He was consultant, not only at Harper, but also at Woman's Hospital and Providence Hospital. He was a vice-president of the American Medical Association and a member of the Detroit Board of Health for four years. "Keenly interested in the problems of sanitary science and preventive medicine . . . he gave the community the fruits of his study and experience." [23] His daughter, Abbie Scott, married Dr. Theodore A. McGraw, Jr. Thus, two families, whose names are an imperishable part of the Harper medical tradition, were united. Howard Longyear died June 2, 1921, and his obituary concluded with the statement that "he was indeed the beloved physician." [24]

The first attempts to expand and departmentalize the Harper staff, beyond Dr. McGraw's insistence to strengthen the lying-in department, were not immediately successful. The trustees, or at least some of them, were aware of the need for expanded services, and in the spring of 1872, a committee was appointed and instructed to report "a revised and full medical staff for the Hospital." [25] Evidently, the committee was unable to come to any sort of agreement, because after three months' deliberation, it reported that it was not yet prepared and asked for further time. That there may have been some dissension about the matter is indicated by the directive to the committee "to consult with members of the present staff in the matter." [26] This strongly suggests that the staff had not, up to that time, been consulted about changes. Another sign of dissent was the resignation of Dr. Jenks as attending physician in December, 1872. Jenks expressed a willingness, however, to accept a position as special physician for female diseases. The matter was referred to Dr. Russel who recommended Dr. A. S. Heaton as Jenks's replacement. Meanwhile, it had been proposed that "the question of appointing one or more oculists be also referred to the medical chief of staff." [27] Along with the recommendation on Heaton, Russel reported "that in his opinion it was not advisable at the present time to create special departments in the Hospital, and he could not therefore recommend the appointment of Dr. Jenks as physician in the department of female diseases." Neither, he declared, was he ready to make any suggestion concerning the oculists.[28] If, then, there was a rift, it would appear that Dr. Russel was involved, along with Dr. Jenks.

Staff dissension was not new. As early as June 12, 1866, Dr. Duffield was asked by his fellow trustees "to see the Medical Board and harmonize the differing views of the Consulting and Visiting members of the Board." [29] Later, in 1872, the trustees went so far as to reprimand Russel who "has not found it convenient to meet with and share with them [the trustees] the responsibilities of their trust, and participate in the management of the institution." [30] About the same time, Dr. J. F. Noyes, who was an oculist and ultimately became a Harper staff member, complained to the trustees that certain of his patients "had been tampered with" by Dr. Eugene Smith.[31] In an effort to resolve some of these and other staff and professional cross-currents, a set of rules was adopted, defining the duties, prerogatives, and respective areas of the attending and consulting physicians and surgeons. Apparently, these regulations, even though they were from time to time amended, did not wholly soothe ruffled feelings. In mid-1875, Russel resigned as chief of the medical staff, to be immediately replaced by Dr. Farrand. At the same time, the trustees decreed that "hereafter the appointments to this office shall be made from the members of the active medicine staff of the Hospital." [32] By the end of the year, the staff was enlarged. Dr. Foster became a staff surgeon and Dr. David Inglis was named assistant physician. But more significant was the appointment of Dr. Noyes as oculist.[33]

At the annual board meeting in 1878, the staff submitted its own recommendations to the trustees. Among these were the following proposals:

1. The surgeon-in-chief should be nominated by the attending physicians for a term of one year, and the chief medical officer was to be elected from among the members of the staff, "they to serve in rotation as such." The duties of the surgeon-in-chief would be "to look after the general management of the Hospital (in all matters pertaining to the the surgical and medical departments thereof)."

2. New members of the staff would be appointed only upon nomination by the attending physicians.

3. Candidates for resident physician must be graduates of "some regular school of medicine," and must pass competitive examinations before their names could be submitted to the Board of Trustees. "It is clearly the opinion of this committee," the staff added, "that as long as the duties of the resident physician and superintendent are continued in one person, it will be for the best interests of the Hospital to re-nominate a good resident physician from year to year as he may be contented to remain."

4. Inasmuch as attending physicians and surgeons give their services gratuitously to the charity patients, it was recommended that a notice be placed in each private room, stating that patients who are able are expected to pay a moderate fee to the visiting physician or surgeon in attendance.[34]

These recommendations, with the exception of the fourth, were approved by the trustees and put in operation. The result was that troubled waters now were quieted. More important, the position of chief of staff had been strengthened, and the staff itself had achieved a larger degree of professional responsibility and independence.*

Under Farrand's direction as chief of staff, Harper's affairs prospered. He was a strong, able man, devoted to the Hospital for which he understandably felt a proprietary interest. It was a great loss, then, when David Osburn Farrand died March 18, 1883, at the untimely age of forty-five.[35]

Harper was still a young institution when, in 1868, it fulfilled one of the functions of a hospital, described by Malcolm T. MacEachern, by providing for the education of physicians. Harper did this in the role of godparent (or would the term midwife be more apropos?) to the Detroit Medical College, the direct ancestor of the College of Medicine of Wayne State University.

The guiding spirits behind the founding of the school were the staff members, and particularly Dr. Theodore A. McGraw. McGraw was an aristocrat of his profession, and one of his abiding ambitions was to raise the level of medical practice by setting up improved educational standards. Medical education at that time still was largely under the preceptor or apprentice system. A young man would attach himself to a doctor for a period of months, tending his fires and sweeping out his office. In return, the student was given access to the doctor's medical books and allowed to accompany him on his rounds and visits. Eventually, he would progress to mixing prescriptions and assisting at operations. By that time, he was deemed qualified to hang out his shingle and start practice on his own. The trouble was that many young men, seeking a way to quick success, attached themselves to incompetents and quacks. A few, having completed their apprenticeships, added a few weeks' training at a medical school, most of which were privately owned and operated for profit. Many of them were little more than diploma mills, graduating "physicians and surgeons" no more qualified than the apprentices. This undesirable practice endured for many years. It was not until 1899 that Michigan adopted a medical licensing and registration law, setting up standards which could be met only by graduation from an accredited medical school.

McGraw and a few of his associates sought to eliminate the worst evils of the preceptor system and the diploma mills by a formalized educational course, employing the teaching talents of the best medical men and the clinical facilities offered by such hospitals as Harper. Dr. Zina Pitcher attempted earlier to improve conditions by establishing a University of Michigan clinical summer course at St. Mary's and Marine Hospitals in 1857, but he was forced to drop the project because of faculty opposition, based upon the University's unwillingness to have any of its operations removed from the Ann Arbor campus.[36]

Many progressive-minded younger men, of whom McGraw was one, served in the Civil War, and one of the lessons they brought back was that the army hospitals provided a vast reservoir of clinical material which could and should be used. In 1865, while Harper was still occupied principally by soldiers and veterans, several of the resident physicians proposed setting up a medical school within the Hospital. Beyond a promise of co-operation on the part of the trustees, nothing was immediately done.[37]

McGraw and his associates learned that under state law a charter was required if degrees were to be granted. A charter cost more than either the Hospital or the supporters of the medical school plan could afford. Dr. Duffield suggested that arrangements might be worked out to take over the charter of an existing college. Marshall College, in Marshall, Michigan, had a charter, but the school was not operating. McGraw wrote to the Marshall trustees to learn if they would be interested in granting degrees to graduates of the Harper school.[38] Nothing came of those inquiries, and a year later, in April, 1868, the trustees' minutes record that "Dr. McGraw submitted some suggestions to the Board relative to the organization of a Medical College," whereupon the trustees agreed to lease the north half of Park lot 25, with the buildings on it, to Drs. Edward W. Jenks, Samuel P. Duffield, David O. Farrand, George P. Andrews, and Theodore A. McGraw "with the understanding that the said lease shall be transferred to the corporation of the Medical College proposed to be organized." The majority of the stock, to the value of $20,000, was to be transferred by the lessees to the Hospital in return for the lease which was to run for twenty years. The rent was to be not more than seven per cent on $20,000.[39] Shortly after that, on June 11, 1868, articles of incorporation were filed.[40] In its annual report for 1868, the Harper Board of Trustees stated that:

. . . a portion of the ground and buildings have been leased during the past year to the Detroit Medical College, which has been incorporated under the laws of the State of Michigan, and is now open for the reception of students. It has no direct connection with the hospital, but is conducted and maintained entirely by the private enterprise of its own stockholders.[41]

It could hardly be expected that the young doctors who organized the college would be able to raise the money, about $30,000, necessary to get it started. They had the help of some of the wealthiest and most influential people in Detroit. James F. Joy became president of the Board of Trustees. Serving with him were Dr. McGraw and his father, A. C. McGraw, Philo Parsons, W. A. Butter, Buckminster Wight, Allen Shelden, C. H. Buhl, M. I. Mills, C. VanHusan, John Owen, George Frost, Hiram Walker, Henry P. Baldwin, W. B. Wesson, Dr. Jenks, Dr. Andrews, and Dr. S. P. Duffield. From these names, the close link between the college and Harper becomes evident. Most of the faculty came straight from the Harper staff and included Jenks, T. A. McGraw, Andrews, S. P. Duffield, and James F. Noyes.

The college occupied two of the north Hospital buildings, and, with alterations, these were combined into a single structure of 60 by 100 feet.* Said the original prospectus:

A part of the central portion of the building will be used for a lecture room, semicircular in shape and provided with seats on an inclined plane for about 250 students. Near the main entrance will be a vestibule with a staircase on each side running up to the top of the amphitheater, and the dissecting room and laboratory will be in the rear of the lecture room.

A preliminary course was started in November, 1868, and the first regular course began February 2, 1869. It ran to June 5, when degrees were given 38 students.[42]

The success of Detroit Medical College prompted interest in others, and in 1874, the Detroit Homeopathic College asked the Harper trustees for similar accommodations. Homeopaths were regarded by the Harper "regulars" in much the same way that modern doctors view "naturapaths," and the proposal got a cool reception. The Homeopathic College had been occupying rented quarters in the Coyl Building, at Woodward and Campus Martius. It is a coincidence that very shortly the Coyl Building became Harper Hospital property through one of the most significant bequests in the Hospital's history. Meanwhile, the homeopaths were put off with the excuse that Harper would probably soon be erecting a new building, and for that reason the trustees found it inadvisable to make any commitments regarding the property.[43]

Students now became a familiar and sometimes distracting element in and around Harper. It has been related that they became favorites of Nancy Martin. At times they were a problem to the trustees who, on one occasion, had to threaten expulsion of the next student who walked on the lawn and failed to use the proper rear door.[44] That the school was open to all is indicated by the matriculation in 1871 of Henry Fitzbutler, a Negro, who a few years later founded the Louisville National Medical College.[45]

A rival school, the Michigan College of Medicine, was founded in 1879. It was located near St. Mary's Hospital, and for the next few years, Detroit's two medical schools operated in competition with each other.[46]

One of the required courses was vivisection, which became a "specialty of the college." This led to some bizarre incidents. It was not until 1881 that a state law provided that unclaimed bodies from prisons and poorhouses should be turned over to the demonstrators of anatomy at medical colleges. Until then, there were occasional scandals as the so-called resurrectionists prowled the cemeteries on dark nights, seeking bodies. Such incidents provided the newspapers with lurid and eerie stories. A police raid on the Detroit Medical College and the Michigan College of Medicine turned up a disinterred body stolen a day or two earlier from Mt. Elliott Cemetery. On two occasions, the Harper trustees were confronted with the serious problem of what measures to take after bodies had disappeared from the hospital "morgue." Whatever the outcome, there was a minimum of publicity, as may easily be imagined. If the trustees discovered the answer to what had happened, or if they took any action, the records are discreetly silent. It takes little imagination, however, to form the conclusion that the "resurrectionists" had been at work, and that the anatomy classes had specimens upon which to work.[47]

In 1883, the Detroit Medical College abandoned the quarters on the Harper grounds and moved into a new building on Farmer Street, between Gratiot and Monroe. The Harper trustees were not really insincere when they told the homeopaths that they were thinking of a new hospital building. The fact that plans for a new hospital were being discussed and the college's need for larger and more modern facilities were reasons new quarters were obtained.

In 1885, the Detroit Medical College and the Michigan College of Medicine consolidated under the new name of the Detroit College of Medicine.[48] It continued well into the twentieth century when financial difficulties developed. These were partially resolved in 1913 when an alumni group, under the leadership of Dr. Burt R. Shurly, purchased the college, with public assistance. Because of increasingly higher educational requirements, a premedical course was inaugurated in Detroit Central High School, which soon evolved into Detroit Junior College, a forerunner of Wayne State University. Thus, the link between Detroit Medical College and the present university became closer. The bond further strengthened after World War I when, through the efforts of Dr. Shurly and Dr. Andrew P. Biddle, the Detroit College of Medicine was absorbed by the Detroit Board of Education into the public school system.[49] It was at that time that the medical college became an integral affiliate of Wayne State—and through that affiliation Wayne was enabled to trace its origins, through its oldest college, back to 1868.

The Harper trustees in 1868 may have meant it when they stated that the Detroit Medical College and the Hospital had no direct connection. Technically, they were correct, but the two institutions have been so close as, at times, almost to defy distinction. The association of the two was confirmed beyond question in 1887, when the Hospital's medical staff expressed its feelings by adopting a rule that all candidates for positions on the house staff must be graduates of the Detroit College of Medicine.[50] The affiliation continued, with the students enjoying the benefits of clinical instruction in the Hospital—a privilege they still have. The stamp of Harper was indelibly placed upon the college by the Hospital's staff which founded it, and by the college's graduates who have been mainstays of the Harper staff for close to a century.

Chapter 12

NEIGHBORS AND BENEFACTORS

The Detroit Medical College
was neither the first nor the last institution, serving a community purpose, to have its origin within Harper Hospital or to be aided by it. In
the earlier army years, a good part of the building space was unused by
the Hospital. Other institutions or organizations, eyeing available room
in the structures or on the grounds, appealed to the trustees for free
or leased quarters. Whenever the request was felt to be within the definition of the public interest, it was granted. The trustees themselves were
men whose civic interests were broad and varied and not confined solely
to Harper Hospital, its operation, and development. Reasonable requests
for use of Harper facilities were freely granted whenever it was possible
to do so. As a result, many civic enterprises, some of which are still
flourishing, can be regarded as offshoots of the Hospital. These included
a wide variety of activities: medical, charitable, religious, scientific, educational, and recreational.

Harper's doors had not long been open as a private hospital when the
trustees received the first plea for assistance. It came from an Episcopalian establishment, St. Luke's Hospital and Home. St. Luke's had been
incorporated in 1861 through the efforts of parishioners of St. Paul's Episcopal Church, assisted by a bequest of $1,500. More a "home" for the
aged and infirm than a hospital, it originally occupied a residence on the
south side of West Lafayette between Griswold and Shelby. Its first patients entered July 18, 1864. Two years later, in April, 1866, the Lafayette
Street property was sold, and a new site was obtained out West Fort
Street, near Clark. Inasmuch as the new building could not be ready for

about two years, it became necessary to find temporary quarters, and the St. Luke's directors appealed to the Harper trustees.[1]

On May 3, 1866, the Harper board granted the Episcopal home the use of:

> . . . a part of the southerly building extending back as far as the unfinished part known as the carpenter shop, with all of the second story and the use of the land between said building and the South Ward, and of a strip of land 20 by 100 feet in front of the West side, with the right . . . to take away all fence posts and boards that they may put on said land and also a free right of way along and over the plank road through the first gate to and from said building and premises.[2]

It was stipulated that St. Luke's would put up no signs bearing its name which could be seen from Woodward Avenue, that it would not operate a general hospital, and that it would insure the quarters allotted it for $1,200.

St. Luke's occupied the building on the Harper grounds until 1868, when its new hospital on Fort was completed. It remained there until 1917, when it relocated on Highland Avenue, Highland Park, where it still operates as an Episcopal, church-supported institution devoted to the care of elderly members of that faith. It was the first institution to benefit from an association with Harper. That association still continues; both Harper and St. Luke's, as joint beneficiaries of a generous bequest, are owners of a downtown building on the northeast corner of Woodward and Campus Martius.

The Harper "campus" soon became a very busy place. In July, 1868, the Mission Sabbath School, which seems to have had some connection with the downtown Westminster Presbyterian Church, was granted permission to use space in the rear of one of the wards, a room which had been used for school purposes. The Harper trustees soon found to their satisfaction that it had "grown into a useful and much needed school in that locality."[3]

The next "tenant" by courtesy of the trustees was an important one. In 1872, the trustees of the Woman's Hospital and Foundlings' Home, an institution almost as old as Harper, found themselves in the same situation St. Luke's had experienced a few years before. The hospital was occupying a rented building at 499 Beaubien Street while preparations were being made to move into better quarters which had been purchased on Thirteenth Street between Linden and Mulberry. These were not ready for occupancy, and Woman's Hospital had to find temporary housing. An appeal was made to the trustees of Harper and their response was prompt. Permission was granted to move into the building "lately occupied by St. Luke's." Woman's Hospital and Foundlings' Home, as its name suggests, had been organized to meet a social problem, primarily that of caring for unmarried women. Fearful, perhaps, that sin might rub off, the Harper board insisted that its new tenants be isolated from the Hospital proper by constructing a fence seven feet high, "to prevent all communication." The only other occupancy requirement, beyond insuring the building and promising to keep it clean, was to construct a water closet for the inmates.[4] Woman's Hospital remained a part of the Harper complex for four years, and then it moved out and into its new home on Thirteenth. On June 6, 1876, the Harper trustees received a letter of thanks from the trustees of Woman's "for the gratuitous use" of one of the Harper buildings.[5]

Another Detroit landmark became closely associated with the Hospital in 1872 when Westminster Presbyterian Church found temporary haven in one of the unused ward buildings. Westminster had been organized in 1837 and was first located at Lafayette and Wayne Streets. In 1861, a new church was built on Washington Boulevard. About 1872, evening services were held at Harper, and the next year, when the Washington Boulevard Church was sold to St. Aloysius Roman Catholic Church, all services were held at Harper. This continued for about a year, or until May 10, 1874, when Westminster moved into its own church home which had been completed at Woodward and Parsons. Westminster occupied that location until 1919 when Orchestra Hall, the home of the Detroit Symphony, was built on the site.[6]

At the same time Woman's, Westminster, and the Medical College all occupied Harper buildings on various parts of the grounds, the Home for the Friendless, another institution for wayward girls, was provided with temporary quarters, while awaiting completion of its new building on West Warren Avenue.[7] Two years later, in 1876, room in an unused building was given to the Ladies Protestant Orphan Asylum to house some of their charges.[8] That same year, Emmanuel Episcopal Church, which had been a near neighbor at Woodward and Fremont, found accommodations at Harper. Emmanuel had to vacate its site which was on the grounds of the Peninsular Cricket Club. It bought a new lot on

West Alexandrine between Cass and Woodward and moved its church building there. During that process, services were held in rooms provided free by the hospital trustees until 1877.[9] In 1880, the Detroit Scientific Association was permitted to set up in a Harper building its museum and collection of rock samples and stuffed birds.[10] In 1882, a Methodist church, in process of being organized, came under the Harper wing.[11] So did a Congregational church which was allowed to use a piece of ground owned by the Hospital on Woodward.[12]

In 1887, when Harper was enjoying a new hospital building of its own, it extended the use of its maternity section, known as the Nancy Martin Ward, to the Children's Free Hospital Association. The result was a hospital within a hospital—Children's being responsible for the admittance and treatment of its patients and paying Harper three dollars per week per patient, while Harper furnished board, laundry, nursing, medicine, and medical attendance. Children's, of course, was a charitable institution. The arrangement between it and Harper continued until February 15, 1891. By that time, or very shortly thereafter, Children's own hospital was built at its present location, Farnsworth and St. Antoine Streets. One of the early large contributors to Children's was Hiram Walker, who donated its first building. He was a generous benefactor of Harper and one of its trustees. James Couzens, also a trustee of Harper, made substantial gifts to Children's Free Hospital which, consolidating with the Michigan Hospital School of Farmington, became today's Children's Hospital of Michigan.[13]

It was not just religion, charity and science which benefited from Harper Hospital's willingness to share its facilities with the public. The sound of voices raised in hymns sometimes must have been offset by shouts of "kill the umpire," or whatever warlike cry came from the bleachers of the 1870's, for it was in 1879 that the trustees gave the use of part of the grounds, including a portion of Nancy Martin's grove, to Recreation Park, a large-scale sports enterprise promoted by several Detroit citizens.[14] The corporation which controlled Recreation Park was formed in 1878 and acquired part of the Brush farm between Brady Street and Fremont Avenue, and Beaubien Street on the east. The tract consisted of eighteen acres which, it soon was discovered, were not enough, causing the directors to ask for use of the east portion of the Harper lands. By the early part of 1879, the development plans were ready; Recreation Park would have just about every kind of sports facility, including two baseball diamonds and grandstands for 1,000 spectators, a three-quarter mile trotting track, a cricket ground, a lacrosse field, a skating and curling rink, an archery range, a croquet grounds, bowling alleys, courts for lawn tennis, and other summer games. There were also to be a club house, a gymnasium, and a caretaker's house. All this was to be surrounded by a nine-foot fence, the grounds to be leveled and provided with a drainage system. The entrance was at the southwest corner, near Brady Street.[15] The prospectus materialized, and the Park became all that the promoters promised. As a special attraction, the owner of a professional baseball team was prevailed upon to use Recreation Park.[16]

On April 1, 1879, the Harper trustees received a formal request from the Park directors for the use of "a portion of the grove for their players." The idea of turning this beautiful grove into a play field must have been more than the staid trustees could assimilate at one swallow. Their reaction was to place the matter "on the table for further consideration." [17] But, by May 6, they were either convinced or reconciled. The petition of Recreation Park was cautiously granted with appropriate safeguards which included:

. . . the use of 100 feet on the eastern end of the grove, under conditions reserving the right to revoke all privileges upon giving reasonable notice and under such other instructions as they [the trustees] shall deem proper, and at a reasonable charge in the way of yearly rent for said use.[18]

With that permission, the baseball club, the "Hollinger Nine," began the sale of season tickets; a crew of sixty workmen moved in to plow, smooth and sod the grounds, and install drain tile and water pipes. On May 13, all was in readiness, and 1,200 spectators turned out to see Detroit lose to Troy, New York, by a score of seven to one.[19] The fans went away disappointed, but they all agreed the park was beautiful. In 1881, regular league games were played at Recreation Park, Detroit then belonging to the old National League. In 1887, Detroit beat St. Louis in fifteen innings to win the world championship.[20]

Recreation Park proved to be a good neighbor to Harper Hospital, so good, in fact, that the Archery Club, which in summer used the Park's range, was permitted to move into one of the vacant hospital buildings in the winter.[21] Recreation Park continued to be a place where Detroiters—players and spectators—could enjoy themselves until 1894, when it closed down and subdivided. The professional baseball team moved out to a new park at Michigan and Trumbull, and the amateur players found new facilities at Grindley Field on Woodward at Canfield, where the old Detroit Athletic Club was established.

Whether it was psalms or stolen bases, orphans or stuffed birds, Harper Hospital's spare facilities were at the disposal of the people of Detroit.

During Harper's first two decades, the character of the institution was determined more by the Board of Trustees than by the staff. The original seven members, aided by Divie B. Duffield as secretary, firmly implanted the mark of their own dedication and awareness of their responsibilities under the Harper-Martin trust. It was due to them, even more than to Walter Harper and Nancy Martin, that Harper Hospital so quickly became a flourishing establishment. Because they held life tenure, a continuity was established, which, as far as the original board was concerned, lasted for thirty-two years, until the death of Jacob S. Farrand, in 1891, and the resignation in the same year of Dr. George B. Russel. But perhaps the sharpest blow fell on June 26, 1868, when Dr. Duffield died at the age of seventy-four. He had remained active and interested in the Hospital's affairs right to the end. As late as April, he was present at meetings which, because of his apparent feebleness, were held at his home. His fellow trustees attended his funeral en masse, the services being held at the First Presbyterian Church on Sunday, June 28. He was eloquently eulogized, but there was no better assessment of the loss to Detroit, and to the Hospital particularly, than was expressed by the trustees in a resolution which they adopted on July 7.

Resolved, That in his death the Harper Hospital has lost its earliest friend, its judicious organizer, its influential and ardent upholder and advocate, and the man whose word and deed contributed largely to secure its present usefulness and success; and it is the pleasure of this Board here to say that but for Dr. Duffield's influence and efforts, Harper Hospital would never have had an existence and the City of Detroit would still be deprived of the blessings of a Protestant hospital.[22]

If there was any consolation for the sorrowing city, the board, and the staff of the Hospital, it was to be found in the fact that there were Duffields left to carry on, as they did for many years, the good works of the head of the family.

As a going, thriving concern, Harper could not long pause in sorrow. On July 7, immediately before adopting the Duffield memorial resolution, Buckminster Wight was elected the new president.[23] He would hold that post until his own death, eleven years later. It became necessary, too, to fill the vacancy on the board occasioned by Dr. Duffield's death, although no action was taken until December 5. On that day, Trustees Wight and Buhl were appointed "to give notice to the Pastor and Session of the 1st Presbyterian Church of a vacancy on the Board, and to request their action in reference thereto as required by the Deed of Trust." [24] The church officials nominated three men. They were David Preston, of Central Methodist Church; Robert W. King, a member of the Congregational Church; and General William F. Raynolds, of Westminster Church. Meeting December 6, 1868, the Harper trustees elected King, who thereupon began a trusteeship which lasted until 1899 and which proved to be of great value to the Hospital.[25]

Born in Pittsburgh in 1821, King had gone to Detroit in 1842, after graduating from Washington and Jefferson College. He soon established himself as a successful businessman, the proprietor of a china and glassware business which, later operated under the name of his son, is still known as the L. B. King Company. He met all the traditions of public service which had marked the board from the beginning. He was foreman of the Fifth Ward Volunteer Fire Company and president of the Young Men's Society, a member of the Board of Education, and the Board of Estimates. Perhaps even more important than these distinctions in bringing about his election was the fact that he was the husband of Elizabeth Buhl, daughter of Frederick Buhl.[26]

There were, as could be expected, more breaks in the chain of trusteeship. David Cooper was the next member to die in 1876. He was replaced by Dexter M. Ferry. Wight died three years later. His place on the board was taken by the Rev. D. M. Cooper, son of the original trustee. Buhl became the third president in 1880, holding that office until 1884, when he resigned from the board. Jacob Farrand then became president, and the vacancy was filled by Sullivan M. Cutcheon.[27] Through all of these changes, as well as the others which inevitably took place during the ensuing years, only the personnel changed; the level of ability and leadership, drawn from the best Detroit had to offer, remained constant.

Looking back upon the heavy demands made on the time and

energy of the individual trustees, one wonders at the physical and financial sacrifices they made and admires the great sense of civic responsibility that kept them at the job of running the Hospital. Each of them gave money, not once, but many times, in response to the Hospital's needs. They met regularly, usually once a month in formal session, and frequently more often. And that did not take into account the committee work and other duties which were placed upon them. Involved as they must have been in their personal and business affairs, it is difficult to comprehend how these men were also able to devote so much time to the Hospital.

In the formative years, the task of the trustees was a dual one: they were the Hospital's real administrators approving expenditures, handling personnel matters, and even having a good deal to say about the housing and care, if not the actual treatment, of patients. In addition—and this became their biggest job—they had to assume the grave financial responsibility of administering assets, investing funds, and raising money to meet ever-growing needs. The financial stewardship also was a two-phase affair. There were the current expenses to meet, and there was the future to prepare for. Almost from the beginning, the trustees knew that the barracks-type buildings taken over from the government would not answer a long-term need. The wooden wards were admittedly temporary structures. Hospitals in the 1860's were not supposed to last. Destruction, it was believed, was the only way to get rid of infection. There is no doubt but that the trustees were looking ahead to the day when it would be necessary to replace the original hospital, and as time passed, the necessity became more urgent. It will be recalled that in 1874, when the hospital was less than ten years old, a request for use of a building for a homeopathic college was turned down because of "the probable early necessity of erecting new and permanent Hospital buildings." [28] Again, in 1881, the board resolved "that when a new Hospital building shall be built, it be placed on that portion of the Hospital grounds lying east of the line of John R street." [29]

The trustees never lost sight of the fact that Harper was intended to be a charitable institution. While it was not a free hospital, it was not operated for profit. This meant that if public care was to be expanded to meet the demands of a growing city, additional income would be required. Patients were charged according to their means; the difference had to be made up through some other income source.

It has ever been the effort and aims of the board to keep the charges to patients down to the lowest point consistent with their proper care and comfort, and thus to extend the advantage of the Hospital to the largest number of sick who have but moderate resources, and it is believed that the charges now are lower than in the majority of similar institutions in the country.[30]

So stated the board in 1883, reflecting a long-standing policy which recognized there would be recurring operating deficits. This was admitted as early as 1868 when, in the annual report for 1867, the trustees stated:

We have already for use, the buildings and furniture and finest hospital grounds in the West. All that is now needed to relieve the numerous cases of sick and homeless sufferers who are daily seeking admittance, is more funds. It now remains to be seen whether or not the citizens of Detroit will contribute liberally for the support of a general public hospital in this city.[31]

The year 1874—about the half-way point between the opening of the military hospital and the construction of a new one—may offer fairly representative indications of the operating costs. The annual report covering that year indicated the average daily cost for maintaining a patient was 74¾ cents; the average daily income per patient was 71 cents. While the figures varied slightly from year to year, the deficits went on. In 1880, Hospital expenses, that is, the cost of patient care, was $8,794.61, and the collections, or what was paid by the patients and their friends, were $8,710.75. In 1882, the receipts were $8,015.48 against expenses of $11,-732.22. With spreads of this kind, wide or narrow, occurring year after year, it is obvious that Hospital capital resources had to be tapped. Also, because the resources with which to make up these deficits were limited, the possibility of accumulating enough assets to permit expansion of facilities annually became more remote.[32]

The original financial base was the Harper-Martin property which was sold off, the proceeds being invested, in some cases, in government bonds, but more often in private loans secured by mortgages. The trustees endeavored to get ten per cent return on their funds, but inasmuch as some of the borrowers defaulted, it is doubtful if the overall average yield was as much as ten per cent. Even that, however, was not enough, the Hospital itself stating that the revenue from the Harper-Martin properties:

. . . was expended in paying the constantly increasing taxes on the real estate owned by the corporation, and paying the annual deficiencies between the Hospital earnings and expenses, so that the funds could not increase by accretion of interest.[33]

It will be recalled that when it became necessary to acquire Park lot 25 to meet the requirements of a military hospital, a public solicitation for funds was made. This was the first time that public assistance had been asked, and the appeal was not repeated for several years—not until it became essential to raise money for a new hospital building. Between appeals, there had been a few supplementary gifts. The balance of the Fifth Ward Bounty Fund, monies collected for the relief of families of Civil War soldiers, was given to Harper. It amounted to only $270.[34] Some other voluntary contributions also came in. One of them was a bequest of $5,000 from the estate of Oliver Newberry, a prosperous and civic-minded businessman. That fund was used to replace the Hospital's capital contribution for the Park lot 25 purchase.

With the exception of the Newberry bequest, Harper received no further donations or bequests until 1871, when the income from the original trust no longer was adequate. To raise some money, a Free Bed Fund was started, a money-raising operation not much different from that employed in 1864 when free hospital care was offered in return for the Park lot contributions. The Free Bed Fund, to which were added larger gifts for the perpetual endowment of beds, amounted to $8,320.87 by 1884. Among the donors were various churches, most of the trustees, and a number of charitable-minded citizens. Contributions ranged from $1,758.86 (from the First Presbyterian Church) to very small sums in the $5.00 to $10.00 range. Altogether, there were twenty-six donors.[35] In later years, more beds and rooms were endowed, sometimes by such organizations as the Fire Department and the Detroit school teachers, or again by private individuals. As these endowments carried a guarantee of free care, the trustees ultimately were forced to fix minimum amounts which would be accepted for this purpose.*

The idea of the Free Bed Fund seems to have originated with Jacob S. Farrand. At least he brought the matter before the Board of Trustees on March 17, 1874. The plan was immediately adopted, along with a set of rules fixing the time that a patient could be taken care of according to the size of the donor's contribution. The cost of care was fixed at $4 per week in a ward and $8 per week in a private room. A subscription of $200 would provide for a ward patient for a year, while for $350, a

11. LYSTRA EGGERT GRETTER — Principal of the training school for nurses from 1888 to 1907, Mrs. Gretter was recognized as a pioneer in the field of nursing and helped establish new professional standards in nursing. She was author of the Florence Nightingale Pledge, first administered to the Harper class of 1893.
courtesy Harper Hospital

12. THE OLD AMPHITHEATRE — This early picture, taken in 1889, shows a group of student nurses observing a clinical demonstration in the amphitheatre in the old John R building. The woman in black at the left is Lystra E. Gretter, principal of the Farrand Training School.
courtesy Harper Hospital

13. WILLIAM KIEFT COYL — An early Detroit merchant and philanthropist, Coyl left the bulk of his sizable estate to Harper to establish a fund for the free care of indigent patients. *courtesy Burton Historical Collection*

14. NURSES: CLASS OF 1889 — Only five women graduated from the Farrand Training School for Nurses in 1889. Although the nurses are not identified in this photograph, they were: May Gage, Mary Moses, Isabel Cochrane, Mabel Rockwell, and Alice Bowen. A gray-blue checked Scotch gingham dress, floor-length, and large muslin cap was the first official uniform worn by Harper nurses.
courtesy Harper Hospital

patient could have a private room for a year. "It is understood and stipulated," the trustees declared, "that the above charges include board, washing, fuel, light, nursing, medicines and medical attendance." [36]

Farrand was delegated to take this plan before a Protestant convention on March 18 and seek support of the member churches. The scheduled date of the convention explains why the Free Bed Fund plan was so quickly adopted at a special board session. The Free Bed Fund income was expended for care and treatment. None of it was available for new building purposes. Thus, there was early formed a distinction between endowments and bequests—the former was always used for specified purposes, generally, the care of the sick, while the latter was used at the discretion of the trustees, usually for new buildings, maintenance, or equipment. For the time being, then, there was very little money, far from enough, for a new building. All that was on hand until 1879 was the "original foundation"—the $18,578 which had been realized from the sale of the Harper-Martin properties, plus the $5,000 Newberry bequest.

Beginning in 1881, however, some unexpected developments occurred. In a casual conversation with a friend in 1879, Trustee King was told of an eccentric farmer at Almont, Lapeer County, who had accumulated a fortune of about $20,000. He was supposed to have expressed a desire to leave his money, most of it in bonds and mortgages, to some charitable institution where it would benefit the poor and afflicted. King sat down and wrote to the Almont man, James Thompson, suggesting Harper Hospital as a worthy recipient. King's letter was never acknowledged, and in time, the matter was forgotten. Then, in 1881, after a lapse of two years, the Harper board was notified that Thompson had died, leaving a will which provided that, after a few small bequests were taken care of, the residue of the estate was to go to the Hospital.[37] Harper's share amounted to $11,200.*

It was almost as if the Thompson bequest opened the financial floodgates. Before the year's end, another $5,000 came to the Hospital from the estate of Fanny Davenport (Mrs. J. W.) Waterman.[38]

In 1874, sometime prior to the receipt of the bequests, the trustees had loaned $17,135.00 to a man named Partridge. The loan was secured by a mortgage on part of Park lot 29, sometimes known as the Partridge lot. This piece of property was north of the Hospital at what is now the

corner of Woodward and East Willis Avenues. Partridge did not keep
up his payments, and on April 9, 1877, the mortgage was foreclosed, the
trustees bidding it in at a foreclosure sale for $26,000.00, approximately
the amount of principal and interest due from Partridge.[39] In 1881, in
order to raise money toward a new hospital, the Partridge lot was sold to
Ashley Pond for $31,000.00.[40] A year later, the ten-acre lot at Woodward,
Harper, and Medbury Avenues was put up for sale. This was the property which Nancy Martin, in her dotage, had bought in 1864, and which
the trustees had been forced to take off her hands. Now they had reason
to think a little more highly of Nancy's acumen and to be grateful to her,
because the Medbury lots were sold for $54,325.74.[41] With that amount
added to the Partridge lot which brought $31,000.00, the Thompson be-
quest of $11,200.00, and the Waterman gift of $5,000, the trustees, at the
end of 1882, had on hand a total of $101,525.74 in cash and negotiable
securities. It was enough, they were confident, to build their new hospital.

In anticipation of this forward step, a building committee had been
appointed March 1, 1881. It was made up of Trustees Buhl, McGraw,
Russel, Alanson Sheley, a builder and contractor, and Dr. David O. Farrand.[42] Then, with all the money on hand except from the Medbury sale,
and with good prospects of soon having that, the trustees definitely com-
mitted themselves. At a special meeting on December 5, 1881, "it was
resolved that plans and specifications for the proposed new Hospital be
procured as early as possible." The cost was not to exceed $60,000—a pipe-
dream which would quickly be shattered once the builder's estimates
were received.[43]

The Hospital over the years was the beneficiary of other gifts on
which it is impossible to place a monetary value, things intended for the
pleasure and comfort of the patients, which the Hospital itself was unable to provide. They included a wide range of items—from the complete furnishing of a room, a pair of slippers, a subscription to a newspaper or magazine, to a case of beer. The Hospital kept meticulous
records of the gifts and the donors, entering them in a "contribution
book." The records cover the period from 1878 to 1907. The donor list
reads like the *Who's Who* of Detroit's best families and institutions.
Many of the churches and their women's organizations are represented.
So are many of the well-remembered business firms: R. H. Fyfe, Calvert
Lithographing Company, G. & R. McMillan, Parke, Davis and Company, Breitmeyer & Sons, the Goebel Brewing Company, and the Ameri-

can Eagle Tobacco Works. The St. Andrew's Society made contributions, and so did Company D of the Detroit Light Guard. The Detroit, Belle Isle and Windsor Ferry Company donated a pass which permitted the Harper ambulance to go over to Windsor to pick up patients without paying toll. Hiram Walker could be counted on at frequent intervals to send over a couple or three cases of "Club Whiskey." Mrs. James F. Joy donated fourteen novels; Mrs. John Mix Stanley, wife of the noted Indian painter, sent half a bushel of strawberries. There were flowers in profusion. The card of Mayor and Mrs. Hazen S. Pingree accompanied one bunch of flowers. There were also fans in warm weather, bottles of wine, jelly and jam, bed sheets, nightgowns, mineral water, candy, fruit, ice cream, and Bibles. It was obvious that the kind and generous people of Detroit felt a sense of responsibility for Harper and its patients. But it should also be mentioned that this feeling was shared by people in other parts of Michigan, and the contributions flowed in from many other cities of the state.[44]

It was not until thirty-one years after its incorporation that Harper Hospital received its first really large contribution to its endowment fund. On July 27, 1894, Miss Jean Coyl died, leaving a will which specified that the bulk of her substantial estate should go to the Hospital. Jean Coyl was the daughter and sole heir of William Kieft Coyl, who had amassed a fortune in Detroit as a merchant and property owner. At the time of his death in 1883, he made some important bequests to various charities, but he left the bulk of his estate to his daughter with the understanding that she, in turn, would pass most of it on to Harper. Miss Coyl, described as a beautiful young woman with philanthropic interests which she must have derived from her father, took good care of what he left. In her own eyes, she was his steward, and under her careful management, the assets of the estate increased.* She carried out his wishes to the letter. Besides a bequest of $10,000 to the University of Michigan to establish a library collection in memory of her brother, and some small amounts given to friends and relatives, the main portion of the estate went to Harper.[45]

Her will declared:

The estate thus conveyed is to be kept as a perpetual fund, and only the net income is to be used. Such income is to be devoted to affording free hospital accommodations to such worthy and indigent persons as may be selected by the Trustees. If the estate hereby devised proves sufficient, I direct that a wing be added to the present building in which free hospital accommodations may be furnished to such persons. If the estate do not prove sufficient for the erection of such additional building, then I ask that a certain portion of the present building be appropriated to such purposes, and the portion of the building, whether new or old, so set apart for such free patients, to be named in honor of my father, The William Kieft Coyl Free Hospital.[46]

One of the executors was Dr. Helen F. Warner, a close friend of Jean Coyl. Dr. Warner was the first woman to serve on the staff of Harper Hospital.*

The estate consisted of several pieces of valuable property, a few securities, and cash which amounted to $80,500. The real estate was made up of the following parcels: a thirty-five-foot lot on East Congress Street, near Woodward; two lots on High Street (now Vernor); one lot on Miami (now Broadway); one lot on Farrar Street (now Library); and a lot on the west side of Park Place. Also, and most important as far as value was concerned, was the lot at the northeast corner of Woodward Avenue and Campus Martius, still owned in part by Harper and occupied by a clothing store.[47] All of the property was improved and had buildings, either commercial or residential, on it. Some lots were divided, those on Congress and High Streets each having three buildings. The Woodward and Campus Martius plat, even then one of the most valuable pieces of downtown Detroit property, was the site of the Coyl Building, erected by William Kieft Coyl in 1860. This building, although altered, is still the same structure.[48] The Miami (or Broadway) site later was occupied by the Capitol Theater.

The real estate was inventoried at its assessed value, the total amount being $107,150. The Coyl Building's assessed valuation was $54,350. Together with cash and securities, the entire estate was inventoried at $189,650.[49] The assessed value of the real estate was, of course, not the true value which was then, as now, substantially greater. Various estimates of the actual worth of the estate were given. In 1913, a newspaper account of the Hospital's financial position valued the Coyl endowment at $420,000 which, at the time, was no doubt reasonably accurate.[50] In 1909, the trustees' annual report referred to the original benefaction as being worth about $250,000. Its value could very possibly have increased to the larger figure given by the *News Tribune* nearly twenty years later.[51]

Immediately after the will had been probated, the Harper trustees amended the association bylaws to conform to Miss Coyl's wishes as to the use of the fund. No addition to the Hospital was built, or even seriously considered. Instead, the fund was given the name of the William Kieft Coyl Free Hospital. As such, it became what might be described as a social service agency within the Hospital proper. The administration of the fund posed no real problem because it conformed precisely to the spirit of the original Harper-Martin trusts. The bylaws specified that patients admitted to the "Free Hospital," would be cared for in either rooms or wards "in the same manner and be subject to the same rules and regulations as other patients of Harper Hospital." The fund was to be charged for the care of patients at the same rates as applied to private patients, and "if patients are able to pay in part for such accommodations and service they will be expected to do so, and the residue only charged to the said Free Hospital." [52] As a result of this provision, the records show that many patients were assessed a certain amount, say five dollars a week against a regular seven dollars a week rate, with the Coyl Fund contributing two dollars.

Because of somewhat restricted facilities, not more than fifteen Coyl patients were to be in the Hospital at one time, without special permission of the trustees. This rule was not a hard and fast one, however, and before long, as many as forty or more applications were being approved at one time. A committee was set up to pass upon applications. Its members were to be the president and two other members of the board, or the president, a member of the medical board, "and two ladies." [53] This rule also changed, and before long, the committee consisted of a trustee, the superintendent, and the superintendent of nurses. Meetings were to be held once a week, a schedule which was faithfully followed.

The Coyl Fund performed a highly useful function, benefiting thousands of persons over the years. Applicants were carefully screened; their admittance depended as a rule upon the recommendations of their doctors or ministers, or some other reliable individual who could vouch for the fact that their circumstances were such that they needed help. Frequently, care of beneficiaries of free bed funds was taken over by the Coyl Fund when the free bed time or money ran out. Patients were not limited to Detroit residents; they came from all over Michigan, although Canadian applicants were rejected. Special attention was given to certain groups. "Worthy newsboys," for example, were regarded as a special class for whom care was almost automatically provided.[54] Apparently, the Horatio Alger influence was strong—a newsboy was regarded as a sturdy, honest, and ambitious youngster who deserved all the help he could get. This idea may also have been fostered by General Russell A. Alger, then a trustee, whose charity to paper boys, which included gifts of new suits at Christmas, was well known and widely publicized.

On March 26, 1896, the superintendent "was instructed to place all nurses and employees who became sick, on this fund." [55] As a result, the records are filled with the names of nurses and even doctors who became beneficiaries. At one time, when a diphtheria epidemic struck the Protestant Orphans' Home, all those afflicted, six in number, were taken into the Harper contagious department, the expense being assumed by the Coyl Fund.[56] Patients received care and treatment for every sort of ailment. One patient, a Mrs. Knight, was kept in the Hospital for a month after she normally would have been discharged. This concession was made at the request of her physician "in order to enable him to experiment on her with some special treatment for the cure of the opium habit." [57]

From time to time, the Coyl Fund made loans or grants to the Hospital, as in 1896 when money was advanced to "pay for improvements now being made for heating, lighting and new elevator." Again, the Coyl committee put up the money for a surgical nurse "to take charge of the operating rooms of the Hospital and to do such special nursing with Coyl patients as may be deemed necessary." [58] At the time of the Spanish-American War, sick soldiers and veterans were admitted under the fund. As time went on, the Coyl committee appears to have assumed the character of a social service department, passing on applicants for free bed fund care, as well as care under the Coyl Fund.

Dr. Helen Warner, executrix of Miss Coyl's estate, her close friend, and confidante, served for many years as a member of the Coyl committee, and no one was better able than she to summarize the benefits of the fund or the good accomplished by the donor. Said Dr. Warner of Jean Coyl:

Hers was a life of quiet, unobtrusive, but none the less heroic self-sacrifice. A life almost without pleasure save that of good work well done. Verily she hath rest from her labor, and her works do follow her.[59]

How very well Jean Coyl's works followed her may be learned from a report made by J. L. Hudson, president of the Board of Trustees in 1909, fourteen years after the Coyl Fund was established:

By reason of her wise disposition of her property, we were enabled to give during the year [1908], 9,728 days' free care to 493 patients; the cost of this was $13,583.69 which is the income that came to us from the Coyl estate, so that Miss Jean Coyl by reason of her splendid will has enabled us to take care of twenty-five people free of charge every day during the past year.[60]

Chapter 13

THE NEW HARPER AND
THE FARRAND TRAINING SCHOOL

Harper Hospital's
old wooden military buildings had outlived their usefulness by 1884. Hard wear, time, and weather had combined to make the barracks, constructed twenty years before, a group of dilapidated structures, no longer fit for hospital purposes. Fortunately, the Board of Trustees, with money in the bank, was at last able to build a new hospital which would be structurally and architecturally modern, and scientifically up to date. A dream was to be fulfilled which would be a credit to the trustees and a monument of enduring brick and stone to the memories of Walter Harper, Nancy Martin, and all the others whose efforts and means gave a growing Detroit the kind of institution it needed and deserved.

Even back in the late 1860's and early 1870's, the trustees were looking ahead to a permanent structure. On February 3, 1874, the trustees' proceedings carry the cryptic note that "Trustee Buhl read a letter from the Rev'd. William Passavant."[1] Nothing was said about the contents of the letter, but inasmuch as Passavant was considered the country's foremost authority on hospital planning and financing and because a decade earlier he had offered his services to the trustees, it is safe to assume that he was writing about a new Harper project. If there was any doubt about the trustees' intention to build, it should have been dispelled in 1881 when Trustee Farrand moved "that when a new Hospital building shall be built, it be placed on that portion of the Hospital grounds lying east of the line of John R Street."[2] John R, at that time, had not been opened north of Brady; therefore, the trustees again disclosed their intent when, in 1883, "the President was authorized to sign on behalf of the Board of Trustees a petition to the Common Council for the opening of John R Street." [3] That was followed not long after by a vigorous protest against a proposed plan to build a streetcar line on John R. Incidentally, the John R right of way through the Harper grounds was dedicated to the city by the trustees.[4] This was a strong hint of what was to come. But it was all out in the open when, with money available in 1881, a special board meeting was held at A. C. McGraw's office at 130 Jefferson Avenue and "it was resolved that plans and specifications for the proposed new Hospital be procured as early as practicable." [5] It was at that meeting that a cost ceiling of $60,000 was placed upon the project. Before long, receipt of the Thompson and Waterman bequests permitted the trustees to raise their sights to a more realistic level. But for the time being, the board had definitely committed itself to action.

As the trustees sat around McGraw's office, the subject of an architect came up. McGraw suggested E. E. Meyers, an architect of considerable local reputation. Trustees King and Ferry strongly favored the firm of Mason & Rice. The argument grew warm. Jacob S. Farrand had left the meeting early, and Frederick Buhl refused for some reason to vote. McGraw could have been outvoted, but as he was a man of strong opinion, King and Ferry did not care to oppose him too vehemently. It was decided to obtain the views of all the trustees, as well as that of Dr. David O. Farrand, who, with Alanson Sheley, was a member of the building committee. King was assigned the task of making the canvass, and he reported back that the majority concurred in the McGraw choice. Meyers was the architect, and before long the trustees were meeting in his office in the Moffatt Block, examining with critical eyes and inner satisfaction what he had laid out on his drawing board.[6]

The beginning of 1883 saw the work well under way. In their annual report for 1882, the trustees had had this to say:

The present hospital buildings, erected by the United States government more than 20 years ago, for a temporary and special use as a military hospital during the continuance of the war of the rebellion, were not built in a substantial or permanent manner, and they are now in a dilapidated condition, costing large outlays annually for repairs. The board have long felt the necessity of replacing them with a new and substantial structure, provided with all the conveniences and appliances of a first-class hospital. A building that would at once meet the needs of the public and largely increase the usefulness of Harper Hospital. They did not, however, as custodians of the property given by the late Walter Harper and Nancy Martin for establishing a hospital, deem it best to anticipate too early in this direction. The property was, yearly, enhancing in value, and in their judgment would ultimately yield sufficient funds to pay the cost of a new and ample hospital building. The timely and unsolicited bequests of the late James Thompson, $11,225, and of the late Mrs. J. W. Waterman, $5,000, determined the board to take immediate steps for the sale of real estate held in trust by them, and to proceed at once to erect the new building.

Plans and specifications, furnished by E. E. Myers [*sic*], architect, were adopted, and contracts were let to put the building under cover during the fall and winter, leaving the interior work to be contracted for in the ensuing spring. The contracts already let with the following well known firms:

For the mason work, Messrs. Topping & Fisher . . .	$40,063
For the carpenter work, Messrs. Nuppenau & Clark . . .	12,194
For the painting and glazing, Godfrey, Dean & Co . . .	1,389
	$53,646

Contracts will be let early in the spring [of 1883] for the interior work, and it is expected that the building will be ready for occupation in the early fall.

It is believed that when completed the new building will be a model of its kind, and fully equal to any similar institution in the country—a credit to our city, both as to its architectural style and in all that constitutes a first-class hospital.

The site of the new building is one of peculiar adaptation and of great beauty. It is immediately in the rear of the present hospital buildings, lying between John R Street and the westerly line of the Brush farm. It comprises about four acres, covered with original forest trees, most of which will be left standing.

The entire cost of completing and furnishing the new Hospital building will probably exceed the amount now at the disposal of the board for this purpose, but it is confidently believed that the benevolent citizens of Detroit will readily come forward with whatever amount may be needed to complete the building and to put it in full, efficient preparation for its benevolent work in this community. Already have several ladies asked the privilege of furnishing one or more rooms, and doubtless others will do likewise.

When three comparatively obscure persons—Walter Harper, Nancy Martin and James Thompson—of little social distinction, after long lives of hard toil and industry, of economy and self-denial, gave the bulk of their life long accumulations to found and establish this noble charity, it cannot be doubted that the Christian intelligence and benevolence of this highly-favored city will see that it shall have the support, both moral and pecuniary, that it may need.[7]

A good deal of careful study went into the plans for the new Hospital. The Johns Hopkins Hospital in Baltimore, built a few years before, was considered the last word in design and construction, and there is evidence that Architect Meyers, in consultation with Dr. David O. Farrand and other medical staff advisers, drew freely on the Johns Hopkins plan, a detailed copy of which was made available to Harper by the officials of the Baltimore institution. Originally, the new Harper was to have been considerably larger, with extensive north and south wings. A newspaper story of February 8, 1882 indicated that a number of plans was considered before that of Meyers was approved. The trustees also decided to continue to use the old wooden buildings until the new Hospital was ready for occupancy. At this time they appear to have been undecided about what disposition to make regarding the old Hospital and the grounds upon which it stood, a legal question being raised about whether, under the terms of the Martin trust, the land could be used for any purpose other than that of a hospital. There also was the matter of what to do about the Medical School. Trustee King recommended that a new school plant be erected on the Martin property on the west side of John R, facing the new Hospital.[8] Gradually, these issues were resolved or pushed for the time being into the background until the more pressing matter of building the new Hospital was settled. Once Meyers' plans had won approval, an exhibit was set up at Roehm and Wright's jewelry store in the Coyl Building for public inspection.[9]

It very soon became apparent to the trustees that they would never be able to complete the Hospital for the specified amount of $60,000. They quickly realized, in fact, that this sum would be totally inadequate. As a result, the building committee, at its second meeting on March 14, 1882, decided to eliminate the north and south wings, one of which had been intended to house contagious cases.[10] Even with that modification, it was clear that costs would be higher than originally anticipated, and a new estimate of $95,000 was approved. The design, however, was such that future expansion would be possible. The completion date was scheduled for November 1, 1883. Like the cost estimates, that too proved to be a bad guess.[11] In May, 1882, things had so far progressed that sealed bids were called for and the contracts were awarded. But once more the cost disturbed the building committee which, in August, again discussed modification of the specifications "so as to lessen the cost of the proposed new Hospital below that of the original plans as submitted by the architect." However, after discussion, it was decided to confirm the original arrangements.[12]

Meanwhile, the upper end of the old Park lots 24 and 25 was a beehive of activity. John R Street was being cut through and graded; on the Hospital site the excavators were at work, followed by a swarm of masons and carpenters. Gradually, the new structure began to take shape. Still, the costs which seemed to mount as rapidly as the walls, were worrisome, and in June it was decided that for the time being only three floors would be finished.[13] The shell of the building, imposing as it may have been, was not a hospital. The rooms, wards, kitchen, and all the rest of the interior had to be furnished, another considerable item. In May, Meyers was instructed to procure proposals for furnishing the interior, each floor to be bid on separately.[14] This covered, primarily, the wards, kitchen, laundry, and other utility rooms. The private rooms, it was rightly expected, would be furnished by individual donors, including church and other organizations.[15]

The work progressed. Construction of fences was ordered; a wooden walk was put in along John R Street, utilizing, as far as possible, materials taken from the old buildings.[16] Both a barn and cottage stood on the grounds, the latter being used as living quarters for the engineer. On April 18, 1884, John Morehead was appointed to that post at a salary of $50 per month.[17] The grounds were graded, and a road was opened to the rear of the Hospital building, presumably to Brush Street.[18] Then, at long last, the structure stood ready for occupancy, saving only a few last-minute touches. The trustees met on June 5, and set June 19 as the formal opening date, "and the secretary was instructed to prepare notices for the press and 200 cards of invitation. Trustee Farrand was appointed to request Dr. Baker [Dr. Duffield's successor as pastor of the First Presbyterian Church was Dr. George D. Baker] and D. B. Duffield to deliver addresses on that occasion." [19] Awaiting the big day, one of the trustees took another look at the cost sheets, and his disillusionment was complete.

That a house is never built at a less cost than the builder counted on, is doubtless the experience of everyone who has ever built a house, and it has been our experience. We were led to believe by our architect that the cost of the building completed would not exceed $95,000, while the construction account shows, as the total cost of the building, including heating apparatus, plumbing and gas fitting, $107,505.73.

The furnishing account, which includes the kitchen department, the steam laundry and furniture generally, shows an expenditure of $7,365.05, or a total of $114,415.78.[20]

General unhappiness over the manner in which Meyers' estimates had been exceeded led to a dispute about the bill for $1,350 which he submitted. He finally settled for $700.[21]

Quite obviously, the trustees would have to dig again into their own pockets, or start ringing the doorbells of faithful benefactors. However, there still was work to be done, besides raising more money in preparation for the grand opening. Second thoughts about the legal restrictions on the sale of the Martin property convinced the trustees they would be within their rights in disposing of that part lying west of John R where the old Hospital stood. After all, one of the five-acre lots had been purchased by subscribed funds and was not covered by the original trust. The new Hospital stood on part of Nancy's lot; it would not be disposed of entirely.

Patients were moved from the old barracks into the new building as soon as the latter could accommodate them—on April 12.[22] Then the wooden buildings were torn down, and a new street, Martin Place, was opened from Woodward to John R, leading to the main entrance of the Hospital, and the vacated property was platted. Soon there were offers coming in to purchase the property for development. There was discussion about selling some of the Woodward Avenue frontage to the Detroit Arts Association, but nothing came of that.[23] An offer to buy a Woodward corner lot for $150 per foot was turned down; so was an offer made by a Cleveland real estate man to purchase the entire tract on both sides of Martin Place for $100,000. Instead, the trustees convinced themselves they could do better by selling the lots themselves, and they set up a price schedule. Corner lots fronting on Woodward would cost $150 per foot; other Woodward lots would go for $135 a foot. Martin Place lots were priced at $80 a foot with the exception of a lot on the north side of Martin Place for which $75 a foot was asked. The first sale, a Woodward lot north of Martin, was made to Dr. John K. Gailey, the superintendent, for $150 a foot.* [24] In the end, the income derived was enough to provide balm to the financial wounds the trustees sustained when they were forced to exceed their building budget by some $12,000.

June 19 was a fine summer day, and several hundred Detroiters turned out to inspect and admire the new Harper Hospital. It was an important occasion. Not since the City Hall was completed in 1871 had such a splendid building in a striking setting been erected. The public was justifiably proud of it. The dedication ceremonies which began at 2:00 P.M. attracted a crowd estimated at between 1,000 and 1,500. A platform had been erected and was filled with dignitaries, including the mayor, aldermen, the trustees, and members of the staff. At 8:00 P.M., a formal dedicatory service was held in the chapel, the audience being limited to the seating capacity of about 200. Mr. Baker, the press agreed, outdid himself in eloquence with his opening address which called attention to the value of the institution to the community. R. W. King, treasurer of the Hospital, gave a history of its inception and growth. Other trustees also spoke, and the program was completed with musical selections. The *Detroit Free Press* called attention to the fact that the "spacious corridors were properly embellished with foliage plants, while the several wards and other apartments were beautified with flowers, which with neat furnishings and general atmosphere of wholesome comfort, made the place entirely inviting." [25]

The public really knew what to expect by the time the grand opening took place, because several days before, the Hospital had been visited by a reporter for one of the papers who, after a thorough inspection of the premises, described the Hospital for his readers. It was, he declared, "one of the most admirably located, most complete, convenient and beautiful establishments of the kind in the United States, and it will long remain one of the leading special objects of interest in the city." [26] The architectural style, it was pointed out, was modern semi-Gothic. Eighty years after its construction, anyone desirous of seeing how it looked need only to stand on the sidewalk on John R Street at Martin Place. The old building upon which he would gaze is only slightly altered from its original appearance. "A bird's-eye view of the structure," said the reporter of 1884, "shows a building in the form of the letter E, with the open side of the letter on the east side, and with pleasant and spacious court yards between the three rear extensions or arms of the letter." [27]

A main corridor ran north and south the length of the building, with corridors branching off in each arm of the E. A large main center hall extended from the front door to the intersecting corridor.

The trustees' official description was of a building five-stories high, "including the attic, but not the basement, all of which are connected by an elevator and four spacious stairways." On the first floor, opening off the center hall, were the superintendent's office, the trustees' room, and a parlor or waiting room. To the rear, beyond the center corridor, the amphitheater opened on one side, and the chapel on the other. Each had room for about two hundred persons. The rest of the first floor was given over to a dispensary, instrument room, two dining rooms, six baths, and four wards, at least one of which was occupied by soldiers.[28] The second floor had four wards, accommodating twenty-eight patients, twenty-one private rooms, quarters for the house physicians, assistants, and officers. The third floor had four wards, twenty-five private rooms, two dining rooms, and a trunk room. On the fourth floor, there were ten wards, accommodating fifty-three patients, eight private rooms, and a children's ward for twenty-two patients, as well as two dining rooms. The fifth floor, or attic, was finished off into two wards for eight patients and three private single rooms.

The kitchen, diet kitchen, pathological room, morgue, smoking room, utility rooms, servants' quarters, and dining room were in the basement. There, too, were the engine and pump rooms and the laundry. There were two operating rooms on the first floor, one of them being part of the amphitheater; the other was in the north end of the building adjoining the surgical ward. Nurses were provided with quarters on the fourth floor. The entire Hospital contained about 240 beds, although at the time it was formally opened, there were but 75 patients being cared for.

Apparently the original plan was to have contagious wards on the fifth floor, and the first newspaper accounts so reported.[29] But a later history of Harper says "the contagious wards for diphtheria and scarlet fever were . . . in a separate pavilion where the Hudson Building now stands." [30] It may be conjectured that this pavilion was one of the original military hospital buildings, moved to a new location for the purpose stated.

By comparison with the old military pavilions, the new Harper was luxurious. As far as possible, the rooms were separated and safeguarded by brick fire walls. "Each floor," it was explained, "is deafened." The furnishings were comfortable and, being new, quite attractive. "Each single room is covered with matting and is furnished with a bedstead, a commode, a wardrobe, a rocking chair and an ordinary chair, the woodwork in the rooms and the furniture being in natural oak, beautifully finished." [31] In the interests of economy, the floors were of pine instead of the oak originally specified.

Another reporter, this one from the *Detroit Free Press,* paid the Hospital an early visit and became almost ecstatic at what he saw.

The new Harper Hospital, now finished and occupied, is one of the handsomest and most commodious public institutions of the city, everything in and about it being conducted on a scale commensurate with the magnitude of the establishment.

He went on to describe "spacious grounds" and "the handsome entrance" which he approached "with an appreciative sense of the still summer beauty which rested like a benediction on this retreat for sick and wounded humanity. Even in their newness the ample grounds had blossomed into garden beds, and starry geraniums sent forth a greeting of homelike sweetness." [32]

Inside, the journalist was ushered into the trustees' room, he having noted with a touch of regret that "no patients were visible, for this was the lunch hour." He stood, hat in hand, beneath the pictures of "the benign face of Nancy Martin" and "Father Harper." Then Dr. Gailey, the superintendent, came in, accompanied by a huge black Newfoundland dog.

"What can I do for you today?" Gailey politely inquired.

"Is it in order to go through the hospital?" asked the reporter.

"The hospital is in order, if that is what you mean. It always is," was the superintendent's reply, leaving the hope that medical humor has advanced since 1884 as far as medical science.

Anyway, Harper was in order. "Cool, new, clean and immaculate, it seemed as if sickness and such conditions might be a luxury." The scribe was given the grand tour, and he had a chance to look in on some of the patients. He provided a graphic and somewhat macabre account of a woman, the victim of an attack, whose "bandaged throat throbbed and gurgled as she breathed." He passed on, and was mightily taken by a circus performer recuperating from an accident. The dialog went like this:

"How were you injured?"

"I was thrown from a camel in a race in the ring and stepped on."

"How long had you been with the circus?"

"About a month."

"And are you going back?"

"Why certainly. They have paid all my expenses since I have been sick."

"What do they pay you?"

"Twenty-five dollars a month and board."

"Did it take you long to learn how to ride the camel?"

"I practiced Sundays."

Few hospitals have ever opened with so brilliant a nonsequitur.

The general satisfaction which resulted from completing and opening the John R Street hospital was tempered by the death of Dr. David Osburn Farrand. He died March 18, 1883 without having had the opportunity of treating patients in the new building with all of its up-to-the-minute facilities. Dr. Farrand's entire professional life had been connected to Harper, and his usefulness, climaxed by membership on the building committee, was as great as any one person's in making Harper the success it had become. It was fitting that, after his death, his friends and colleagues on the staff and Board of Trustees should seek some suitable memorial to him. Of course, there were the usual formal resolutions, "lamenting the death of the late D. O. Farrand, M.D.," eulogizing him, and expressing appreciation of "his noble character, his self-sacrificing devotion to the duties of his profession and especially his deep interest in everything connected with the prosperity of this institution. . . ." [33] But words were not enough. On the evening of April 21, twenty gentlemen met at the home of the Rev. George D. Baker for the purpose of doing something tangible and permanent to honor Farrand. Out of that meeting came the organization of the Farrand Memorial Training School for Nurses. As an adjunct to Harper Hospital, it was to provide a service to the community which compared in usefulness and importance to that furnished by the Hospital itself.

The original name of the school, the Farrand Memorial Training School for Nurses, had been shortened by the time the school opened in

1884 by dropping the word *Memorial*. Even so, it was a unique title, said to be the only one named after an individual.

Establishment of schools to train young women in the arts of nursing and to raise that vocation to a high professional level was a relatively new concept in 1883. The idea that Harper should have such a training program was one which for some time had been very close to Dr. Farrand's heart. He had anticipated that the new Hospital would offer the room and the facilities to start such a program, the object of which would be to furnish trained nurses not only for the Hospital but also for the community at large. It is said that he had fully worked out the details for such an institution, and it was his chief ambition "to live to see the realization of his hopes in this direction." [34] Certainly it was a worthy ambition, and its fulfillment improved the whole level of medical science. Nursing, in its professional development, had lagged behind the advancements made by the other branches of medicine. Until about 1880, most nurses were menials, often slovenly, drunken, and immoral. Nursing was done by untaught hirelings, the cooks, scrub women, and convalescents.[35] There is frequent reference to nurses being recruited from the criminal classes. Charles Dickens, deftly exposing social evils, did not overlook nursing. In *Martin Chuzzlewit,* he pictured the Betsey Prig school of nursing, exemplified by Mrs. Sairey Gamp entering a room: "At the same moment a peculiar fragrance was borne upon the breeze, as if a passing fairy had hiccoughed, and had previously been to a wine vault." In Sairey Gamp, Dickens caricatured the nursing profession and revealed an underlying but sharply discernible element of truth. Hospitals and sick rooms, unfortunately, were full of Sairey Gamps and Betsey Prigs.

It was not until Florence Nightingale lit her lamp during the Crimean War that nursing began to acquire professional habiliments. The training movement reached the United States after the Civil War, and the first school of nursing was established in connection with Bellevue Hospital, New York, in 1873.[36] It was followed by a few more, but by 1883, there probably were not more than a dozen in existence in the United States, and they were mostly in the East. A few trained nurses, products of these schools, found their way to Michigan and to Harper, but nowhere in sufficient number to supply the demand. For years, Harper had to rely upon the "Charleys" and "Old Marys," who, faithful, hard working, and compassionate as they may have been, were not technicians.

It was Farrand's idea that a nurses' training school in connection with Harper "would be open to women of culture and stability, who would consent to become pupils with a view to making it a life work." [37] With these hopes and plans in mind, Dr. Baker's friends, some of whom were Harper trustees, had a blueprint to follow in establishing the memorial to Farrand. The details of what took place at that meeting are sketchy, but it has been explained that Dr. Baker:

. . . briefly explained the object of the assembly at the same time presenting the benefits of the proposed school of instruction. . . . The proposition met with a most hearty and spontaneous approval, and the meeting was organized by the selection of Jacob S. Farrand as chairman.[38]

After some discussion, Robert W. King scribbled out a resolution which he offered and which was quickly adopted. It called attention to the need for a training school for nurses in Detroit, pointing out that such a school could be more efficiently and economically operated in connection with a hospital. The resolution then called for a public subscription of not less than $10,000.00, the money to be placed in the hands of the Harper Hospital trustees, who would invest it. The income from this trust was to be used to maintain the school. Many, if not all, of those present had been Dr. Farrand's friends, so it is not surprising that they would be the first to contribute. In fact, when the meeting ended, $3,000.00 had been pledged. Other fund-raising meetings later were held in various parts of the city and, it was reported, "equal interest was manifested." It must have been, indeed, because within a very short time— "much shorter than was anticipated"—the full $10,000.00 had been contributed. Within a year, the paid-up fund amounted to a very impressive $17,711.72.[39]

Altogether, there were 133 subscribers. They included the best names in Detroit. Aside from the trustees or their immediate families, all of whom were represented, such well-known people as James McMillan, David Whitney, Jr., Mrs. Zach Chandler, Don M. Dickinson, the Prismatic Club, Dr. Herman Kiefer, Magnus Butzel, and Charles A. Strelinger contributed. It was not entirely a local effort. A contribution was received from the influential McPherson family of Howell; other subscriptions came from various places around southern Michigan; and one was received from Chicago.[40]

The first action of the trustees was to appoint in the fall of 1883 a training-school committee which consisted of Dr. Russel, Jacob S. Farrand, King, and Superintendent Gailey. The next few months were given to organizational work, preparatory to opening the school officially at the same time the new Hospital opened.[41] The next thing to be done was to obtain a principal. The committee selected Miss Emma Hodkinson, who had graduated from the New York Hospital. She was described as a woman of "rare ability and special qualifications eminently fitting her for the responsible duties of her position." [42] Particularly mentioned were her enthusiasm, zeal, and "energy and industry that rarely knew a limit." With the help of Miss Hodkinson, an announcement was prepared which stated the purpose of the school. This announcement was released in January, 1884, and soon thereafter one hundred applications were received. Those who applied usually submitted recommendations of doctors, clergymen, or citizens of good repute. The backgrounds of the young ladies were carefully looked into, particularly their moral character. This was especially true of applicants, of whom there were several, who were or had been married.[43]

Out of the first group of applicants, seventeen young women were accepted between April 5 and July 21 as members of the spring class. First was Alice D. Morse, accepted on probation, as were all the others. She was followed by Annie Richards, Mrs. Susie (or Susan) Knight, and Maggie Brodie. These are mentioned because they were the only ones to survive the eighteen-month course and to be graduated in the first class in December, 1885. The others dropped out or were dismissed for various reasons, including sickness and incompetence. Miss Helen Fitchell, for instance, won the unenviable observation: "work not satisfactory." Jennie Smith was "found incompetent and rejected"; Hattie Gurton's deportment was not good; Maria MacKenna "gave up the thought of being a nurse" after friends persuaded her to resume the study of music; Nellie Hendricks was expelled "for impertinence to head nurse"; and Minnie Hazard, like several others, discovered she was "not adapted to the work." Some stayed only a few days before deciding that another career held greater charm. But those who remained and graduated became nurses in the best sense of the word and according to the best professional standards. Annie Richards' record, for example, carries the notation: "deportment and work excellent. She passed her examination satisfactorily." Maggie Brodie, whose record was only "fair," unfortunately contracted diphtheria soon after graduation and thereafter was not strong enough to do much nursing.[44]

There were, originally, two terms, or classes—spring and fall. The entering student served the first six months as junior assistant, the second six months as senior assistant, and the third six months as head nurse. The age limits were originally between twenty-five and thirty years. A common school education was required. Those accepted had to serve their first two months as probationers, during which time they received board and lodging. Having completed the probation period, the student signed an agreement to serve out the entire eighteen months, plus an additional six months if her services were required. Upon graduation, she received a diploma and a pin, upon which was embossed a likeness of Dr. Farrand. Students were given allowances of six dollars per month for the first ten months and eight dollars thereafter. Board, lodging, and laundry were provided, as was free hospital care in case of illness.[45]

The uniform was made of gray-blue checked Scotch gingham, and originally included a muslin cap with a ruffled edge,

. . . narrow cuffs and collar inside the cuffs and collar of the uniform; no bib or kerchief; a full apron which came to the bottom of the skirt; three ruffles on the skirt which came to the floor; long and fairly tight sleeves; and a tight bodice.

Later, from time to time, the style changed, but not the "checked Scotch gingham" which still was being worn in 1963.[46]

The students were assigned living quarters on the fourth floor of the south end of the new Hospital. A parlor, set aside for their use, was completely furnished by Hiram Walker. It contained a Steinway piano. Walker also donated books and other equipment for the classroom.[47] Instruction, which was given by the Medical Board of the Hospital, the principal, and the head nurses, consisted of "didactic lectures relating to the general principles of nursing, the observation and recording of symptoms, practical instruction in the preparation of the diet of the sick, and the method of managing helpless patients."[48] At the bedside, the pupil was instructed in dressing wounds, applying blisters, cups, and leeches, using the catheter, administering enemas, applying friction, bandaging, making beds, changing draw sheets, moving patients, and preventing bedsores. The life was rigorous and demanding, but it must have had its rewards because there were always applicants seeking admittance. The trustees, too, must have approved heartily of the work of the school. On June 1, 1886, with the first class having completed its work and graduated, the training-school committee reported with a ring of satisfaction:

The school is now thoroughly organized and first class in all its equipment. The amount of instruction is greater and in many important respects the school is in advance of any similar school in the country. The committee believe that the instruction and training given are fully the equivalent for the services rendered. Heretofore applications for admission have been largely in excess of the number of people required and, in the opinion of the committee, there would be no difficulty in filling the classes with the best material without the monthly wages heretofore. And they therefore recommend that as to the pupils already enrolled the monthly wages be continued in accordance with the terms of their admission, but as to the future admissions there be no wages paid and in lieu thereof and as full compensation, each pupil shall be furnished annually with two suits of regulation uniforms with board quarters and washing, and on graduating with a badge of the F.N.T.S.[49]

There were many changes in the organization and curriculum of the nursing school as the years went by, but perhaps nothing was as significant as the appointment on February 1, 1889 of Mrs. Lystra E. Gretter as principal.* Miss Hodkinson, worn out by the energy she expended in getting the school started, died in 1886. She was succeeded by two acting principals, one of whom was that same Annie Richards who was a member of the first graduating class. But with the appearance of Mrs. Gretter, the Farrand Training School for Nurses entered an era of greatness, a period in which it won recognition as one of the great nursing schools of the nation and, perhaps, of the world.

Mrs. Gretter was a most remarkable woman possessing the talents of organizer, administrator, and teacher. During her long tenure—she held the principal's post until 1907—she was one of the dominant personalities of Harper Hospital. Born in Ontario in 1858, Mrs. Gretter was the daughter and wife of physicians. She was privately educated, married at nineteen, and widowed at twenty-six. After the death of her husband, she took up a nursing career and trained at the Buffalo [New York] General Hospital Training School, graduating in 1888. When she went to her new post at Harper a year later, it was said that she took with her "a quiet dignified personality, intelligence, and clear vision." [50] Mrs. Gretter took hold immediately, and under her direction, the curriculum was revised; and, along with a general raising of the educational standards, there was a corresponding rise in the professional standing of the school. For example, the enrollment was increased, sixty-five students being admitted, and the course was extended to two full years.

Some idea of what was accomplished can be ascertained from the tenth annual report of the school—that for the year 1894. This was, in reality, a brief history of the Farrand School during the decade, and it clearly reveals the progress made.[51] The school had graduated 103 nurses by the end of 1894. Of these, according to Mrs. Gretter:

. . . sixty-three are engaged in private nursing; thirteen are occupying positions of responsibility in different institutions; five (two of whom are physicians) are in foreign mission fields; fourteen are married and have given up their profession; three are engaged in other pursuits; one other has taken up the medical profession; two are doing district nursing among the sick poor, and two have died.

In the spring of 1891, an important innovation was made by introducing an eight-hour day to Harper students and nurses. As a result, Harper became a pioneer in social progress in the field of female employment. Another of Mrs. Gretter's ideas was to give students experience in private nursing. Under this plan, each student, after having completed a specified period of training, was sent to the home of a patient for a short time. According to Mrs. Gretter, this arrangement made the student responsible, self-reliant, and able to accommodate herself to the different circumstances existing in private homes. Students doing their stint of private nursing in this fashion were paid, although three-fourths of their earnings were retained by the Hospital. This experiment did not work out satisfactorily and was discontinued after a year. For several years, Harper students were assigned for training periods to Woman's Hospital and Children's Hospital, and still later, each trainee was required to spend six weeks (later three months) on duty with the municipally-operated Herman Kiefer Hospital for experience, primarily with contagious cases.

In 1897, the course of instruction was extended to three years. Two years of high school later became an admission requirement. As the curriculum was enlarged, student nurses were required to take certain elementary courses in materia medica and chemistry at Cass Technical

High School through arrangements with the Detroit Board of Education. From time to time, small allowances, sufficient only to provide spending money, were reinstated, only to be revoked again. In 1931, a twenty-five dollar tuition fee was required for entrance.[52]

By 1923, allowances had been replaced by scholarships and a loan fund. From time to time over the years, the financial foundation of the school was buttressed by endowment contributions. In 1902, Hiram Walker gave $20,000 which permitted a strengthening of the curriculum. Again, in 1921, a group of Harper doctors and training-school graduates undertook to establish a scholarship in honor of Mrs. Gretter. Its purpose was to provide financial aid to graduates desiring further university training relating to some special branch of nursing. Quickly raised were $1,300. Then, in 1925, Farrand graduates began a drive for $50,000 to endow a bed for alumnae. This money was raised by direct solicitation, dances, baked goods sales, and similar devices.[53]

Within a short time after the school's founding, there developed a remarkable *esprit de corps* on the part of students and graduates which was reflected by their dedication and self-sacrifice. No more perfect instance of this can be cited than the selflessness of Student Nurse Shirley (or Charlotte) Wright of the class of 1904. Her roommate and classmate, Nellie McComb, contracted smallpox in the course of her duties and was sent to the pest house. The nursing facilities there were virtually nil; even the doctors did not relish looking after the patients. Some doctors, never having seen a case of smallpox, refused to attend stricken patients. The outlook, then, for Nellie McComb was bleak. But she was not abandoned. Her friend Shirley did not think twice about what she felt to be her duty. She at once volunteered to accompany the sick girl to the pest house and nurse her. She was allowed to do so, with the happiest of results. Nellie recovered under the tender ministrations of Shirley who, fortunately, did not contract the disease. Miss Wright's noble act of devotion to a friend won recognition from the trustees, who recorded what she did in their minutes.[54]

Another Farrand woman of heroic stature and great appeal was Alice Bowen. A frail girl, she entered the school in the late 1880's, but was forced to drop out for a while, probably because she was susceptible to tuberculosis and was forced at intervals to enter a sanitarium. She re-entered the school with the class of 1889 and graduated. During her dropout period, she had gone to Philadelphia where she had a year of training and nursing experience in that city's slums, working as a visiting nurse. She became imbued with the idea that a similar service for the poor was needed in Detroit. After completing her course at Harper, she dedicated herself to that work. With virtually no public or official support, and existing only on the small donations a few friends made— about forty dollars a month—she became Detroit's first visiting nurse. She was indefatigable, and, making her calls day and night, she became a familiar figure in the city. She rode a bicycle from one house to the next. During the first nine months of this service, she made more than 1,000 visits. In 1898, her health broke, but she had accomplished her purpose. Her indomitable spirit won the attention and interest of the community, and out of her work developed the Visiting Nurse Association of which, as far as Detroit is concerned, she remains the patron saint. Miss Bowen retired, finally, after twenty-seven years of selfless service to Put-in Bay, Ohio, where she later died of tuberculosis on June 16, 1921.[55]

The life of the students was by no means all hardship and self-sacrifice. The course of study, combined with work in the wards, was arduous, but there were lighter moments, time for such social diversions as dances, parties, and sleigh rides. Friends of the Hospital, and particularly the trustees and their wives, took an interest in the girls, and the school's annual reports list many incidents that made life pleasant. Captain Gilbert Hart each year invited the young ladies to be guests on his yacht for a trip to the Flats. Frequently, there were tickets for lectures and to the theater, and Christmas remembrances were generous. Books, both for entertainment as well as instruction, were donated to the nurses' library. Supper parties were often given for the students. One list of acknowledgments covers, in addition to those things mentioned, gifts of candy, flowers, fruit, and articles of furniture for the nurses' quarters. Cards from appreciative members of the medical staff often were attached to these gifts.[56]

Over a period of time, the excellence of Farrand training became widely recognized, and the Farrand badge was seen and appreciated in many parts of the world. Harper-trained nurses became superintendents of nurses in many of the nation's leading hospitals; several became principals in other training schools. Their services were called for in at least three wars. A number of Harper nurses went on to become physicians themselves. They served on the staffs of hospitals across the country and carried their healing arts into countless private homes. Many a foreign medical mission in Asia or Africa was able to function successfully because a Farrand graduate was attached to it.

The excellence of the Farrand School's reputation stirred pride in the hearts of the hospital trustees and officials. The Thirty-fourth Annual Report (for 1897) had this to say about Farrand:

> The School is doing splendid work, and stands so well in public esteem that, out of ninety-four graduates in active service, thirty are now at the head or in responsible positions in other training schools and hospitals in the United States. This is a record of which the School may well be proud.[57]

Not all the respect accorded the Farrand Training School was local. Its international reputation was revealed in 1903, when it was the subject of an article in a leading British journal. In describing the school, its operation, and curriculum, the article stated that "the facilities for practical work and study are exceptionally good, including the nursing in Harper Hospital." [58]

Chapter 14

SURGICAL GIANTS

Dr. Andrew Porter Biddle,
a mainstay of the Harper Hospital staff for half a century, once made the cogent observation that it was the physicians and surgeons of a staff who made a hospital possible.[1] The new—or 1884 Hospital—having been built, the trustees wisely selected a staff which made the institution a great one and earned for it world-wide renown. The staff proved beyond doubt that brick and stone were not enough for a successful hospital—the first ingredient must be a group of physicians and surgeons of outstanding ability, recognized by both the profession and the public for their skill, knowledge, and humanitarianism.

Before construction of the John R Street building was well started, thought was being given to a new staff. As early as March 6, 1883, Dr. Frederick P. Anderson of Grosse Ile, Michigan, offered his services to the trustees as clinical instructor in connection with the staff. His application was carefully considered, but "it was resolved that no changes in or addition to the staff be made before entrance into the new Hospital building." [2] But within six weeks, the trustees, having felt the loss resulting from the death of Dr. David O. Farrand, realized that a bigger institution would require a larger staff, and one of the first quality. As a result, a new policy was considered and it was decided to review the action taken on Dr. Anderson's application. Trustees Russel, Farrand, and King were appointed as a committee "to report to the board the names of surgeons and physicians to compose a full medical staff for the Hospital." To fill the Farrand vacancy, Dr. H. O. Walker was temporarily named chief of staff.[3]

In 1884, two weeks before the John R building was formally presented to the public, the Board of Trustees made appointments to a new staff which, from the standpoint of size and individual prestige, was a credit to the institution. Altogether there were twenty-six members, not counting the house or resident staff. The original Medical Board, which had served the Hospital from its beginning, had consisted of four surgeons and four physicians. This number had been increased by one or two members from time to time, including the addition of a microscopist. But, beyond the distinction between physicians and surgeons, there was no departmentalization until 1884. At that time, there were established departments of surgery, medicine, gynecology, ophthalmology, laryngology, pathology, and, in addition, a microscopist was appointed.[4] The significance of this organization, of which George P. Andrews was made chief, was that it made Harper a modern medical institution, fully equipped, so far as professional facilities were concerned, to handle all cases brought to it. Of course, this was not the final word. Five years later, a neurologist and a dermatologist were added to the staff which, over the years, continued to expand as new fields of medical science were developed.[5]

The 1884 staff remained a creature of the Board of Trustees, not yet having attained the degree of professional autonomy and specialization which, like those of other hospitals, it would eventually enjoy. For example, in 1884, and for a year or two after that, the chief of staff was chosen by the trustees. In 1886, Trustee Cutcheon offered a motion, which was adopted, to the effect that the medical staff would be required to submit to the trustees, in writing or by committee, its recommendations "concerning the medical management of the Hospital as in the judgment of the staff will promote its efficiency and prosperity."[6] This meant that while the medical staff might propose changes in the rules and regulations, the final decisions lay with the trustees. From that time on, however, while the staff and board worked closely together, the former gradually assumed more and more authority where purely medical policy was concerned.

Among matters the staff took upon itself to decide were some involving the rights and privileges of non-staff members in treating private patients. This issue was first raised at a staff meeting in 1888 when the members were asked: "Should physicians not members of the medical board be admitted to treat patients in the public wards?" If the Hospital was "opened" to this extent, it was argued, costs of operating the institution would be materially increased because a larger house staff would be required, expensive special diets would be ordered, and—possibly of most concern—the value of staff positions would be decreased. The proposition was first turned down; then, a modified version was accepted that permitted the outsiders to practice in the Hospital with the approval of the attending physicians and surgeons.[7] A short time later, this rule was further amended to read:

No physician or surgeon *not* a member of the Medical Board, nor any member of the Medical Board not on duty at the Hospital shall be allowed to treat patients in the public wards of the Hospital except for very special reasons to be decided upon by the president of the Medical Board and the member of the Medical Board on duty; no member of the Medical Board shall at any time treat patients in the public wards not falling to his department.[8]

This rule applied until 1893, when the Medical Board instructed the officers to prepare a list "of physicians residing in the City who may have the privilege to treat private patients in the Hospital." [9]

Two years later, in 1895, it was ordained that all city-supported cases in the Hospital must be treated by the staff and not by city physicians. But at the same time:

It was also agreed that any physician in good and regular standing, who had attended a case previous to entering the Hospital, could continue in attendance with the treatment of the case, if the patient occupied and paid for a private room; or through the courtesy of the attending staff physicians be allowed to attend the patient in the ward as a private case if [the] patient paid his own way; thus would those who are not in hospital practice have an opportunity of doing more hospital work which would be for the good of the Hospital.[10]

The first set of up-to-date rules governing staff organization and duties was adopted on March 31, 1886. It does not vary greatly in principle from the table of staff organization in effect ever since, including the Harper Hospital of 1963.[11] The medical management was to be under the immediate control of the senior member of the house staff, designated the house (or today, resident) physician. The house staff was to consist of three members, graduates in medicine, appointed by the Board of Trustees upon recommendation of the Medical Board which, in turn, would have general supervision over the house staff. The three members would each serve eighteen months: the first six months as second assistant, second six months as first assistant, and third six months as house physician. The Medical Board was to be composed of attending and consulting physicians and surgeons. The consultants "shall be considered as counsellors and shall be invited to attend all capital operations in the Hospital, and to examine such critical cases as the attending physician may desire." A member of the attending staff was expected to "visit every medical and surgical patient who may be afflicted with an acute disease at least once every day and every patient in the Hospital without exception twice every week." The Medical Board was empowered to elect annually its president and secretary. (Before the year was over provision was made also for a vice-president.) The first chief of staff elected under these rules was Dr. E. L. Shurly, and the secretary was Dr. J. K. Gailey, former superintendent.

The 1884 staff included such familiar names as Drs. Theodore A. McGraw and George P. Andrews, who had been members of the original staff. McGraw as consulting surgeon and Andrews as consulting physician were the only remaining members of the 1866 group. However, there were many new members already prominent or who, in time, would become equally well known. The other surgeons were Drs. Donald Maclean, consultant; and H. O. Walker, J. K. Gailey, J. B. Book, and E. T. Tappey, attendants. C. B. Gilbert was the other consulting physician; the attending physicians were H. S. Cleland, Charles Douglas, I. E. Emerson, H. F. Lyster, John Flinterman, C. A. Devendorf, and A. E. Carrier. There were three gynecologists: Drs. Howard Longyear, Helen Warner, the first woman staff member, and John Henry Carstens. There were two consulting ophthalmologists: J. F. Noyes, another veteran, and George E. Frothingham, who, as a professor at the University of Michigan, had profoundly influenced one of his students, William J. Mayo.[12] The attending ophthalmologist, Leartus Connor, won wide recognition as a great teacher and an even greater medical writer. Drs. Ernest L. Shurly, a long-time chief of staff, and J. W. Robertson were the laryngologists; F. W. Brown and W. R. Chittick were the pathologists and curators; and George Duffield had replaced his famous uncle, Samuel, as microscopist. Three years later, on April 25, 1887, another star was added to this galaxy when the name of Angus McLean first appeared in the Hospital records. On that date, he was accepted as second assistant house physician.[13]

15. Groundbreaking Ceremonies for the Hudson Memorial Building—Prominent trustees and staff of Harper were on hand in November, 1911, when J. L. Hudson turned the sod for the new Harper building. Left to right: F. E. Moulder, Lem W. Bowen, Walter P. Manton, Preston Hickey, Louis Hirschman, Stewart Hamilton, H. O. Walker, J. L. Hudson, Clarence A. Black, W. R. Farrand, unidentified, Richard H. Webber, Max Ballin, and Daniel La Ferte.

courtesy Harper Hospital

16. Harper Hospital with the Hudson Wing — Seen in the background, the Hudson Building was named in honor of one of the Hospital's benefactors. It was completed and first occupied in 1913. The Swain Home for Nurses is seen in the foreground.

courtesy Burton Historical Collection

That these men were considered giants in their profession, that their reputations extended far beyond Detroit, is borne out by their mention in nearly every reference to medical practice and to Harper Hospital in the last quarter of the nineteenth century and the first quarter—and even beyond—of the twentieth. Of that original 1884 staff of twenty-six members, the post of president of the Michigan State Medical Society was held by Maclean, McGraw, Frothingham, Walker, Ernest L. Shurly, Connor, and Carstens. Angus McLean also held the presidency, as did Andrew P. Biddle and Louis J. Hirschman, who came on the staff a few years later. Three Harper men—George Duffield, Biddle, and R. B. Schenck—held the Society's secretaryship every year from 1886 to 1910 with the exception of the 1891–99 period.[14] So eminent were these men and their associates who joined them that Dr. Shurly, chief of staff, became almost lyrical in praising his colleagues in his 1890 annual report to the Board of Trustees:

The labor on the part of your staff has resulted in placing the institution in the foremost rank in this country, and her name is favorably known to almost every physician in the land. She is therefore in a high position among the institutions identified with medical science and art.[15]

There were "medical giants" at Harper in the 1880's, the 1890's, and beyond into the 1900's. Through skill, personality, and professional competence, they gained a national reputation for the Hospital. To name them all would require a long listing. But during this period from 1884 on, one man does stand out, not only because of his accomplishments as a surgeon, but also because his name was so closely identified with that of Harper Hospital that he became the dominant Harper figure of the era. He was the German-born John Henry Carstens. To paraphrase someone who may have said it better, if there had never before been a physician, it would have been necessary to invent one to explain the character of Dr. Carstens. He was one of those rare individuals who loved everybody and in return was loved by everybody.

Having chosen to be on the wrong side in the revolution which swept Germany that year, Carstens' father was in prison when his son was born in Kiel, June 9, 1848. The elder Carstens, a staunch individualist and liberal, planted the seeds of that philosophy in his son, who gave expression to it through an unsurpassed understanding and sympathy for humanity. Once out of jail, with his ardor for active revolutionism considerably cooled, the senior Carstens gathered up his family and possessions and, like so many of his compatriots, headed for America. Some lucky chance led him to Detroit, where he settled on a farm on the lower west side, in Springwells near Fort Wayne. There John Henry grew up. He attended public school and the German-American Seminary, and as a youth, he worked for a year or two in drug stores, becoming a competent pharmacist. One of his employers was Dr. Samuel Duffield, the chemist; another was Frederick Stearns. Carstens decided to become a doctor and enrolled in the Detroit College of Medicine. He graduated in 1870, and his diploma was a virtual ticket of admission to the Harper Hospital staff.

Having served his medical apprenticeship under such men as McGraw, Andrews, Jenks, Noyes, and others of equal renown, Carstens selected gynecology as his specialty. It was not long before he was recognized, locally at least, as a leader in that field, and he became known to his associates as the "stork of Detroit." But as time went on, his interest expanded, rather than shifted. He became impressed by the work being done by a brilliant young surgeon up in Minnesota—William Mayo—and in time, the two became fast friends, sharing a mutual admiration. Mayo was doing some remarkable work in abdominal surgery, a field which many surgeons at that time found too hazardous. But, impressed by what Mayo and a few others were doing, Carstens decided to become an abdominal surgeon too, and before long he had an established name in that branch of surgery.

Successful abdominal surgery became possible, among other reasons, through a better understanding of the causes of infection and because of improved anesthetics. Yet, like many an early colleague in that field, including the elder Mayo, Carstens thought that the germ theory, while containing elements of good sense, could be overemphasized. To him, skill, confidence, and speed—particularly speed—were the prime essentials. As he always wore a full beard, he rebelled at having to wear a face mask. By sure, fast work, he felt he could outrace a germ and a doubtful anesthetic. As a result, he became one of the most rapid operators in the profession. It was said that he took pride in entering the amphitheater smoking a cigar. He would lay it aside, complete the operation before the cigar went out, and leave the operating room puffing away triumphantly.*

Not only was Carstens a fine technician, but he was an even greater teacher, and for most of his professional life, he was on the faculty of the Detroit College of Medicine. To hundreds of students and graduates he was "Dad" Carstens, and he is so referred to by an older generation of doctors of this day. He was as soft-hearted in the college classrooms and examination halls as he was skillful in the amphitheater. A student in trouble, or teetering on the precipice of dubious grades, could count on being pulled back to safety after an appeal to "Dad" Carstens.

He became a familiar figure in Detroit. He always wore boots and a silk topper, and he prided himself on the splendid carriage and pair of high-steppers which carried him on his visits. It wasn't all medicine with him; from his home and office on Macomb Street, it was but a short step to the hall of the Harmonie Society where he lifted his voice in song or acrimonious debate on metaphysics. As time went on, he developed an aldermanic pouch which gave him the appearance of a jovial Santa Claus in a frock coat. Along with the appearance went the inclination, and John Henry Carstens found an avocation in politics. A solid Republican, like most of the Germans of that day, he held numerous offices. He sat on the Board of Education and was president of the Board of Health. He served as city chairman of the Republican party, and in 1892, he was one of Benjamin Harrison's presidential electors. Three times he was an unsuccessful candidate for mayor of Detroit with a platform that has, even at this late date, something familiar about it. In 1908, he advocated

. . . permanent settlement of the streetcar problem, enough school buildings so that all children will have educational facilities; a convention hall that will help make Detroit the convention city of the entire country, and all public improvements that are needed to make Detroit clean, healthy and beautiful.

Detroit had to wait quite a few years to catch up with "Dad" Carstens' ideas.

Carstens was many things to many people. He was a philosopher who once told a medical class that "if a man's mind is not so evenly balanced that he can study each case and treat it as it deserves and needs, he is not fit to practice medicine." He was a voluminous writer, and the medical profession in the United States relied heavily upon his translations from German and French journals. The range of his interests can be discerned from the titles of some of his original papers, selected at random: "Care of Infants in the Summertime"; "Medical Education"; "Hospital Disinfection"; "Magnetism in Relation to Disease"; "Embolus"; "Reorganization of the Detroit Board of Health"; and "Treatment of Dysentery Without Opium." He was president of the Michigan State Medical Society, one of the founders of the Detroit Medical and Library Association, a forerunner of the present Wayne County Medical Society, and president of the American Gynecological Society. To repeat that he possessed "a striking personality" is almost a superfluity.[16]

The general surgery, some of it bold and imaginative, performed at Harper during the last decade of the nineteenth century began to overshadow the medical work, and once that shadow was cast, it lengthened rapidly. In 1890, the medical cases—879 of them—almost doubled the 437 surgical cases. But by 1893, surgery had moved ahead, 751 to 617, and in 1895, surgical cases ran ahead of medical by almost two to one. While the ratio fluctuated from year to year, the amount of surgery performed increased very rapidly. In 1899, the surgical cases outnumbered the medical by 1,508 to 656. From that point on, the number of medical cases remained fairly constant, around the 700 to 800 mark, while more and more surgery was being performed. In 1900, there were 1,843 surgical cases; in 1904, 2,089; in 1908, 3,691; and in 1909, 4,024 cases with 4,632 operations performed. In 1923, there was a total of 9,899 operations, 3,063 of them major ones.[17] Observing this rising curve in the amount of surgical work, it is easy to understand how Harper Hospital, beginning in the 1890's, began to gain national and world recognition as one of the foremost surgical hospitals.

Although the work at Harper included just about every kind of surgery, the greater emphasis on that branch of medical science can be attributed very largely to the advances made in abdominal surgery. And that, in turn, can be attributed to the work being done by Dr. Carstens. Most of his interest centered upon abdominal work, and in 1897, he was given the title of abdominal surgeon by the trustees and placed at the head of a special department of abdominal surgery. The appointment was short lived. The Medical Board protested vehemently against what it considered an unfair distinction, pointing out that other staff surgeons besides Carstens were doing that kind of work. Under pressure of the staff, the trustees rescinded their action, and Carstens was restored to his original position as attending surgeon.[18] However, this appointment, so quickly taken away, was in a sense deserved. He was performing a useful service of public and professional education, which soon paid off in lives saved. In addition, he was really pioneering in a new field, the appendectomy, and getting remarkable results. Dr. Louis J. Hirschman, who had the opportunity to watch Carstens work and evaluate the results, stated flatly that the impetus given abdominal surgery in this period largely was the result of appendectomies.[19] In the annual report for 1898, Carstens made what was, from the standpoint of Harper, a most significant statement:

There were 1,027 operations performed during the year, including 324 abdominal sections of all kinds, the latter class of operations being more than in any other hospital in the country as far as I have been able to find out. This is not due to the fact that we operate more than in any other city, but to the fact that there are comparatively fewer hospitals, and our territory is large, reaching north for 1,200 miles and taking in western Ontario and the whole Lake Superior region, as a great many of our patients come from outside of the city.[20]

Carstens might have explained that Harper had become a medical magnet with a large field of attraction because the graduates of the Detroit College of Medicine, hanging out their shingles over a wide area, remembered their old teachers and referred their troublesome cases to Harper. The Hospital, even in that early period, took on some of the aspects of a medical center.

Two years before Carstens made the statement referred to, he drew attention to a paper read by the famous New York surgeon, T. Gaillard Thomas, before the staff of Woman's Hospital of that city. In this paper, the work done in abdominal surgery in six leading eastern hospitals was cited. A compilation of statistics showed Woman's had the most cases and the lowest death rate—the mortality varying from fifteen per cent at Woman's to twenty-five per cent in the others. Carstens declared:

I am happy to say that at Harper Hospital we had 228 abdominal sections, being far more than any other hospital in the country, as far as I know, and although the most desperate and hopeless cases were given the benefit of the last hope, the mortality was lower than in any of them.[21]

There were others ready to acknowledge Harper's remarkable record in surgery. A Detroit newspaper editorial of 1905, commenting on the previous year's 2,903 operations with only 88 deaths, called the record "admirable." It recognized the accomplishment as a sign of "the great strides made by surgery in recent years." Wrote the editorialist:

The knife and the antiseptic have made new things possible. An evil suggestion lies in the keen-edged blade, and it is natural that the mind should shrink from the idea of its use. The dangers of septic poisoning have not been hidden. These things served to make surgery unpopular. But records like that established by the Harper Hospital and those yearly established by the great institutions of the east, will soon break down whatever prejudice may stand between the suffering and the surgeon's skill. The careless, the unclean, the ignorant, the hasty and the brutal use of the knife must be entirely supplanted by the scientific mastery, or a record of only 88 deaths out of 2,903 operations could not have been made.[22]

Appendicitis, which was the big reason for the advances in abdominal surgery, was a term which did not appear in the medical dictionaries prior to 1886. In June of that year, Dr. Reginald Fitz, a Boston pathologist who had grown up in Ontonagon County, Michigan, coined the term in a paper he delivered before the Association of American Physicians titled "Perforating Inflammation of the Vermiform Appendix." In this paper he stated "that virtually all cases of perityphilitis actually originated in the appendix and ought therefore to be called appendicitis." [23] Prior to that time, appendicitis had been diagnosed many ways and called many things. The sharp, identifying pain in the abdomen was often called acute indigestion or inflammation of the bowels, and it was treated by laxatives, or hot or cold packs, or ignored as something that would soon go away by itself. It was a frequent cause of death and inflammation of the bowels "was at that time very justly regarded as a summons to the cemetery." [24] "The recognition of appendicitis and the application thereto of surgical measures is one of the greatest of late nineteenth century benefactions," proclaims one medical history book.[25]

Carstens not only was one of the earliest surgeons to recognize appendicitis, but he also wanted every other doctor, particularly physicians, to recognize it. The educational campaign which he conducted was of as much value in saving lives as his skill with the knife. He kept hammering away at the general practitioners with one theme: "Get your patients with the belly ache to the hospital quickly, and we'll save them." A warning he once directed to the public was: "Don't wait to enter the hospital until you are in the agonies of death." [26] Giving an account of an acute appendicitis case in which the patient died, Carstens added a stern word of caution to his medical brethren:

These sad cases always occur in spite of all our efforts and our boasted diagnostic acumen. It is simply another case which proves we are right when we say that in all abdominal troubles we must look out for the appendix; no matter how severe the pain is in the stomach or extensive the diarrhea, pay no attention to the degree of dyspepsia or severity of the cholic, but always look for the appendix. There is the serious pathologic condition nine times out of ten.[27]

Of course, there were prominent medical men who believed that Carstens and his followers were dramatizing through overemphasis. They were particularly dubious about the need for immediate surgery to the extent that Carstens advocated. To these men, Carstens replied in the *Harper Hospital Bulletin* in 1908. He insisted that appendicitis was both a medical and a surgical disease; the general practitioner should learn to recognize it and properly "diagnosticate" it, and then get the patient into the hands of a competent surgeon.

I am happy to say, as a result of our continued efforts and talk about appendicitis in and out of season—so much so that we have been considered cranks on the subject—that at the present time the diagnosis of appendicitis is readily made by the general practitioner. Formerly, he would not think of it; he would call it everything else. But now, having his attention continually called to it, he looks for it and finds it easy to diagnosticate.[28]

The result of increased knowledge was lives saved, and Carstens and his colleagues could prove this as his campaign progressed. In 1892, 2 appendicitis cases entered the Hospital, and 1 of them died—a 50 per cent mortality rate. That rate continued in 1893, when 6 out of 13 cases died. Often these admissions were in moribund condition; they were sent to the Hospital in desperation, but too late to save them. However, as more cases appeared under Carstens' persuasion, the mortality rate declined. In 1896, 47 cases were treated, with 8 deaths. The following year, 65 cases were admitted, and only nine were lost. By 1900, conditions really began to improve. The number of cases operated on was 147, and the mortality rate (10 deaths) was down to 6.7 per cent. Ten years later, the death rate was down to 1.7 per cent, with only 6 out of 355 patients operated on dying.[29]

In time, the most deadly thing about appendicitis was the conversation it generated around the bridge table or at afternoon tea parties. Carstens had proved his point and, in doing so, established Harper

Hospital's reputation as one of the foremost, if not *the* foremost, surgical hospitals in the country.

Despite the increase in surgery, the Harper medical staff did its share in the combat against contagious diseases—scarlet fever, erysipelas, and that dread killer, diphtheria, which was the most dramatic—if the term can be used—of the contagious diseases treated at Harper because it was the most deadly. It has been seen that Michigan, until about 1921, was annually afflicted with diphtheria. Not until vaccines were perfected and generally used did this scourge abate in Detroit and Michigan.

Few cases of diphtheria found their way into hospitals during the nineteenth century, because few hospitals, and particularly general hospitals, would accept them. The danger of contagion was too great. Harper was no exception when it first opened to civilian patients in 1866. It will be recalled that its advertising cards offered to accept all cases except contagious ones. When the new Hospital opened in 1884, however, there was a change. Harper offered to receive patients afflicted with any disease "except smallpox and insanity." A small ward was set up in the new building, on the fifth floor, directly over the main entrance. A few beds were provided for diphtheria, scarlet fever, and erysipelas cases. Although these were, to some extent, isolated from the rest of the Hospital, they were not segregated. But the important thing is that, by accepting them at all, Harper for many years thereafter operated the only contagious department in Michigan. This pioneering effort paid off handsomely in lives saved.

Within two years after the opening of the John R building, it became evident that more room was required for contagious patients than the fifth-floor attic provided. Early that year, the medical staff went on record advocating:

. . . the erection as soon as possible of a cheaply constructed building detached from the main building, for occupation by patients suffering from contagious diseases. . . . This is becoming imperatively necessary as the hospital is filling up with patients, and proper isolation is difficult, to say nothing of the lurking danger of contaminating the whole building with these latent disease germs by the aggregation of cases of an infectious nature.

It also was the staff's recommendation that "a post-mortem room and dead house be added to or located in such a building." [30]

On March 12, 1888, the trustees voted to erect the contagious building. However, their authorization was subject to the approval of the Children's Free Hospital, which suggested that the latter contribute some financial assistance. No description of the building has been discovered. Before many years had gone by, it was enlarged by the expedient of setting up old streetcars on the grounds with their interiors remodeled to accommodate a few beds.[31] The contagious building was placed in the back, or on the east side, of the John R hospital, where the Hudson Memorial Building now stands. Dr. Ernest L. Shurly, in a brief history of Harper written in 1900, stated:

I believe this [Harper] was the first institution in the United States which engaged in this beneficent enterprise of providing a place where cases of diphtheria and scarlet fever could be accepted, isolated and treated.[32]

Isolation, it was shortly proved, benefited and protected the patients in the general hospital, but proximity to and attendance upon the contagious patients took their toll of the staff. Several nurses contracted diphtheria, and one student, Ella McKelroy, assigned to the care of an infant diphtheria patient, contracted the disease and died. In order to isolate the staff as well as the patients, Mrs. Divie Bethune Duffield and her two sons, Dr. George and Bethune, in 1893 gave the money for construction of a two-story brick cottage, to be built alongside the contagious building for living quarters for nurses on duty in the scarlet fever and diphtheria wards.[33] While the Duffield Cottage, as it was called, was comfortably furnished and offered more agreeable surroundings for the nurses, the problem of staff contagion was not solved. It was stated in the 1896 annual report of the Farrand Training School:

Several of our nurses have contracted diphtheria in the discharge of their duties in the Contagious Hospital. Two are still incapacitated for work. In no other part of the institution are the duties so trying as they are there, and the bravery and the faithfulness of the nurses are nowhere more conspicuous.[34]

At one time a wall was built, separating the Hospital proper from the contagious building and the Duffield Cottage. Apparently, it was not high enough, because it has been told how one young swain, visiting his girl friend, a nurse on contagious duty, courted her with the wall separating them. He received a goodnight kiss across the barrier and, unhappily, contracted diphtheria.[35]

Dr. George Duffield, at a staff meeting, recommended that the member of the house staff in attendance at the contagious building "be isolated and not attend the cases in the general hospital. At present this member is a menace to the health of the hospital." [36] The staff not only agreed that the house physician caring for contagious cases "should not mingle" in the general hospital, but also recommended to the trustees that an extra house physician be appointed so a full-time man could be on contagious duty and, in his spare time, do most of the laboratory work.[37]

Facilities were soon outstripped by the demand for beds in the contagious wards. In 1890, when 77 diphtheria and 28 scarlet fever cases were admitted, the contagious hospital was operating at close to capacity. But by 1902, when there were 115 diphtheria and 122 scarlet fever cases, capacity was so badly exceeded that the staff and trustees were calling for enlarged facilities "at the earliest possible date." [38] In 1902, the contagious building was so overcrowded that Superintendent Shaw was authorized "to purchase a tent for the temporary care of contagious cases during the warm weather." [39] But relief was at hand. At the October 20, 1902 meeting of the trustees, a letter from Dr. F. W. Mann was read, in which he stated that Mrs. John Avery "proposed to erect a new contagious building for us." [40] The offer was quickly accepted, and in 1904, the new building, erected at a cost of $10,000 in memory of Mrs. W. L. Smith, the mother of Mrs. Avery, was receiving patients. For the present time, the old building was retained, used for treatment of measles, whooping cough, and the less dangerous diseases. The Avery building was unique in that a solid wall through the center divided it into two parts, with no inside access from one part to the other. This permitted the isolation of the diphtheria from the scarlet fever cases. Up to this time, they had been more or less intermingled.

Yet, even the addition of this fine new facility did not solve the problem. The number of cases being admitted continued to increase, and soon the overcrowding was as bad as before. "I do not know that there is more sickness in the city than ever before," explained Superintendent Shaw, "but I think people are using the hospitals more." [41] A clamor had been raised for a public contagious hospital, and it did not subside even after the Avery building was in use. A city-operated hospital was strongly urged by Dr. Guy L. Kiefer, a member of the Harper staff who became Commissioner of Health. He spoke of "the present small accommodations at Harper Hospital." [42] A city hospital for "incurables," which included contagious diseases, became a local political issue, and mayoralty and councilmanic candidates began campaigning on promises to provide one. Dr. Kiefer proposed that a city hospital be built near Harper, so it could be attended by the Harper staff.[43] At first, those associated with Harper opposed the idea, claiming it would be more advantageous to the city to provide funds with which Harper could expand its facilities.

Serious consideration was given Kiefer's plan for awhile, but loud protests began to be heard from neighborhood property-owners who did not want to live near a large contagious hospital. This opposition developed into a campaign in which Harper and its women employees became victims of a smear. At a protest meeting, a speaker made slurring remarks about "the Harper girls." A neighborhood Mrs. Grundy used the contagious issue to denounce the moral conduct of the young women employees who had quarters in the Hospital. This lady declared that on weekends, when the domestics had a free night, they and their escorts, on returning from their dates, would appropriate the porches of private residences for lovemaking, and those peeking through the curtains could see them "where they hugged and kissed each other like fury." [44] This line of attack backfired. Fair-minded people, even though they opposed the Hospital, came to the defense of the girls, as did the newspapers. Before long, the woman who first circulated the libel publicly apologized, and once again the issue was debated on something resembling its merits.

Kiefer made a good case. He pointed out that in the 1903–04 fiscal year, Detroit had 1,433 cases of diphtheria, of which 1,252 were treated at home, with 185 deaths resulting. This was a 14 per cent mortality rate. The remaining 181 cases were cared for at Harper. There, only 7 deaths occurred, a mortality of 4 per cent. The conclusion was plain. A large enough hospital to care for all or almost all city cases would result in lives saved.[45]

Gradually, the Harper staff came around to Kiefer's point of view, and when the Common Council appropriated $100,000 for a municipal contagious hospital, Dr. Longyear agreed that "no surgical hospital should handle contagious cases." [46] Several members of the Harper staff concurred at a hearing held by the aldermen. The upshot was that in 1906 a new municipal hospital for contagious diseases, the Herman Kiefer, named for Dr. Guy Kiefer's father, was built on Hamilton

Avenue, at Pingree, adjoining the old pest house where the city had cared for smallpox cases in "the small building in the woods" since 1893.[47]

Harper continued to accept contagious cases for a few more years, until the Hudson Memorial Building was erected in 1912. The results continued to be good, justifying the statement made earlier by the chief of staff, who reported:

There was, virtually, a mortality of only two per cent [in 1896] in this very malignant disease [diphtheria] which has always shown a mortality of 30 to 40 per cent when treated in the old fashioned way at the home of the patient. All the cases of diphtheria were verified by the cultures of the Klebs-Loeffler bacillus, and it shows the wonderful benefits of scientific treatment with antitoxin and good nursing.[48]

By providing medical leadership, Harper Hospital demonstrated that diphtheria could be licked, and the "killer" is all but eliminated from the community.

Chapter 15

PILLS, AMBULANCES, AND PATIENTS

On the third day
of December, 1867, the Harper Hospital trustees carefully weighed a suggestion made by the medical staff, and after some discussion, they adopted a resolution to the effect:

. . . that a dispensary for the poor of the city be established in connection with this hospital, to be arranged and conducted by the attending board of physicians and surgeons, the rules and regulations to be hereafter submitted to the trustees by the physicians and surgeons.[1]

This action prepared Harper to serve two additional functions. It provided the means whereby the original concept of a charity hospital could be enlarged to reach people who needed medical attention and medicine but who were not sick enough to be hospitalized, and it added an important teaching facility, available to the medical college then in process of being organized. In giving their sanction to the operation of a dispensary, the trustees again were pioneering in an undeveloped field. The dispensary became, in turn, the Outdoor Department, the Polyclinic, and finally, as it is known today, the Out-patient Department. H. L. Corwin, an authority on American hospitals, has pointed out that "the growth of out-patient departments is to a large degree a metropolitan development of the present century." He has added that "of the 461 general out-patient departments in existence in 1937, only 26 per cent were established before 1900."[2] That figure clearly puts Harper in the forefront.

The dispensary, as the name suggests, was originally a place to which people came for free consultation and medicine, but not for treatment. When the services were expanded to include medical, surgical, and, in time, dental treatment, the dispensary became a polyclinic (a term which has a teaching connotation) or an out-patient department. On January 7, 1868, the Medical Board presented the trustees with a set of rules for the arrangement of the dispensary. They were really quite simple. A staff physician was to take charge immediately; he was to be on duty from 10:00 in the morning until 12:00 noon daily except Sunday "to dispense the medicines prescribed, and to prescribe for the patients in the absence of the attending physician and surgeon." All "poor persons shall be furnished with medical and surgical advice and medicines gratuitously," although the attending staff was given the power to refuse medicine to those able to pay for it. Finally, a full record of each case was to be kept by the physician in charge, a post given to Dr. H. O. Walker, a house physician on whose medical diploma the ink was barely dry.[3] The rules were approved by the trustees who immediately ordered that handbills be printed and circulated and that a sign be nailed on the gate "so that the poor may know of the dispensary."[4]

The public took advantage of this new facility. Those unable to pay for medical advice had the services of the same talent available to the richest family in Detroit. The attending staff of the dispensary was the same as that of the Hospital. A caller could make his choice of conferring with Drs. Jenks, Andrews, McGraw, or Farrand. The doors officially opened February 1, and during that month, 134 persons visited the dispensary. For a while thereafter, the callers averaged 20 a day.[5] In hailing the dispensary's initial success, the *Detroit Advertiser* pointed out that the poor were not the only beneficiaries. The medical profession gained, too, by getting good experience in diagnosis and prescription for ills which they did not commonly see.[6]

Exactly a year after the dispensary had been set up, Dr. McGraw appeared before the Board of Trustees with an offer from the Detroit Medical College to take that unit over, and "keep it up at the expense of the college in as liberal a manner as heretofore." This was a proposition which made sense and the trustees quickly accepted. The college itself had just been established, and the dispensary presented itself as a natural teaching facility.[7] "Certain teachers of medicine are of the opinion that the major part of hospital training should be concentrated in the out-patient department," Corwin observed. "It is here also that the hitherto largely neglected phase of preventive medicine, including the handling of occupational diseases in their incipiency could be put into actual practice." [8] If, therefore, hospital training should be centered in the dispensary, under what better supervision could it be placed than in a school, particularly when the school was as closely affiliated with a hospital as the Detroit Medical College was with Harper? The arrangement worked out, as far as can be determined, to the complete satisfaction of all concerned. The indigent patients got free advice and medicine as in the past, under the supervision of the same doctors who manned the Hospital staff. And through clinics conducted regularly on Tuesdays and Saturdays, the medical students gained valuable knowledge and experience.[9]

If there were those who sometimes took advantage of the opportunity to obtain free what they could pay for, the incidents were sufficiently infrequent so as to cause no comment or concern on the part of the trustees or those directly operating the dispensary. Again Corwin is quoted as saying:

. . . the percentage of persons who take undue advantage of dispensary service is small. Moreover, it is being increasingly realized that providing adequate care for the people is of greater moment than the occasional measure of medical charity.[10]

When the new hospital was built on John R Street in 1884, the Medical College moved to new quarters in the Y.M.C.A. Building, which then stood on the south side of Farmer Street, between Monroe and Gratiot. The dispensary went with it, and for the next couple of years, Harper had none. It was a lack which the Medical Board felt keenly, with the result that on June 1, 1886, a committee of trustees was named to confer with the doctors regarding "establishing an outdoor clinic in connection with the Hospital . . . on the first floor of the hospital building." [11] An outdoor clinic was set up along the lines of the dispensary, and it operated within those limits for more than two years. Its limitations were apparent, however, and the medical staff wanted something more suited to Harper's prestige and capabilities. The result was a recommendation to the trustees in February, 1888, expressing the Medical Board's desires that:

. . . provision be made as soon as possible for an out-patient department; it is well known that an out-patient department where the indigent poor come for treatment daily is one of the great "finders" so to speak of a hospital. Many patients who would not otherwise do so, find their way into the wards of the hospital through such a channel, and thus receive benefits which they would not otherwise obtain. Besides, it will be remembered that one of the signal benefits to a community of the establishment of hospital institutes consists of the facilities offered to the medical profession and students for the study and advancement of medical science, the accomplishment of which is greatly aided by a well-regulated out-patient department.[12]

Apparently there was some delay, because it was not until the following November 12, 1888 that the details were worked out, and the expanded outdoor department became operative. The Medical Board asked simultaneously for a separate contagious hospital and a separate outdoor clinic building, each of which was provided with gratifying alacrity.[13] The new clinic was a two-story brick house, very similar in appearance to the contagious building. It was built facing John R, at the north end of the Hospital proper. In time, a passageway connecting the two buildings was built.

About the same time the new building came into use, the name of the clinic was changed to the Harper Hospital Polyclinic.[14] Some of the old rules were reaffirmed and new ones were adopted. It was stated that gratuitous treatment would be provided only "for such persons as are unable to pay their own doctors for services rendered." The Polyclinic was to advance medical science by study and treatment of actual cases of disease, instruct medical students, and advance the "common interests of the Hospital, the needy sick poor, the profession of Detroit and tributary country, and all classes of people." Unlike the dispensary, the Polyclinic offered complete medical treatment, and to accomplish this, separate departments were established. These were medicine (which received the greater portion of the cases), surgery, gynecology, laryngology, neurology, opthalmology and otology, and dermatology.[15]

The results spoke for themselves. In 1890, after two years of operation, the out-patient department had 1,045 visits, and 1,442 free prescriptions were provided. Of those seeking free medical advice, 16 were sent into the Hospital for more intensive treatment.[16] The following year, 1891, business fell off. "The Polyclinic did not accomplish as much during the year as was expected," President Cutcheon reported. This was attributed by the chief of staff to the illness and absence of the director. The result was a reorganization program by which a separate Polyclinic staff was established, "composed of the younger members of the profession." [17] At the same time, it was recommended that the Hospital hire a "live, bright young man" for director.[18] The position was given first to Dr. Storz. He was succeeded in a year by Dr. W. J. Brand, who was assisted by a staff of 7 members, among whom was a woman, Dr. Emma D. Cook, in charge of gynecology.[19] This reorganization proved to be a wise step, because shortly thereafter, full Hospital-staff membership became contingent upon a doctor's devoting a prescribed period of time to the clinic. That having been provided, the number of visits in 1894 reached a total of 2,177.[20] Thereafter, the work of the Polyclinic, or out-patient department, steadily increased, until 1961 when Harper Hospital reported a total of 53,702 visits.[21]

A visible weakness of the out-patient service, pointed out by Dr. Cook, was that many patients, particularly women, insisted upon continuing treatment when their condition could best be remedied by an operation. The trouble was, she said, too many patients were terror-stricken at the prospect of an operation. Citing twenty-five cases in which operations were obviously called for, only three were performed.

The dread which prompts patients to seek palliative rather than curative treatment results from erroneous ideas, which are born of ignorance and nurtured by false reports, until they look upon an operation as dangerous to life and not necessary. There is also a tendency on the part of such patients to go from one clinic to another. As soon as one physician advises an operation she immediately tries to gain the opinion of others, hoping in this way to evade the prescribed treatment.[22]

It took time, but eventually abuse or overuse of out-patient privileges was partially corrected by instituting a system of moderate fees which required a $.25 registration, and from $1.00 for salvarsan to $15.00 for tonsillectomies. Among the reasons given for putting this fee schedule into effect were the greater value placed upon a service if the patient paid for it, a reduction in the number of "floaters," removal of the stigma of charity, and "the small sums collected from many people bulk large in the aggregate."[23] In the first 10 months, the fees totaled $12,898.65, received from 7,480 visits.[24] There was, according to Hospital authorities, no decrease in the number of out-patients. Also, at that time, the Hospital reaffirmed what had been proved by the dispensary back in 1868: that "an out-patient clinic is avowedly both charitable and educational. The maintenance of real educational privileges enables us to command for our out-patients the services of the most highly-qualified young physicians of the city. . . ."[25]

In 1926, the out-patient service was again expanded, and the fees in some cases increased. Alice H. Walker, director of the Social Service Department, reported in 1927:

We are now able to treat patients who hitherto were deemed ineligible. Detroit, the mecca for job seekers, has so long been regarded as the seat of the proverbial pot of gold at the end of the rainbow, that the necessity for this extension of clinic services might be questioned.[26]

But, Miss Walker continued, the factory production worker too often found the gold pot empty, and the average Detroit family of five had an income of only $1,952 a year, which did not provide much for medical care. The new out-patient system geared charges to family means or income, which was a great benefit to small wage-earners. Thus, although the social and economic climate of Detroit had undergone marked changes since the days of Walter Harper and Nancy Martin, the intent of their benevolence was being observed, fitted to the new times.

While out-patients were flocking to the clinic under their own motive power, patients entering the general hospital were under a handicap. If they were too sick or too badly injured to use the streetcars, which involved a walk of a block, they came in whatever conveyance, public or private, was available. Located on what were still the city's outskirts in the 1880's, Harper's ability to care for emergency cases was limited by the difficulties in getting accident victims, or those seized by sudden illness, into the Hospital promptly. The question of ambulance service came up at a trustees' meeting on June 7, 1887, and it was decided to provide free ambulance service to patients and patrons.[27] Equipment was soon obtained, consisting of a light spring wagon, painted white, with a gong under the dashboard. There was already a barn for stabling the horse on the northeast corner of the lot, so shelter presented no problem. Soon the rig was answering calls, and by the end of the year, it had made 366 runs. The driver was a man named J. S. Fletcher,[28] and the usual procedure was for a junior member of the house staff to accompany the ambulance on its calls.

In a way, competition forced the trustees into providing ambulance service. Beginning about 1879, the first regular hospital ambulance in Detroit was operated by the Michigan College of Medicine, in connection with the old Emergency Hospital with which it was affiliated. This first ambulance, manned by medical students before a regular ambulance surgeon was appointed, was a converted grocery wagon. Its response to emergency calls meant that such cases ended up in Emergency Hospital instead of in Harper. Another factor influencing the trustees was Harper's arrangement with industrial firms, particularly the railroads, to take care of accidents, for this required a means of getting the victims to the Hospital.[29] When the Detroit-Windsor railroad tunnel was being built, the ambulance averaged a call a day, so common were accidents.[30]

The Harper ambulance entrance was off John R Street, at the north end of the building. When, within a year or two, the out-patient building was erected, the drive went between the two structures, dipping down so as to permit the vehicle to clear the passageway which connected the clinic and Hospital. The receiving station was in the rear, close to the operating rooms. A need was soon felt for expanding the service. Detroit was a sprawling city, and a good deal of time was involved driving from the Hospital to the patient's residence, or the scene of an accident, which often occurred in the factories or railroad yards on the edge of town, or on the downtown streets. The result was the acquisition in 1889 of a second ambulance which was stationed on St. Antoine Street, probably in or near a convenient livery stable. This arrangement permitted faster runs, particularly on emergency calls, but the trustees found the service to be a heavy expense. After a year of operation, the board took a second close look at the downtown station, and in 1891 voted to discontinue it, requiring thereafter that "the whole service be from the hospital." The use of the telephone, plus the use of two wagons and three horses which the Hospital now had, made it possible to carry regular patients back and forth and, at the same time, keep one rig on hand for emergencies. The availability of the ambulance for emergencies was advertised through the co-operation of a boys' church group, the Boy Door Keepers. To all who wanted them, the Door Keepers circulated gummed labels to be pasted on telephones, giving the Hospital number, 13, and giving assurance that service was on a day and night basis with a surgeon always accompanying the ambulance.[31] In time, the "surgeon" very frequently turned out to be an intern, or even an extern.

The ambulance service was expensive, a fact which worried the thrifty trustees, and they noted with alarm the "great wear and tear on vehicles and horses." [32] The shine had scarcely worn off the original ambulance in 1887 when it was the object of disaster. A young blade of the town, driving two young ladies—sisters—in his carriage, was tempted to show off, and he began driving recklessly. At Woodward and Grand River he collided with an omnibus; the two girls were thrown out and rather badly battered. An emergency call went out to Harper, and the ambulance set out on the run. En route there was another collision, this time between the ambulance and a beer dray, driven by August Ruoff. The ambulance was all but demolished, and the horse, whose jaw was broken, had to be fitted with a set of false teeth. Apparently, the ambulance driver was at fault, because the trustees were told they had no claim against Ruoff. They admonished their driver, as they often did thereafter, to hold down his speed to a comfortable and safe six miles per hour.[33] One of the things that caused the most trouble was the desire of the ambulance driver, called out on an emergency, to get to the scene of the accident first. There developed a rivalry which took on the aspects of a horse race. It must have been exhilarating for the drivers and attendants, and the dashing wagons, with their gongs pounding, were quite a stirring spectacle for bystanders. But it gave the trustees gray hairs.

In 1888, Harper acquired a new neighbor when the Grace Hospital * opened two blocks north on John R Street at the corner of East Willis Ave.[34] The competition between the two institutions was keen, but nowhere was it keener than between the ambulances. All sorts of tricks and strategies were employed by the drivers to get to the scene of an accident first. Whichever ambulance picked up the victim, that hospital got another patient. The result was that Detroit was frequently treated to a scene resembling the chariot race in *Ben Hur*. Dr. Stephen H. Knight, of Grace, in a mellow mood many years later, recounted how someone at Grace would keep watch up the street, and press an alarm when the Harper ambulance dashed out. At the signal, the harness in the Grace barn would drop onto the horse, just as it did in fire houses. The Grace driver and intern would scramble aboard and off they would go in pursuit. "It happened that out in front of Grace there were two big mud holes, so when the Harper ambulance went by, they had to slacken up a bit," Dr. Knight recalled. That gave the Grace rig a chance to catch up, and the race would be on. Sometimes it would be a three-cornered contest, with the Emergency Hospital ambulance taking part.[35]

All of this was hard, not only on the ambulances and horses, but also on the drivers, interns, patients, and general public. Accidents became too commonplace, and the authorities and the newspapers began to find fault. Criticism was leveled particularly at the practice of leaving a victim in the street if he demanded being taken to a rival hospital. If Harper was first on the scene, and the prospective patient insisted he wanted to go to Grace, the Harper ambulance would refuse to carry him there, and vice versa. This led to an effort to zone the city, with each ambulance having its assigned area, but nothing came of that idea.[36]

The drivers were sometimes a trial to the interns. Dr. J. Milton Robb recalled his days of riding the Harper ambulance as an intern. The driver was a squeamish chap, and after collecting a particularly gory accident case, he would feel compelled to stop on the way back to the Hospital and fortify his shaken nerves with strong spirits. Ambulance, intern, and patient would be left at the curb while the driver went inside to settle his stomach. The interns, conspicuous in their white coats, fidgeted on seats of the rigs, as bystanders, listening to the moans of the victim, delivered caustic observations about the Hospital's ambulance service. One exasperated intern finally threatened the driver with physical violence if he ever did such a thing again, with the result that the nuisance was more or less abated. Dr. Robb also recalled that ambulance service was given an added filip because the horse was blind.

There were other occasional embarrassments for the trustees, such as the time that two lovelorn interns appropriated an ambulance one night and took two student nurses for a ride in the moonlight. The young men were called on the carpet, roundly berated, and suspended. But the suspensions were quietly lifted a few days later. Perhaps the trustees remembered they, too, had once been young and in love.

The medical staff sometimes favored fast ambulance service, regardless of the consequences. The staff annual report for 1893 contained a pinch of sarcasm in referring to the six-mile-per-hour limit ordained by the trustees.

The ambulances have done good service notwithstanding your honored president has unequivocally embarrassed the fast runs. There were 758 trips made, of which 213 were for accident cases. The ambulances brought 434 patients to the Hospital, took 240 to their homes, and made 84 futile trips.[37]

In 1893, there arose the need for a new ambulance barn. The old one was falling apart, and the site was required for an addition to the Hospital. Unfortunately, the trustees lacked funds—the depression of 1893 was responsible for that. But they solicited subscriptions and raised enough money to build a new barn closer to the edge of Recreation Park.[38] This proved a boon, because the ambulance attendants constructed bleacher seats in the opening to the hay mow from which the ball games could be watched.[39]

From time to time the old ambulances were replaced by new ones which were more comfortable and efficient. In 1894, a local medical journal described one of these vehicles as being "so arranged that the padded sides swing upward and inward to meet in the center, where iron supports are adjusted to hold the upper berth in place." As the description indicates, this ambulance was designed to hold four patients, "which will prove of great service in large accidents."[40] In 1899, a new ambulance was acquired, "lighted by electricity with rubber tires and all other modern equipment."[41] In 1911, Harper entered the automobile age with its first motor ambulance. This was a Ford chassis with a specially built body. In 1914, a Cadillac costing $3,600 was donated by Trustee C. A. Black, an official of the Cadillac Motor Car Company.[42] In 1918, Harper Hospital ended its ambulance service, relying thereafter upon the various private ambulance services.[43]

After having built the John R Street hospital, and having established the Farrand Training School, the Board of Trustees discovered that the problems of administration had substantially increased. Running the institution was not something that could be done by a superintendent who also wore the resident physician's hat, aided by seven trustees who got together when time from their personal involvements permitted. In 1887, it was realized that the Hospital management had to be strengthened. For five years, Dr. J. K. Gailey had been both superintendent and resident physician. Now, either job, by itself, was enough to keep a man fully occupied. What Harper needed was a manager who had business and administrative experience, and it was decided to replace Gailey with a non-medical superintendent. On June 14, William C. Bagley was hired as general superintendent at a salary of $600 a year. This move indicated no criticism of Dr. Gailey, who welcomed the opportunity to practice medicine instead of devoting at least half his time . and energy to being an institutional housekeeper. He retired, with an expression of the board's appreciation for his past services. He continued for several years to be a valuable and influential member of the staff, serving as one of the attending surgeons.[44]

The next step was to relieve the burden upon the seven trustees. One obvious solution was to enlarge the board so that the responsibilities could be diffused. The necessary action was taken, and on October 10, 1887, the Articles of Incorporation were amended, increasing the number of trustees from seven to fifteen.[45] As a result of this expansion, such prominent men as Christian H. Buhl, brother of Frederick Buhl, Russell A. Alger, Henry B. Ledyard, David Whitney, Jr., William K. Muir, William H. Elliott, J. L. Hudson,* George F. Moore, and Clarence Black, along with others equally devoted to the trust given them, went on the board. With the increase in trustee membership, it was now possible to reorganize the board, setting up a number of standing committees. Prior to 1887, the board had functioned, with occasional exceptions, as a committee of the whole, with special committees being appointed from time to time to deal with specific and usually temporary matters. In other words, all the business of the Hospital was the concern of each trustee. Fifteen trustees permitted a division of labor, with more attention to specific duties and problems.

The reorganization did not take place until 1891 when a new list of committees was decided upon. They were: (1) Finance, Real Estate, and Law; (2) Auditing; (3) Contracts for Purchases and Supplies; (4) Buildings, Furnishings, and Repairs; (5) Visiting, Complaints, Admissions, and Rates; (6) Statistics and Free Beds; (7) Training School and Admission of Nurses; (8) Cabinet and Library; and (9) Polyclinic. Membership on these committees varied from three to six. Members of the medical staff were invited to sit on three committees—Cabinet and Library, Training School, and Polyclinic.[46] This division proved to be an excellent arrangement, and from then on, the Board of Trustees worked largely through committees. Occasionally, special committees were appointed for extraordinary purposes, and when they were required, new standing committees were created. In 1891, the bylaws were amended to provide for a Committee on Housekeeping. This was to consist of:

. . . three ladies, whose duty it shall be to make weekly inspection of the Hospital with the housekeeper; give her the aid of their counsel, and report to the Board of Trustees in the months of June and December of each year, the condition of the Hospital housekeeping with such recommendations as they shall deem for the good of the Hospital.[47]

Committees of ladies also were appointed to advise on furnishings for parlors, reception rooms, halls, wards, and private rooms. For the most part, the women appointed to these committees were the wives of trustees or medical staff members. But the important thing is that, from that time, the role of women in the Hospital became increasingly important.

The trustees learned what every homeowner knows: that the expense of upkeep unrelentingly follows the original cost. The proceedings of the board are filled with such husbandry as painting, calcimining, plumbing repairs, maintaining the heating and power plants, keeping the lawns and grounds in trim, and a hundred other chores, in season and out. Awnings were obtained, and it became necessary to provide window screens. In 1891, stone sidewalks were installed along John R Street, and the Hospital had to bear its share of the cost. Gas bills seemed unduly high, and the trustees turned their attention to electric lighting. Conversion to electricity was a decision not easily made. Debate on the issue began in 1889; committees studied and reported, and were directed to study some more before the big decision was made and electric lights were installed in 1890. Telephone service was subscribed to in 1897, and in 1903 a generous donor, Henry Stephens, installed an interinstitutional communications system which replaced messengers, pull bells, and speaking tubes. In 1896, the Hospital was completely renovated at a cost of $50,000. Sometime before, the kitchen had been moved from the basement to the fifth floor, which involved considerable expense.[48]

While physical improvements were being made, Harper Hospital never lost sight of its obligation to be of service to the community in every way possible, and during the 1890's, it engaged in many good works. In 1889, for example, a huge "world's fair" was held in Detroit, known as the Detroit International Fair and Exposition. A site was selected in Delray, a southwestern suburb. The grounds later became the property of the Solvay Process Company, which still stands there. Intended to run for three years, the Exposition, a costly and elaborate affair, never really got off the ground, being overshadowed by the projected Chicago Columbian Exposition planned for 1893. Nevertheless, the Detroit Exposition attracted large numbers of people, and as its contribution to the fair's success, Harper established a temporary hospital on the grounds which it operated during three summers.[49] In August, 1891, the National Grand Army of the Republic Encampment took over the Exposition grounds, naming it Camp Sherman, and a tent city was set up to house the thousands of veterans who attended what up to that time was Detroit's largest convention. With such men as General Alger and Captain Hart and other ex-warriors on the board and the staff, and considering Harper's own Civil War origins, it is no surprise that the Hospital agreed to keep its Exposition hospital going from August 3 to 8 and to offer the facilities of the Hospital proper for the free care of such patients who might be sent from Camp Sherman.[50]

This generous gesture, unfortunately, was marred by a tragic incident. Diphtheria broke out among the members of the Leadville [Colorado] Drum Corps, and two members were rushed to Harper's contagious hospital, where one died soon after admittance. Annie Gilroy, a student nurse from Traverse City, who had entered the Farrand Training School the previous April, was on duty and was assigned to the care of the two diphtheria patients. Less than a week after their admittance, Annie developed symptoms and died within a day or two. She was the first Harper student nurse to die in line of duty, and her death saddened the entire Hospital. Among the floral offerings at her funeral was "a beautiful tribute from the Leadville Drum Corps." [51]

The Michigan State Fair provided another annual occasion for Harper to perform a community service. A "Little Harper Hospital" was established at the fairgrounds, land now occupied by Wayne State University. First aid was provided, and a staff of doctors and nurses was in attendance. Free ambulance service also was made available.[52]

In June, 1899, several hundred young people went to Detroit to attend the National Convention of Christian Endeavor. Harper was asked to staff with nurses the tent grounds, which were on the fairground property, as well as the chief meeting place on Belle Isle. The trustees regretfully had to turn down the request for nurses, but they did offer, for five dollars per week, to care for visitors who were taken sick and unable to pay more. Free ambulance service also was offered to transport the sick to the Hospital, either from Belle Isle or the tent camp.[53]

Major disasters, when they struck infrequently, elicited prompt and whole-hearted response, with all of the Hospital's resources placed at the disposal of the victims. When a terrific explosion ripped apart the plant of the Penberthy Injector Company in 1901, causing thirty deaths and injury to more than fifty persons, Harper ambulances, doctors, and nurses were among the first to appear at the scene.* When the city of Dayton, Ohio, was threatened with obliteration by flood in 1913, Harper rushed a relief train carrying medical supplies and a detachment of nurses to the stricken town. And again, in 1927, when a madman blew up a rural schoolhouse at Bath, Michigan, killing almost the entire student body, Harper nurses and medical supplies were rushed there to aid the injured survivors. The Rev. Dr. Duffield's ideal of Harper's role "for the wider welfare of the city" was expanded to include as large an area as the Hospital could reach in times of trouble and distress.

Because a doctor must have access to the best and latest information, an adequate hospital library is essential. Harper had a library of sorts as early as 1873 when Trustee Robert W. King called to the board's attention "the small library in use at Harper Hospital has become greatly reduced from constant use." The trustees appointed him librarian, a title which he used primarily to solicit books, magazines, newspapers, and Bibles for the use of patients. The present professional library is the result of evolution. Upon establishment of the Farrand Training School, Hiram Walker donated a nurses' library, composed largely of textbooks. This was the first real collection for professional purposes. The medical library had an informal beginning. It started with a few volumes and some journals, donated by staff members. Occasionally the widow of a doctor gave her husband's collection to Harper. As the medical library grew through acquisitions of that nature, the books were kept wherever space could be found. As time went on, they more or less gravitated to the office of the pathologist.

In 1948, the nurses' library and the medical library were combined into a single department under Miss Marion Wells, who was both a nurse and a trained librarian. While this was an improvement, it was still far from satisfactory because the nurses' library remained in the nurses' home, and the medical library was housed in makeshift quarters in the Buhl building.[54] In 1949, the two collections were brought together and placed in new library quarters. What had been the powerhouse was remodeled through financial help from the Greater Detroit Hospital Fund. The lower part became the laundry, and the upper, the library. Henry Fink, then president of Michigan Consolidated Gas Company, gave $12,000 for furniture, and the drapes and carpets were the gift of the J. L. Hudson Company. About the time of the dedication of the new library rooms in 1950, the patients' library, which since the 1930's had been supervised by Gamma Beta Phi as an alumnae project, also was taken over by the department of libraries. As a result of the consolidation of three libraries, Harper had the first integrated hospital library in the Midwest and one of the first in the United States. In 1963, the integrated Harper library, administered by a professional staff, had on its shelves about 30,000 volumes, of which 15,000 were bound medical journals and 10,000 were professional books. The library was receiving some 500 current journals a year.[55]

Another important but not widely known Harper activity has been the intermittent publication of the *Harper Hospital Bulletin*. Over a period of seventy years, it has made a valuable contribution to medical literature. Although the *Bulletin* has been a useful vehicle for circulating information about staff and administration activities, its principal purpose has been in the field of education, offering an opportunity for staff members to discuss technical matters of value, not only with their colleagues, but with the profession at large. It was the latter consideration, perhaps coupled with the staff's desire to enhance its own prestige, that prompted the medical staff in 1889 to ask the trustees to approve and support a publication.[56] After due deliberation, the trustees reported back that they "feel too poor to assume the expense of the publication, but approve of the plan." The staff members, therefore, determined to make it their own project, and decided "that the Hospital Publication be strictly professional." The publication committee, which had previously been formed, was instructed to issue the first number as soon as possible, and Dr. H. O. Walker moved that it be called the *Harper Hospital Bulletin*. The staff agreed that it would make up any deficits which might result. The trustees offered to help to the extent of handling the mailing, although the superintendent was instructed to incur no additional expense to the Hospital.[57]

Volume I, Number 1 bore the date line of June, 1890. This first issue had twelve pages, the lead article being the reprint of a paper by Dr. Walker, read sometime previously before the Detroit Medical Library. It was titled "Report of Three Successful Operations for Surgical Kidney—Two of Nephrectomy and one of Nephrorraphy." Dr. E. T. Tappey offered an article on "Two Cases of Laparotomy"; Dr. Albert E. Carrier had one with the formidable title "The Differences and Likenesses of Papulo-Squamous Affections of the Palms and Soles";

and Dr. Howard Longyear had "A Case of Fibroid Polypus—Simulating Inversion of the Uterus." Filler material included a five-line report by Dr. George Duffield on "The Microscopical Laboratory" which, as he pointed out, had been established in February, 1889 "for the purpose of facilitating the diagnosis of the various diseases." Within a year, 252 examinations had been made, and since January 1, 1890, "there have been 81 examinations of the urine, 34 of sputum and 20 of pathological tissues." There also was an announcement of the new term commencing at the Farrand Training School, a notice of a forthcoming meeting of the Michigan State Medical Society, and the bi-monthly report of the superintendent which stated, among other things, that "since the opening of the Hospital by the Trustees in 1865, a period of 25 years," 10,350 patients had been treated.

The *Bulletin* was a bi-monthly; at first it had no regular editor. The selection and preparation of articles was handled by the publication committee. Later, editors were assigned. Dr. Duffield's name appeared on the masthead in April, 1891 as publisher, a job which also included the chief editorial responsibilities. Dr. Preston M. Hickey became the first regular editor in June, 1893, and others who held that post after him included Drs. Walter P. Manton, Louis J. Hirschman, and John N. Bell. Besides the contributors' papers, the magazine each year carried the annual report, a gold mine of information and statistics. Before long, medical and surgical equipment firms, pharmaceutical houses, and frequently general business concerns were finding the *Bulletin* a useful advertising medium. The Hospital was given a free, full-page ad, and the Farrand Training School and Detroit College of Medicine also used the publication for advertising purposes.

The original lack of fixed editorial responsibility soon threatened the life of the *Bulletin*. Its future was discussed at a staff meeting on October 22, 1901, and it was proposed that publication be suspended because "the Medical Board do not write sufficient." It was pointed out that the entire staff was supposed to be the editors and the publication committee simply the means of conducting the operations. Instead, the committee had been forced to assume all responsibility, including the writing. It was unfortunate, the staff was told, that it had become so hard to get publishable material because "the business of the journal has grown rapidly, the advertising has grown beyond our comprehension." Then Dr. Duffield took the floor in defense of continuing publication.

"Harper Hospital Bulletin," he declared, "was begun under auspicious circumstances in June 1890, and has since been self-supporting, probably the only paying investment Harper Hospital has." He pointed out that the Hospital had received free space worth $400, that the cost of printing was only $85 to $90 an issue, and that 2,000 copies were regularly being mailed out. Duffield said:

> There is no need of dropping this journal. We know that it advertises the Hospital, for cases come to it from all over the state to have operations performed and receive the treatment for various diseases. . . . Every two months the edition is scattered broadcast over the country, and physicians, medical journals, medical colleges and prominent men see that we have a live hospital (though ourselves may be dead).
> We don't want your filthy lucre, what we want are papers.[58]

Apparently he got them, because during 1902, the staff had become quite literary minded. In addition to articles contributed to the *Bulletin,* 13 staff members had a total of 33 papers in other medical journals. Among those contributing were such prominent Harper men as Drs. Don M. Campbell, J. H. Carstens, George Duffield, Angus McLean, Walter Manton, W. F. Metcalf, and H. R. Varney.[59]

By 1897, circulation had reached the 4,000 mark for each edition, and that year, for the first time, the staff was asked to make up a deficit of $114.27, and the Hospital was charged $50.00 for its page advertisement ("a thing never done before").[60] Financial difficulties gradually increased and advertising for some reason fell off. In 1908, Dr. Hirschman recommended that the Hospital assume publication costs, a proposition to which the trustees acceded reluctantly, with the provision that the net cost to the Hospital would not run more than $200.00 a year.[61] Apparently, it was impossible to stay within that figure, because the issue of October, 1912—Volume XXIII, Number 4—was the last, and the first *Harper Hospital Bulletin* quietly expired.

In April, 1917, the *Bulletin* was briefly revived as the second series, under the editorship of Dr. Plinn F. Morse. World War I, and the resultant disruption of the staff, caused this publication to languish after two issues had appeared. It was officially suspended April 22, 1919 by the trustees. That decision was influenced by the Wayne County Medical Society taking over the *Detroit Medical Journal,* and all the Harper material was given to the Wayne County Medical Society.[62]

In April, 1922, however, the *Harper Bulletin* reappeared as the "new series," under the supervision of a publication committee. Volume I, Number 1 pointed out that, because of the increase in staff and personnel, an authoritative means of communication was necessary. It was admittedly a house organ magazine and carried no scientific papers. It continued to be published until 1926 when it, too, quietly folded up.

The hiatus following discontinuance of the "new series" *Bulletin* lasted until 1941 when the executive committee of the medical staff asked the trustees to resume publication of "a sixteen page bulletin to be called *The Harper Hospital Bulletin*" to contain "medical material only." The trustees agreed to "try a publication of such a bulletin and to continue it as long as the Hospital could afford to do so." It was to appear nine months each year, suspending during the three summer months.[63] The first issue of sixteen pages appeared October 1, 1941, with the statement that it was to be a monthly. World War II interrupted operations during all of 1943, but the *Bulletin* resumed publication in 1944 as a quarterly, so continuing until 1947 when it became a bi-monthly journal. The *Bulletin* has since been published without interruption and has maintained a high level of editorial and scientific excellence. It has been edited by Dr. William S. Reveno and Dr. Harold C. Mack. Their work was singularly recognized in 1958, when the *Bulletin* received the award of the American Medical Writers' Association for distinguished service in medical journalism.

During the closing years of the nineteenth century, Harper Hospital became involved in a serious legal matter, which attracted national attention. The outcome affected all hospitals by establishing a principle of law which deferred the responsibility of hospitals and other charitable institutions in regard to responsibility for negligence. On January 26, 1890, a patient by the name of Downes was taken to Harper in a highly disturbed state of mind. He was admitted as an insane person, although his condition may have been delirium tremens. Being violent, he was placed in a third floor padded room which had an iron framework over the window. In order to restrain Downes further, he was handcuffed when he was taken to the Hospital, and these restraints were kept on for a day or two when they were removed by an attendant. On January 29, Downes continued to be violent, and with his hands free, he managed to tear loose the window bars and jump to the ground, thirty-five feet below. He was instantly killed. The suspicion of delirium tremens is bolstered by action of the trustees on February 10, 1890, directing that an indemnity bond be taken out "for use in cases of patients suffering under delirium tremens." [64]

Downes' widow brought suit, charging the Hospital with negligence in not properly restraining her husband, that is, by removing the hand-cuffs and putting him in a room from which it was possible to remove the window bars. The case was argued in the Wayne County Circuit Court, and the verdict was in favor of Harper. Mrs. Downes then appealed to the Michigan Supreme Court which upheld the lower court in an opinion handed down September 25, 1894. The higher court's ruling was of the utmost importance in defining the responsibility of charitable institutions. It was the contention of the plaintiff that Downes was a private, paying patient and that, in accepting such patients who were not charity cases, the Hospital could not claim exemption from liability as a charitable institution.

The Supreme Court replied that, if the Hospital were liable, it would mean that the trust fund could be entirely wiped out and diverted from its original purpose through damage awards.

Charitable bequests cannot be thus thwarted by negligence for which the donor is in no manner responsible. If, in the proper execution of the trust, a trustee or an employee commits an act of negligence, he may be held responsible for his negligent act; but the law jealously guards the charitable trust fund, and does not permit it to be frittered away by the negligent acts of those employed in its execution. . . .

The fact that patients who are able to pay are required to do so does not deprive the defendant of its eleemosynary character, nor permit a recovery for damages on account of the existence of contract relations. The amounts thus received are not for private gain, but contribute to the more effectual accomplishment of the purpose for which the charity was founded.[65]

This opinion, which safeguarded Harper and most other Michigan hospitals, stood as the prevailing law until 1961, when it was modified by a new Supreme Court judgment involving a Port Huron hospital.

17. Brush Street Building — Designed by Albert Kahn, the Brush Street Building opened in 1928, increasing the Hospital's capacity to 690 beds.

courtesy Harper Hospital

18. Dr. Max Ballin — Born and educated in Germany, Dr. Ballin became one of America's great surgeons. During most of his professional life, he was a member of the Harper Hospital staff, serving as chief of staff from 1920 to 1928. *courtesy Harper Hospital*

19. Richard H. Webber — Nephew of Detroit's merchant prince, J. L. Hudson, Webber carried on a long family tradition of service and philanthropy to Harper Hospital. He became a trustee in 1912, was still active on the Board of Trustees in 1963, and was president from 1918 to 1961. His was the longest tenure, both as trustee and president, in the board's history. *courtesy Burton Historical Collection*

Chapter 16

ERA OF EXPANSION

One morning
soon after the turn of the century, Harper Hospital was wakened by
the chug of internal combustion engines and discovered it was in—was
part of—the automobile age. In the space of a few brief years, there
occurred great technological developments which brought about profound changes in social and economic conditions. The face of American
society underwent startling revision, and nowhere in America was it
more noticeable than in Detroit, which almost overnight became the
automobile capital of the world. But the automobile was only a symbol,
perhaps the catalyst, of what was happening all over the world, as the
shift from agriculture to a civilization based upon mass industry took
place. Villages and quiet, peaceful towns became booming cities, crowded
with immigrants who sought the pot of American gold at the end of a
throbbing factory or roaring mill rainbow. Americans moved off their
farms to seek their fortunes in the cities. Both groups, the foreign and
the native-born, created problems such as most of the older cities had
never known. Overcrowding, changed and often lower living standards,
caused serious health and social problems. There was a need for agencies
and institutions, both public and private, to help meet the demands
which these new and unfamiliar social, economic, and health problems
presented.

Harper Hospital, to survive, had to accept a new role in a new community. How it met that challenge comprises a significant part of its
history.

In 1900, Detroit's population was 285,704, and that of the metropolitan area was 304,132. The city, although larger, retained many of the

characteristics of the 1870's and 1880's. Industry had expanded, to be sure. The city had spread out. But gracious homes still lined Woodward and Jefferson Avenues; north of Grand Circus Park continued to be a lovely residential area; and Harper Hospital remained an integral part of a pleasant neighborhood. But by 1910, things had begun to change perceptibly. The decade 1900–10 was one of vast and rapid change. By the latter year, population had grown to 465,766, and Detroit had a much higher percentage of foreign-born and foreign-speaking people than most other American cities. That decade saw the city's economy change from one based primarily on commerce to one of heavy manufacturing. And it was the automobile that did it.

The decade saw the founding of Packard, Cadillac, Ford, Reo, Hudson and Hupp, and the organization of the General Motors Corporation. In 1902, the industry produced 9,000 cars; in 1910, more than 50,000 were turned out, and Detroit hadn't even started to warm up. As it celebrated its two hundredth anniversary in 1901, (Dr. Daniel La Ferte played the pageant role of Cadillac, the city's founder), Detroit was only keeping pace with the rest of the world. The first transatlantic radio message was sent; the Wright brothers gave mankind wings at Kitty Hawk. The Russian-Japanese War, a small fracas by later standards of mass killing, provided the seed from which would sprout two world wars. The adding-machine industry came to Detroit, and the city counted more than fifty millionaires. A new crop of tycoons was calculating wealth which no longer was derived almost exclusively from northern mines and forests. New money was being minted by factory lathes, stamping presses, and high-powered salesmanship.

Yet, there were other things happening, less obvious, perhaps, to the average person, but nevertheless of great significance. Adrenalin was perfected, and with the aid of Parke, Davis and Company, hormones were isolated. Novocaine was introduced, salvarsan was discovered, and the Wassermann test was perfected. A scientist determined blood groupings, and the nation's doctors found new reason almost every month to read their professional journals. Pulling back the curtain of medical knowledge increased the importance to the community of such institutions as Harper Hospital and gave the institutions, with an imperativeness which would allow of no delay, the responsibility to meet intensified social and economic obligations. Fortunately, the right men were available, or soon would be, who made it possible to meet these responsibilities.

A new group of trustees gradually came to the fore as community leaders. Originally, Harper looked for support and guidance to men who had made their mark in mercantile enterprises, building, and specialized lighter industry. As these trustees passed on, a new generation took over, drawn, to a great extent, from the front offices of the automotive companies, the emerging giant financial institutions, and the chambers of legal lights specializing in corporation law. Thus, there are seen on the early twentieth-century roster of trustees such names as Dodge, Couzens, Alger, Joy, Boyer, Bowen, Kirchner, and Hudson. The old names remained, too, and the second and even the third generations carried on the work of the founding fathers—the Duffields, Russels, Buhls, and Farrands. Harper had the managerial resources to enable it to fit nicely into the new era.

Up to 1891, the presidency of the board was held by the original trustees under the Harper-Martin deeds. They were Dr. Duffield (1859–68), Buckminster Wight (1868–79), Frederick Buhl (1879–84), and Jacob S. Farrand (1884–91). When Farrand died, Sullivan Cutcheon, leading Detroit attorney and bank president, was chosen, the first man to hold the post who was not a member of the original board. He served until his death in 1900. A century had ended, and the men of the century disappeared with it. As Cutcheon's replacement, the board elected J. L. Hudson. A rising business and community leader, destined to make his mark as one of the country's great merchants, he was a typical twentieth-century businessman. Selecting him to head the Hospital, until 1912 when he died, was almost prophetic of the era which was beginning. On April 12, 1910, Henry Ford was elected to the board. Unfortunately for Harper, his hospital interests lay elsewhere, and he resigned on the following July 5. There is no record of his having attended a single board meeting.

The medical staff of the Hospital was slower to change than the board. Going into the 1900's, the old names and faces were still in evidence, still doing good work, and exercising an almost autocratic control over medical policy, sometimes to the despair of younger men. In 1908, John Henry Carstens was still chief of staff, performing appendectomies and probing the abdomen with as much skill as men thirty years his junior. Theodore A. McGraw and J. K. Gailey remained stalwarts of the staff, as did H. O. Walker, H. W. Longyear, W. P. Manton, George Duffield, Charles G. Jennings, George Frothingham, and E. L. Shurly. But along with them were new men, men who were winning reputations and who, by the end of the decade and long after, would be giants in their own right. The list included Max Ballin, Burt R. Shurly, Angus McLean, Preston M. Hickey, and Louis J. Hirschman. Soon they would be joined by Clark D. Brooks, Hugo Freund, Alex W. Blain, Plinn F. Morse, George Kamperman, J. Milton Robb, and Lawrence Reynolds, to mention only a few.

Harper Hospital, then, entered the twentieth century with a nice balance between the old and the new manpower—the ripe experience and budding genius typical of the new age in medicine. The balance included both the administrative and the professional phases of the Hospital—the trustees and the staff. "Everything has worked smooth and peaceful," said Dr. Carstens in his last annual report as chief of staff, "except the everlasting demand for more room." [1]

In order to provide the room for which Dr. Carstens cried, as well as extra facilities to make Harper more functional, several new buildings and additions were added in the years immediately following the turn of the century. Of course, there had been some additions before that— the Polyclinic building, the original contagious hospital, and the Duffield Cottage. Another structure of considerable importance was also built about the same time. It was the Hospital's first building to be used exclusively as a home for nurses and to house the Farrand Training School. Prior to 1893, the nurses' quarters were on the fourth floor of the John R building, taking up space which the trustees felt could be better utilized for patients. "They really encroach upon room which should be devoted to patients," the board observed. [2] But for the moment nothing could be done. There was no other place available for the nurses of whom there were thirty-six students and three supervisors.

Then, on February 8, 1892, President Cutcheon disclosed to the board an offer made by Mrs. Eleanor J. Swain to erect a separate building for the Farrand Training School. [3] J. L. Hudson later credited Cutcheon with persuading Mrs. Swain to make the gift. [4] He was undoubtedly correct, because Cutcheon looked after Mrs. Swain's legal and financial affairs.* The conditions attached to the offer were promptly agreed to. Mrs. Swain wanted the building to be named the Swain Home for the Farrand Training School for Nurses. She also requested an annuity of six per cent for life, based upon the cost of the Home which was estimated at $20,000. [5]

The site selected was on the east side of John R Street, south of the Hospital. Work was pushed on the Swain Home, and on November 9, 1893, it was ready for occupancy. The structure was described as "a spacious three-story brick building, erected just south of the Hospital, and connected by an arcade. . . . [It] accommodates forty nurses and the three preceptors. The first floor is furnished in hardwood, and the others in Georgia pine." The principal had a suite of three rooms, and most of the nurses and students had single rooms, although a few doubled up. The furniture and equipment were all given by more than a dozen donors, including several members of the Board of Trustees.[6] The Swain Home proved to be a much-needed facility. Not only did it return some Hospital bed space to the purpose for which it was originally intended, it also provided room so that the nursing staff and the school enrollment could be expanded. The effect splendid new and comfortable quarters had on morale must have been incalculable. Contemporary accounts reveal how the young ladies, formerly under close restraint in the Hospital in which quiet and decorum were necessary, reacted in new surroundings.

Many a ripple of laughter rings through the halls, and as the school is in a different building from the hospital, no attempts are made to suppress the merriment. The rather sober and trying duties of the day demand a reaction and various amusements are indulged in during the evening. At home the nurses dress like other girls. They give dancing and card parties occasionally, and gentlemen acquaintances are not rigorously excluded.[7]

The building housed the library and ultimately a dining room, which was also used by the interns and staff. In 1899, the Swain Home was enlarged "at an expense not to exceed seven thousand dollars." [8] Still later, in 1923, after a new home for nurses had been built, the Swain building was remodeled to furnish a residence for the superintendent and quarters for male employees. In 1958, it was torn down, the site being used for tennis courts for the enjoyment of the nurses and residency staff.[9]

In supplying the Hospital with an adequate nursing staff, the Farrand School necessarily grew, and quarters outside the Swain Home had to be found. For a while, some of the graduate nurses occupied a "nurses' club" on Parsons Street. Then, in 1913, President Milton McRae, of the Board of Trustees, disclosed that Vernor Richmond and his two spinster sisters were willing to deed to the Hospital their property on the southwest corner of John R Street and Martin Place as an annex for the nurses. The building, a terrace, consisted of seven individual dwelling units, one of which fronted on Martin Place, the others on John R. The Richmonds stipulated they should jointly receive $2,500 a year for life. This was agreed to, and the Richmond Terrace, as it was called, provided living room for several nurses until 1922, when it was remodeled into interns' quarters. It continued to serve that purpose until 1962, when it was razed.[10]

Soon after the Swain building was completed, Trustee Gilbert Hart donated the funds for the construction of a power plant, to be located at the east line of the Hospital property, the site of the old ambulance barn, which was replaced by a new one at the northeast corner of the grounds. The Hart power plant continued in use until 1922, when it was replaced by a new one on the same site, the gift of Joseph Boyer. It was the Boyer power plant which ultimately became the quarters of the laundry and library.[11]

All of these additions and improvements were needed and gratefully accepted. But they did not fill the Hospital's major requirements. Commenting on one of these, Dr. Walter P. Manton stated:

> The reputation of Harper Hospital as an institution for the relief of surgical disorders particularly, has extended beyond the borders of the state and become national, and the demand for larger quarters, with all the equipment that such an institution implies, was never so great as at the present time.[12]

What Manton said was only what the surgical staff had been saying for a long time, and the pressure upon the trustees for new operating rooms was applied at every opportunity. The only thing that prevented the trustees from acting sooner was a lack of money. The project was discussed in 1899, and the following year a resolution was adopted to the effect:

> . . . that the Board place on record its purpose to bring about the building of suitable operating rooms and amphitheatre as soon as possible, and that the first money donated to the Hospital without restrictions will be appropriated for that purpose, and every effort will be made by the Board collectively and individually to further that end.[13]

This was a firm commitment, and on April 8, 1901, the building committee was directed "to get plans and specifications for the new amphitheatre and operating rooms, the entire cost of building same not to exceed twenty-five thousand dollars." [14] The site selected was the northeast corner adjoining the John R building. The architect, R. E. Raseman, went to work, with Dr. Carstens and other staff members literally standing around his drawing board, giving him instructions. Raseman was asked by the trustees to submit estimates for remodeling the old amphitheater and chapel:

. . . for the following purposes: store room and help's dining room, sleeping rooms for female help, and if possible strong rooms with the view to tearing down the adjoining building, the present female help's sleeping building, and erecting in its place the proposed operating rooms and amphitheatre.[15]

Later, when the work was progressing on the new operating building, the trustees decided to build an annex to be used as a combined morgue and autopsy room, made possible by a gift of $2,000 from Trustee Lem W. Bowen.[16]

"The Finest In The Whole Country," proclaimed the headlines in the local press, speaking of the new operating building which opened for use December 1, 1903. "In its equipment . . . it is said to eclipse anything of the kind in America, and according to Detroit physicians, recently returned from abroad, it is far ahead of anything in the great hospitals of Europe." [17] It was, indeed, a magnificent temple dedicated to surgery, a temple of antiseptic white enamel, stone, shiny steel, and brick, with "not a vestige of wood in sight." It was three floors in height, covering a ground surface of 50 by 100 feet. The ground floor had a "drive-in" for the ambulance, with an emergency operating room and a recovery room adjoining. The building was connected to the main Hospital, with an elevator providing service to each floor and to the corridors leading into the John R building. The morgue and autopsy room was off the northwest corner. On the second floor were three operating rooms and a small amphitheater or lecture room accommodating about 35 persons. The south end was taken up by the main amphitheater whose tiers rose to the top of the third floor with seats for about 400 spectators. The remaining part of the third floor was divided into smaller rooms, one for sterilizing, one for x-ray, and a third for eye and ear examinations.[18] Of course, it cost more than the specified $25,000. By the time it was completed, $60,000 had been expended, and the trustees had been forced to borrow part of the extra money. Nevertheless, pride proved adequate compensation for estimates exceeded. Observed Dr. Manton:

As a whole the new operating building is a brilliant example of architectural possibilities, and a positive illustration of the efforts of modern surgery for the best in its noble quest for the uplifting of the sick and afflicted and the alleviation of human suffering.[19]

It continued to serve Harper's needs until 1918, when it was replaced by the adjoining Gray Operating Pavilion, which provided new and even more modern operating rooms.

Important and useful as these new facilities were, they did not provide satisfactory answers to the Hospital's chief problem, the growing shortage of beds. It was one thing to have a building in which a patient could be operated on in antiseptic splendor. But he was likely to be little benefited if there was no empty bed awaiting him in a private room or ward after the operation had been performed. The Hospital authorities were fully aware of this and looked forward to an expansion program, which did not materialize for ten years. Meanwhile, steps could be and were taken to prepare for the future. In 1906, the president and treasurer were authorized "to investigate the purchase of the property in the rear of the Hospital on Brush Street belonging to the Brush Estate." Acting upon this authority, 7 lots were purchased in April, 1906, for $10,000.00. Later that month, an additional parcel of 80 feet on Brush was bought at $30.00 a foot, and another lot was obtained for $1,534.12. This property was paid for in part by proceeds from the sale of real estate owned by the Hospital in other sections of Detroit. These purchases gave Harper the room it needed; it had only to await the day when funds would be available for building purposes. In the meantime, a strip of John R Street frontage of 205 feet, extending south close to Brady Street, and some land behind it on Brush Street were acquired for $20,500.00. With the land acquired between 1906 and 1910, the Hospital owned most of the real estate between John R, Brush, Alexandrine, and Brady.[20]

Obtaining substantial funds to provide on this newly-acquired property the bed space to meet Detroit's growing needs now became the immediate concern of many people. One who interested himself was Dr. William F. Metcalf. He was one of those men destined to be the center of controversy. An outspoken critic of the Hospital's policies, he yearned to become chief of staff. Apparently, he felt one way to achieve his goal was personally to raise money from donors who would also back him in a general reorganization of the Hospital—with him as its medical chief. He began his campaign about 1906, soliciting support, raising money, and formulating his plans. He found backers on the Board of Trustees and on the medical staff. By 1909, he was ready and requested an audience with the Board of Trustees. A special meeting was held January 27, 1909. Dr. Metcalf not only told how Harper, in his estimation, should be reorganized, but he also laid before the trustees a subscription list, amounting to $357,000 to be used for expansion under his direction. Among the subscribers were E. L. Ford and family ($100,000); J. L. Hudson ($50,000); Joseph Boyer ($25,000); the Buhl estate ($50,000); L. W. Bowen ($25,000); Henry Ford ($25,000), and other pledges in lesser amounts from other prominent people. Altogether, there were 24 subscribers.[21]

With the backing that Metcalf had, it is not entirely clear why his plan fell through, but the Harper trustees finally turned it down. It may have been largely the pressure of the medical staff under Dr. Carstens which was responsible. The "old guard" was potent and influential. On March 8, 1909, Carstens was instructed to "harmonize the ideas of Dr. Metcalf and the Medical Board." [22] The Carstens' faction, however, had its own plan for reorganization, and neither that group nor Metcalf was in the mood for compromise. Apparently, a majority of the trustees looked with favor upon the staff plan. At any rate, Metcalf lost; the staff plan, with modifications which included some of Metcalf's ideas, was adopted on November 11, 1909. At that meeting, the minutes note that "The request of Dr. W. F. Metcalf for no further appointments on the medical staff was accepted, and the secretary instructed to notify him." * [23]

Picking up what pieces he could, and still with sizeable public and financial support, Metcalf and his backers, including several Harper staff men, organized the Detroit General Hospital. Land was purchased at West Grand Boulevard and Hamilton. Buildings, providing about fifty beds, were put up in 1911. Detroit General was a privately owned and operated hospital. Without any substantial endowment, financial difficulties were soon encountered. Fund raising lagged. By 1914, the hospital was in difficulties. Henry Ford provided the solution. He offered to assume all debts and obligations and take over the operation of the institution. His proposal was accepted, and on October 1, 1915, Detroit General Hospital became the Henry Ford Hospital. In 1917, construction was begun on the present main, in-patient building.[24] In 1916, prior to the beginning of the Ford expansion, there were serious discussions of an amalgamation with Harper to form the Harper General Hospital. Although this plan had the strong support of James Couzens, it never came into being because of legal obstacles.

When the Metcalf bubble burst, the Harper trustees had to fall back on their own resources in order to enlarge the Hospital. The financial outlook was by no means entirely bleak. Over the years, there had been gifts and bequests of varying sizes, and both the endowment fund and the money available for general purposes had increased. At the end of 1911, the total endowment amounted to $778,000. A special building fund of $350,000 had been accumulated, J. L. Hudson and C. A. Black each contributing $150,000, and Boyer and Bowen each giving $25,000.[25] A sizeable amount had been bequeathed some years earlier by Mrs. Mary Stockdale, of Flint, while other funds had come, or soon would come, from the estates of Hiram Walker, Thomas Palmer, and other prominent Detroiters. Altogether, Harper was not faring too badly, and the trustees felt justified, at their February 8, 1910 meeting, in their resolve "that the Board of Trustees proceed at once to expend the sum of $150,000 for necessary additions to the Hospital buildings." [26] If all the required money was not, at that moment, on hand, a little trust in Providence was all that was needed. Plans were prepared, and on July 25, 1911, contracts were signed and construction was ready to be started.[27] Said J. L. Hudson:

I am very happy to announce that arrangements have been made for a new Harper Hospital, which will ultimately have 600 beds. Plans are now being made for the first building which will be erected in the rear of our present main building, and will be connected with it. This new building will have accommodations for about 175 patients and will be known as the Surgical Building—all surgical cases will be taken care of in it. . . . When it is completed we will be able to take care of at least 350 patients.[28]

Work progressed, but not fast enough to suit the medical staff, which sent a note or two to the trustees, demanding to know the reason for not getting the work done faster. By November 20, 1913, it was near enough completion for the trustees to announce the grand opening for public inspection on January 1, 1914.[29]

Soon after the construction started, the trustees and all connected with the Hospital were saddened by news of the death of J. L. Hudson. He died during the summer while traveling in England. As a tribute to his memory, and in acknowledgment of his service to Harper, the new addition was named the Hudson Memorial Building.[30]

In the end, the Hudson Building cost $350,000, plus another $100,000 for furnishings and equipment. In 1913, the task of raising part of the latter amount was given to Couzens. He wasted no time; soon he was able to report he had $65,000 from 8 contributors, including himself. He gave $10,000. It is indicative of the times, and of Couzens' own associations, that all or most of the money he brought in came directly or indirectly from men who recently had made fortunes in the automobile business. The 7 others from whom he got donations were C. Harold Wills, John W. Anderson, John F. Dodge, Horace E. Dodge, Horace H. Rackham, the John S. Gray estate, and "a well known citizen." [31]

While the Hudson Building was going up, Dr. Charles G. Jennings, who had succeeded Carstens as chief of staff, had been talking to members of the Buhl family, trying to persuade them to contribute to the building of a laboratory which could also house the out-patient and other departments. Jennings' success was shown by a letter dated July 15, 1912, signed by Mrs. Theodore D. Buhl and her four children. They offered to erect a building to be known as the "Theodore D. Buhl Memorial," on the site "of the present polyclinic building." The four-story structure was to cost not more than $100,000.[32] "The first and second floors of the building," said the Buhl letter, "are to be used for a free out-door department and the fourth floor for pathology and research department." It was not so stipulated in the letter, but the third floor was turned into quarters for the interns. In 1916, Dr. Jennings presented the board with a further gift, a $50,000 trust fund made by Mrs. Theodore D. Buhl to be used for the upkeep of the Buhl Memorial.[33]

The Buhl building was completed in time so that it, too, could be shown to the public on January 1, 1914. The occasion was used to mark the Hospital's fiftieth anniversary, and the openings turned out to be quite a social event. In the receiving line was the niece of Mr. Hudson, Miss Josephine Hudson Clay, the future Mrs. Edsel Ford. Detroiters came and admired, as well they might. The Hudson Building, in particular, was the last word in hospital design, and it attracted national attention. While the Buhl building stood on the old out-patient department site, facing John R at the north end of the Hospital, the Hudson pavilion was at the rear of the main building, where the contagious hospital and the Duffield Cottage formerly stood.

Rectangular in shape, the Hudson Building extended in a north-south direction. Across the north end, like the cross on a T, was the service building, large enough to take care of a future estimated capacity of 750 patients. The surgical building consisted of 6 floors and a basement, the unit being 196 feet long by 47 feet wide. The service building was 149 feet by 57 feet. It had one story and a basement. The capacity of the Hudson pavilion was 186 patients, 66 in private rooms and 120 in wards of 4 or more beds. Each floor had its utility rooms, and on the south end of each was a solarium. A section of the roof was equipped as a place for patients to sit in good weather. The interior was finished with an eye to easy cleaning and low-cost maintenance, with terrazzo floors. Corridor floors were covered with rubber tile to reduce noise to a minimum. The service building contained the kitchen, storerooms, bakery, help's dining rooms, and diet kitchens in the basement. The first floor had provision for nurses', staff, and superintendent's dining rooms; the superintendent's office; and visiting doctors' rooms. A corridor connected both new buildings with the main Hospital, and another led to the operating building.[34]

The Buhl building was equally impressive. The main entrance from John R Street opened into a vestibule with a general waiting room beyond. In addition to this reception room, the first floor was given over to offices, laboratory, department of dermatology, nervous and children's diseases, as well as the free dispensary. The second floor was occupied by various departments. The fourth floor had special departments and the necessary equipment. The roof was fitted up with a laboratory where animals used for experimental purposes were kept. In the Buhl basement was the hydrotherapy department, along with the orthopedic department.[35] Both the Buhl and Hudson buildings continued to be important units in the Harper complex of 1963.

In 1914, Harper Hospital became the proprietor of its first branch, when the Solvay Process Company established a 105-bed industrial hospital in Delray on West Jefferson Avenue on the southwest edge of Detroit. Delray at that time was a suburb, heavily industrialized, with many manufacturing plants along West Jefferson. Later, Delray was annexed by Detroit. Solvay discovered that it was unable to operate its hospital effectively and applied to the Harper trustees, proposing that it be added to the Detroit hospital and operated as a branch. A merger was agreed upon June 23, 1914, whereby Harper acquired all of the Solvay General Hospital property. In return, Harper agreed to treat injury cases sent in by Solvay Process, its affiliated firm, Semet-Solvay Company, and other companies in the area. Physical examinations, made necessary by the nature of the Solvay operation which exposed its employees to pulmonary diseases, were to be provided for one dollar per person. Patients would be accepted on referral of the Solvay Mutual Benefit Society.[36]

The Delray hospital was renamed the Harper Hospital West Branch. Staff assignments were made by the Harper Medical Board with Dr. Arthur R. Hackett as resident physician. Because it was the nature of the branch to serve the needs of an industrial area and because it was remote from the main Hospital, it was thought wise to set up an advisory board of trustees. This was done, with executives of the leading Delray industries represented. The members were Samuel Mumford, Detroit Edison Company; George H. Barbour, Jr., Michigan Copper & Brass Company; Theodore W. Dunn, Detroit Sulphite Pulp and Paper Company; P. J. Moran, Detroit Iron & Steel Company; T. H. Simpson, Michigan Malleable Iron Company; Joseph S. Stringham, Monarch Steel Castings Company; W. S. Blauvelt, Semet-Solvay Company; J. D. Saunders, Solvay Process Company; John Searles, Detroit Copper and Brass Company; and Harry Stansfield and W. T. Harms representing the Delray municipality.[37] The Harper Hospital West Branch continued to operate in every way as a general hospital, with all the essentials including ambulance service and a nurses' training program. On December 11, 1917, Solvay Process invoked a clause in the 1914 agreement and took the hospital back, without any noticeable objections from Harper. It continued to function, thereafter, first under the name of Delray Industrial Hospital and later as Delray General Hospital.[38]

The Hudson Memorial Building was only one unit in a masterplan which Harper authorities had conceived. Ultimately, a large building on Brush Street was planned, and it was contemplated that the John R. building would be torn down and replaced. Other structures, including a new nurses' home on Brush Street, would give the Hospital a complex which would be the latest in hospital planning design and construction and would have a capacity of more than 700 beds.[39] Such a facility was needed in the early 1920's, because the city's phenomenal industrial development and population growth had not been paced by the necessary number of hospital beds. In this area, Detroit was sadly lacking. The need for more hospital facilities, particularly for the care of city cases, became apparent as early as 1903 when political leaders and newspapers began to call for action.[40] The talk then, as later, was for a municipal hospital. Detroit owned a large piece of property on Hamilton Avenue where it had built its contagious hospital. By 1913, serious thought was being given by the city administration to the erection of a city-owned and -operated general hospital on the grounds adjoining Herman Kiefer Hospital. This movement gained impetus because at this time the city was caring for more than 15,000 patients per year at public expense in private hospitals. Another crying need was for a centrally-located emergency hospital.[41]

The campaign for a municipal facility gave Harper an idea. Why not use the Harper property on Brush Street as a site, persuade the city to put up a building or two which would conform to the Harper master-plan, fill it with the city's patients, but allow Harper to handle administration and provide the medical services? At a special meeting of the trustees on February 22, 1913, this idea took form:

> Harper Hospital will build on the Hospital grounds with funds to be furnished by the city, and in conformity with the general plans of the Hospital, the Brush street unit—so called—and would undertake the care of all the city patients exclusive of contagious cases, up to the capacity of the building, all such patients to be under the care and management of the Harper Hospital; the cost to be paid by the city per patient per week to be agreed upon between the Hospital and the city authorities in the future, but not to be less than actual cost.[42]

A letter containing this offer was drafted and presented to the mayor by Trustee Joseph A. Stringham, who had political connections. The letter called attention to two problems which the city faced and offered solutions: the city should build a small but adequate emergency hospital downtown and a large general hospital for medical-surgical cases on the Harper grounds. Children's Hospital, it was pointed out, could handle all children's cases, and the two existing maternity hospitals could handle all cases in that category. It would be a waste of public funds, the letter continued, for the city to build and operate its own general hospital. The need was for wards, not for duplicated administrative expense. Given the buildings, Harper could supply the administration and provide the staff facilities. The Hamilton location, it went on, had serious drawbacks; it was too far from the center of town; it was served by inadequate transportation; and the distance from other medical facilities would tax the time and strength of visiting physicians.[43]

A week later, a supplementary letter was sent to the Board of Health. Harper suggested that a south wing of the proposed Brush Street building be erected for the care of mentally-disturbed patients at a cost of $375,000, and that the basement and two stories of the north wing be constructed with 50 beds for medical-surgical cases at a cost of $125,000. This arrangement, it was pointed out, would separate the two classes of patients and would provide a total of 190 beds which, with the children's and maternity facilities, would just about solve the city's problems. Harper requested the right to acquire future ownership of these buildings by reimbursing the city for their cost.[44] This proposal was thoroughly debated in and out of the City Hall and the newspapers. Politics became a major consideration, with the result that the Harper offer finally was rejected. Instead, the city proceeded with construction of Receiving Hospital which was opened in 1915 and enlarged in 1920 to give it a bed capacity for 560 patients. Later, too, some new facilities, including a maternity department, were added at Herman Kiefer, prior to the erection of the large tuberculosis hospital on the Hamilton Avenue site.[45]

There were, during these years of expansion, the normal personnel changes which the passage of time ordains for all institutions. Milton A. McRae, president of the Evening News Association, publishers of the *Detroit News,* had come on the Board of Trustees in 1909. Upon the death of J. L. Hudson, he was elected president, holding that post for three years until 1915, when he relinquished it to Joseph Boyer. There were changes, too, in the superintendency. Following the reorganization of 1887, when Dr. J. K. Gailey took a staff post in favor of a nonmedical man, the position was given to W. C. Bagley, at a salary of $600 a year. He remained until 1891, when poor health forced him to resign. His place was temporarily filled by M. C. Strong, "at the pleasure of the board." A permanent replacement was found in the person of A. W.

Shaw, who died in 1907 and was succeeded by the Hospital's chief clerk, Frank Moulder.

On August 9, 1910, following the medical staff reorganization of the previous year, it was felt that the staff should be better represented in the Hospital's administration. To effect that purpose, the position of medical director was created and given to Dr. Stewart Hamilton.* He and Moulder shared responsibility and jurisdiction—Moulder in charge of business administration and Hamilton in charge of medical supervision.[46] In 1913, Moulder retired, and the idea of having a non-medical man superintendent was abandoned. Dr. Wayne Smith, of St. Louis, was brought in at a salary of $416.66 per month and a house allowance of $75.00 per month. Hamilton remained as medical director until 1915, when Dr. Smith died suddenly at the age of 38. Hamilton was then named superintendent, and a new position of assistant superintendent, given to Dr. Thomas K. Gruber,* [47] was created to replace the position of medical director.

Among other comings and goings was the sad case in 1902 of two promising young men, one an assistant house physician, the other an extern. After conducting themselves in a manner which left the Board of Trustees, some of whom had not yet emerged from the Victorian era, in a condition of shock, these two juniors were dismissed for:

. . . taking out two pupil nurses, members of the Farrand Training School, late at night Saturday, April 19, and visiting with them four restaurants successively, drinking wine at each, then visiting a public dancing hall, and finally reaching Harper Hospital on their return at about one o'clock Sunday morning, April 20.

Happily, it is possible to report that the extern eventually managed to live down his disgrace and became a highly respected physician in Detroit.[48]

Of more serious concern was a sore throat epidemic in 1913 which closed the Hospital for three days to all but emergency cases. This outbreak, the cause of which could not be pinned down immediately, started in mid-July. Confined to the staff, the nurses, and employees, it quickly reached critical proportions. So many of the personnel were sick that conduct of routine operations of the Hospital was affected. On July 16, an emergency meeting of the executive committee of the staff was held. It was attended by Dr. Guy L. Kiefer, city health commissioner and also a member of the Harper staff. Every intern and nurse was ordered to have a throat culture taken, as were all persons working or eating in the basement dining rooms of the Swain Home. Superintendent Moulder was instructed to have all doors and windows screened immediately and to have all accumulated rubbish on the Hospital premises cleaned up. Dr. Kiefer expressed the opinion that the Hospital should change its milk supply source; his tests had revealed that "the milk contained a culture of pure streptococci." That appeared to be the root of the trouble, but because so many interns, nurses, and domestic employes were sick, it was thought best to close the Hospital for a few days. After that time, the epidemic was under control and normal operations were resumed.[49]

Chapter 17

THE AGE OF SPECIALIZATION

In 1906,
after three years of discussion and planning, the Harper Hospital medical staff prevailed upon the Board of Trustees to appropriate money for an entirely new and modern method of compiling case histories. Up to that time, case records were kept on a hit-or-miss basis, usually by the physician attending the case. Only the most meager details were recorded, and not enough information was always available to the teaching staff, the house physician, or the nursing staff supervising the case.[1] Modernization of the records was the prelude to a complete reorganization of the staff itself in 1909. That reorganization heralded the era of specialization at Harper.

There were several reasons why staff reorganization was necessary. One, which was as compelling as any, was the general recognition that the balance between surgery and medicine should be restored. From about the time of the opening of the John R building, the emphasis had been on surgery, and Harper had gained the reputation of being primarily a surgical hospital. Medical cases were scattered through the Hospital, and while there were staff physicians as well as surgeons, the line of demarcation was not always clearly drawn. After the turn of the century, more attention gradually came to be paid to medicine, and the profession expected a general hospital to keep abreast of the times. The staff organization of 1908 was much as it had been for forty years or more. Surgery, to some extent, had been departmentalized, but medicine had not been. The only division listed, other than general medicine, was that of contagious diseases.[2] Although agitation for more departmentalization began well ahead of 1909, it was in that year that the matter was brought

to a head by the staff. Early in March, a special committee was ready
to report to the Board of Trustees. This committee was composed of Drs.
Donald Maclean, Charles G. Jennings, Max Ballin, William R. Chittick,
and William F. Metcalf.

Metcalf, as seen, had already made his ideas known to the trustees,
the profession, and to the public generally. In a paper delivered before
the Detroit Academy of Medicine on March 9, 1909, he outlined a program which would have minimized the influence of the trustees by placing more authority in the hands of one man, the president of the board.
He would be made the real head of the hospital; the other trustees
would serve simply in an advisory capacity. Metcalf also wanted more
departmentalization, a social service department, more research, and a
medical director who would be the real head of the staff. In addition,
he called for younger men on the staff with the veterans accepting
voluntary retirement after twenty-five years. This, he pointed out, would
eliminate the evil of older staff members becoming so entrenched as to
have a virtual monopoly of free bed patients. Metcalf also opposed so-
called fee-splitting, a practice whereby a staff member, to whom a patient
was sent, would return part of his fee to the referring doctor. In this,
Metcalf was on the side of the Harper trustees who, in 1912, warned
the staff that any member "convicted of the illegal division of fees shall
be dismissed from the staff." [3] It is hardly necessary to add that in this
program, as it pertained to Harper, Metcalf envisioned himself as chief
of staff and the dominant power.[4]

Metcalf's ideas, as might be suspected, reflected a clash of personalities and ambitions. Factions had developed in the staff. There was the
"old guard," composed of Carstens, G. E. Frothingham, H. O. Walker,
Maclean, and a few others. It had been joined by the brilliant Max
Ballin * who came on the staff in 1906, largely through the influence of
Dr. Donald Maclean. These men had achieved positions of prominence
and professional standing which brought them a good deal of business.
Moreover, they represented a close affiliation with the Detroit College
of Medicine, almost all of them being on its faculty. Metcalf and his
staff friends wanted to crack this entrenchment so that they could prosper
financially and gain prestige. Thus, when the report on reorganization
was prepared, after consultation with Johns Hopkins Hospital after
whose system the new Harper plan was designed, Metcalf filed a minority report to which the staff gave very little attention.[5] He again

carried his case to the trustees, but to no avail. On December 28, 1909, the trustees adopted the staff majority report and directed that it become effective immediately after the annual meeting in 1910, at which time the staff appointments for the year were ordinarily made. When he saw he had lost, Metcalf resigned from the Harper staff.[6] There was nothing wildly visionary in Metcalf's minority report. Much of it, in fact, was sound and was adopted as part of the Harper reorganization. Where Metcalf tripped and fell was in his attempts to reduce the authority of the trustees and to displace the older members of the staff.

The table of organization which took effect in 1910 provided for five main departments: surgery; medicine; gynecology and obstetrics; eye, ear, nose, and throat; and research. These departments, which were familiar ones, were to be at least semiautonomous, each electing its own chairman, who would be a member of the executive committee along with the chief of staff. But the big change was the provision that each department would be subdivided along lines to be determined by the executive committee. Thus, the way was open to general departmentalization and, more important, to a high degree of specialization. The 1910 table of organization had a Department of General Surgery, broken into two divisions, general surgery and special surgery. Under the latter were gynecology, orthopedics, surgery of the nervous system and the thyroid gland, proctology, and genitourinary surgery. The Department of Medicine also had five divisions. They were: internal medicine, neurology, gastroenterology, infectious diseases, and dermatology. The Department of Ophthalmology and Rhino-Laryngology had two divisions: ophthalmology and otology, and rhino-laryngology. The fifth department, Pathology and Research, had three divisions: radiography (x-ray), bacteriology, and pathology.[7]

Here, then, was the blueprint by which Harper became a hospital of specialists. There was no place on this roster for the general practitioner, or at least soon there would be none. A physician who claimed internal medicine as his specialty would not be expected also to be an expert in obstetrics. It soon became necessary for a staff member to qualify in one of the specialties and establish his qualifications in his selected field by membership in one of the "colleges" or "academies."

The new arrangement had hardly gone into effect when certain groups within the staff began to make the most of it. Their principal effort, which was successful, was to restore medicine to its proper place and lay the groundwork for Harper's later achievements in internal medicine. Behind this move were Charles G. Jennings, first chairman of the new medical executive committee, and Dr. E. W. Haass. Between them, they talked the trustees into renovating the fourth floor of the John R building at a cost of $5,000 and using the space to install Harper's first exclusively medical division with beds for 22 patients. Under Jennings and Haass, the division of internal medicine and the other medical divisions assumed great importance. In time, the work was carried on and augmented under Dr. Hugo A. Freund,* one of the great names in internal medicine.[8] How well this shift in emphasis worked out, and how much it meant to Harper, can be seen by the Hospital reports. In 1909, the number of medical cases was 874; in 1920, it had increased to 2,109.[9]

Another innovation under the 1909 reorganization plan was the provision for the new post of medical director. The man holding this position was to be to the staff what the superintendent was to the Hospital at large—an administrator and co-ordinator. The place was offered to a Dr. Burligham of the Massachusetts General Hospital, at a salary of $3,000. He turned it down, whereupon it was given to a young Harper surgeon of promise who also had a flair for administration —Dr. Stewart Hamilton.[10] The effect of the reorganization became evident almost immediately, and within two years, Dr. Hamilton, in his report to the trustees, stated:

Harper Hospital is known all over the country as one of the most progressive up-to-date hospitals in America. The medical men connected with it are of high standing and splendid reputation, and have made the Hospital one of the best in the land. With our new buildings—splendidly constructed, carefully planned and with every modern hospital convenience— we will be a greater blessing than ever to Detroit.[11]

The staff reorganization of 1909 created serious dissension, and the furor drew public attention that was not wholly favorable to the Hospital.

The reorganization and departmentalization added many new members to the staff, men who were specialists in their respective fields. As the staff grew, so did the demand for beds, for these men sought to have their cases admitted. It was not long before the John R building and later the Hudson pavilion were bursting at the seams. It was not at all unusual to find every bed filled and waiting lists for admissions. As this situation developed, the staff members, claiming priority, became resentful of the general practitioners and other outsiders who, as a matter of courtesy under the policy of 1893, were permitted to bring their patients into the Hospital. The first sign of resentment from the regular staff was officially noted in 1911, when the executive committee requested a change in policy, demanding that free bed patients, customarily brought in by family doctors, thereafter be turned over to the attending staff.

Doctors that do not regularly attend the Hospital get patients in that way and often the patient is a friend of a friend who knows the endower of the bed who had no interest in the patient at all. On two different occasions physicians operated here that otherwise would not have been given time or room.[12]

Harper Hospital was under contract with railroads and insurance companies to care for their patients, and these were ordinarily looked after by company doctors who were not always regular staff members. It was demanded that these cases, too, be assigned to the attending staff. Finally, the staff executive committee proposed that Harper be closed to all except staff cases when the Hospital was crowded.

This policy was not adopted until 1919, when the competition for beds had intensified. The staff had continued to grow, and conditions had become more critical because of the post-World War I influenza epidemic, which was sweeping across the country and putting a premium on beds in all hospitals. At Harper, there simply weren't enough to take care of the patients being brought in both by the staff and the city's general practitioners. The result was that on February 25, 1919, a trustees' committee recommended to the board "that at an early date we change the policy of the Hospital from an open to a closed Hospital."[13] This was a serious step, not to be taken lightly. It was not until April 8, 1919 that the board became "satisfied that the appropriate time has arrived"[14] to make Harper a "closed" hospital, and the superintendent was instructed to admit no patients of doctors not on the staff when accommodations were needed for staff cases. Less than a month later, the trustees' executive committee reported that the new policy "is working out in a thoroughly satisfactory manner, and that we have no intentions of changing this policy."[15]

The final clause of that statement indicates recognition of the wave of criticism that had erupted. The general practitioners of the city were up in arms, and their resentment carried over to the general public. For the time being, Harper Hospital was decidedly on the defensive. The Wayne County Medical Society led the attack which became so vitriolic that the trustees felt constrained to explain their position.

Although the Hospital has heretofore been operated as an "open" hospital, this has not meant that any physician could take patients to Harper Hospital and treat the case. The Hospital has always had to recognize the obligation toward each and every patient; and it has, therefore, been the custom to leave to the discretion of the Superintendent, backed up by the Medical Executive Committee, and the Executive Committee of the Trustees, the eliminating of all men about whose qualifications there was the slightest doubt. . . .

A "closed" hospital is one in which the practice of medicine and surgery is limited to those physicians and surgeons who are officially appointed by the Board of Trustees as members of the staff. It has been the aim of Harper Hospital at all times to secure the best men available for the various services in order that the Hospital itself might discharge the obligation which it assumes toward the public. . . .

All members of the staff and of the Executive Committee serve the Hospital without pay and the amount of free work done annually represents a very large sum of money from the standpoint of the value of professional services rendered. Members of the staff are really entitled to special consideration in view of the gratuitous service they render. . . .

Harper Hospital desires to render to the public the best service that can be developed in its particular field and the trustees firmly believe the "closed" policy will not only result in a better service to the public but will enable the hospital to discharge other duties in respect to teaching and research work which will also be of benefit to the community.[16]

Despite the logic behind this declaration, the general practitioners were not satisfied. Neither was a faction within the Hospital staff, lead by Dr. Angus McLean, assistant chief of staff. The criticism did not lessen. At one of the largest meetings ever held by the Wayne County Medical Society, a resolution passed condemning the Harper action. This was done despite a spirited defense by Dr. Max Ballin, who insisted that the change in policy meant nothing because Harper was full all the time anyway, and that making it a closed hospital in no way affected the shortage of hospital beds in Detroit. The flu epidemic had filled every bed—the meeting digressed long enough to discuss erecting temporary barracks for flu cases.[17]

It might not be out of order at this point to define the terms "open" and "closed" hospital. The terms were loosely used and subject to misunderstanding. The modern definition of a "closed" hospital is one that is privately owned and operated with a salaried staff. It receives no patients, either staff or referred, except those who apply directly for admittance. An "open" hospital is generally a tax-supported institution in which all qualified physicians of the community have access. Harper, in 1919 as well as in 1963, might better be called a "staff" hospital. There was nothing new or revolutionary in the trustees' action in 1919. The policy they adopted was in common use, probably in the majority of the nation's leading hospitals. Harper Hospital considers itself a "closed" hospital, in that no doctor may admit or attend patients until he has been appointed by the Board of Trustees to the "attending" staff.

But people in Detroit were too worked up to consider definitions. Politics was injected when Trustee James Couzens, then mayor of Detroit, used his official office to reply to the Wayne County Medical Society. Angus McLean angrily resigned from the staff, thereby ending a valuable association of about thirty years' standing.[18] At the state capitol in Lansing, a bill was introduced into the 1921 session which, if passed, would have banned all closed hospitals in Michigan. Legislative hearings were conducted, and some of the testimony was unfairly slanted. One witness, a Detroit clubwoman, charged that some of Harper's wards had been closed, not pausing to realize that the Hospital itself had been hit by the flu epidemic, and that temporarily so many nurses and employees were sick that the Hospital could not be operated at maximum capacity. The sponsor of the bill, Senator O. G. Johnson, of Fostoria, Michigan, himself a physician, stated that Harper was overcharging its patients and neglecting charity cases under the closed system.[19] Stung by such irresponsible charges, Richard H. Webber, president of the Board of Trustees, could contain himself no longer. He rose to his feet angrily, pointed a finger at Senator Johnson, and shouted: "Senator, you have not yet made a statement about Harper Hospital that is true."[20] The closed-hospital bill failed to pass, but unfavorable publicity had caused considerable damage. "Our hospital," said a *Bulletin* editorial in 1921, "has suffered somewhat from unjust attacks on its motives and methods."[21] But time, as it has a way of doing, eventually soothed wounded feelings and wiped out animosities. A rational perspective was restored, and in 1923 the *Harper Bulletin* could loftily remark that "Henry Ford Hospital is the only closed hospital in Michigan." [22]

The strength and value of the new staff organization—which was fundamentally that in effect in 1963—were in its fluidity and its ability to adapt to new conditions and to keep up with the progress in medical science. The framework remained much the same through the following years. But new divisions were added when need called for them—and others were dropped, or combined, when it was clearly advantageous to do so. Thus, in 1913, obstetrics was made a division separate from gynecology. The following year, under the Department of Medicine, a division of pediatrics was established. Others came along in later years, though not always to be permanent. There was added the Division of Radium Therapy (Department of Pathology) in 1919. In that year, too, a Division of Anesthesia was added. In 1920, there was a Division of Oral and Dental Surgery. Acknowledging the new technical era of industry in Detroit, a Division of Industrial Surgery was formed in 1924. Four years later, the Department of Surgery gained a new Division of Thoracic Surgery, and in 1930 the Division of Psychiatry was added to the Department of Medicine, followed the next year by a Surgical Division of Neuro-Surgery. The year 1947 saw the formation of a Division of Cardiology, under Medicine. In virtually every instance, the emergence of these various new divisions was a reflection of the high professional skills of one or two men specializing in that particular field. Such divisions usually attained preëminence because of the force of character of an individual, usually the chairman, whose reputation and administrative capacity combined to bring to public and professional attention the particular type of work being done. An example might be the significant accomplishments in obstetrics and gynecology which, in 1921, again were combined as a single division.

Much of what was done at Harper can be attributed to the leadership of Dr. George A. Kamperman.* Harper had its noted gynecologists and obstetricians from the time it first opened its doors—such men as Howard Longyear, W. F. Metcalf, Benjamin R. Schenck, J. H. Carstens, W. P. Manton, John Bell, and Ernest K. Cullen. The last of these, who was Johns Hopkins trained, returned from military service in 1919 to resume his place as head of the Division of Gynecology, and Kamperman, a University of Michigan product, became head of the Division of Obstetrics. Following the death of Cullen in 1922, the Department of Obstetrics and Gynecology was taken over by Kamperman, who was described as "no easy taskmaster." He completely reorganized the two divisions, placing particular emphasis upon training and building up a staff of specialists. Within a very short time, the department had outgrown its hospital accommodations, and new and more adequate ones were obtained. A special labor ward was set up, consisting of six or seven beds, and as one disciple of Dr. Kamperman observed, "one can imagine the din and confusion with so many in active labor." From time to time, through Kamperman's influence, new facilities were frequently added. The result was to demolish that often-heard remark that the rarest thing in Detroit is a native-born Detroiter. "When the final history of obstetrics and gynecology at Harper Hospital is written," it was said in a tribute to the "chief," "the influence of George Kamperman, who fostered the present era, will prove to be one of its most brilliant chapters." [23]

Pediatrics was another division which had a remarkable growth, paralleling, as is perhaps natural, that of obstetrics. This division, too, reflects the trend toward specialization which developed so rapidly about the time of World War I. On July 1, 1919, the executive committee of the Board of Trustees stated:

At a meeting of the Executive Committee of the Medical Board of Harper Hospital, held June 23, 1919, it was brought to the committee's attention that the new quarters for the Pediatric Department would soon be ready for occupancy. The Pediatric Department at present has no particular organization so far as staff is concerned. Therefore, it is recommended to the Board of Trustees of this Hospital that in order to care for this department, Dr. R. B. Hoobler be appointed acting head of this department for the remainder of this year; and that the present staff of the Pediatric Department of the Out-Patient Clinic be appointed acting assistants in this department of the Hospital. . . .[24]

So successfully did this turn out that, in 1926, Dr. Hugo Freund, chief of the Department of Internal Medicine, was able to point out that "this department has grown rapidly, in the number of patients cared for, in the quality of work done, and in the results achieved." [25] In June, 1930, a group of pediatricians from all over the United States, meeting at Harper, organized the American Academy of Pediatrics.[26]

Another important function at Harper, as at any modern hospital, is that which comprises pathology, research, and x-ray, the handmaidens of science. The origins of pathology at Harper may be traced back to about 1876, when Dr. Longyear browbeat a reluctant Board of Trustees into spending $125 for a microscope. To the trustees, this was a wanton waste of money for a gadget for which they could see no earthly practical use.[27] For many years after that, pathology was pretty much a stepchild, the laboratories being located in whatever closet was not, at the moment, being utilized for more important things, such as storing mops and brooms. Often there was no regular pathologist, the work being done by the physicians themselves, or by senior medical students. Then, in February, 1889, a microscopical laboratory was set up under Dr. George Duffield, who was able to report that during 1889 a total of 252 examinations was made. In the first six months of 1890, there were 81 examinations of urine, 34 of sputum, and 20 of pathological tissues. Regardless of the importance of his work, pathology was only a side line with Duffield.[28]

This continued to be the general situation until 1899, when the staff requested that the services of a paid, full-time pathologist be obtained.[29] His services were not immediately forthcoming. Instead, beginning about 1902 and continuing for the next six years, laboratory work was farmed out on contract to the Detroit Clinical Laboratory, a private concern in which several medical men, including some of the Harper staff, had a financial interest. Eventually, the trustees became convinced that this work could be better and more economically done by the Hospital. As a result, in 1908, Dr. Joseph Sill was hired as the first regular pathologist, and the emergency operating room was converted into a laboratory which served until the Buhl laboratory building was opened.[30] After that, pathology at Harper began to achieve the status which it deserved, coming into full flower under Dr. Plinn F. Morse,* one of the truly great men in the field of pathology and research. Of him, it was said that:

His supreme forte is analytical thought, in which exercise he invariably displays a high degree of judicial acumen. A life time of study and research has given him that scholastic background which is the salvation of any worker in a special field.[31]

Pathology, under Dr. Morse, was largely a one-man operation, until 1925, when a residency was established and Dr. Hayden Palmer accepted the post. As the department grew, there was built up a staff of chemists, bacteriologists, microscopists, and physiologists.

Plinn Morse's relationship to research was much the same as it was toward pathology. He became a member of the staff in 1913, and in 1914 succeeded Dr. Sill as pathologist-in-chief, a position he held until 1958 when he retired to consultant status. It was said of him that he was primarily a "clinical pathologist," and his interest in research was "clinical" as well. As a consequence, Harper stressed clinical as opposed to basic research.

Research as it is carried on at Harper has been a sometime thing, depending upon facilities available and the time and interest of staff members. In 1939, Trustee Richard H. Webber pointed out that, while Harper had always done some research, "we are not so set up that we can do much research; our job is to take care of patients, teach nurses and teach internes, and do a limited amount of research such as our finances permit." It would be wrong to assume from this that research was being minimized, because, under the leadership of Dr. Morse, significant research contributions were made. The laboratory and staff personnel was early described as "an invaluable part of Harper Hospital and an example for such departments throughout the country." *

The construction of the Buhl building provided facilities which had been sorely lacking before. It enabled the Pathology and Research Division to report that:

. . . an average monthly shipment of 45–50 guinea pigs is needed to provide the laboratory with materials for routine work and research. Some research is being done practically all the time by the technicians and the Hospital residents. The laboratory is available to any member of the staff who wishes to prosecute any line of research.[32]

In 1925, the "Animal Lab" was set up on the roof of the Buhl building, and animals, including dogs, rabbits, guinea pigs, and rats, began to be used for research as well as for regular laboratory purposes. In a booklet which the Hospital published the following year as a fund-raising aid, the work of the Research Department was described in a short paragraph:

Cancer, pellagra, tuberculosis, and bone tumors are the four subjects upon which special research work is being done at present, in addition to the routine work on all current forms of disease.[33]

As the years passed, the list of projects grew much longer. Out of the Harper research laboratories, sometimes in collaboration with other medical, pharmaceutical, and industrial concerns, came many a contribution to the advancement of medical science. Some proved to be of classical quality, attracting wide attention and winning recognition and professional honors for Harper researchers.*

Early in the present century one of the most important aids to medical science for diagnosis and therapy was put in use at Harper—the x-ray. The Hospital's acquisition of this device did not long follow its discovery in 1895 by a German physicist, Wilhelm Conrad Roentgen, who admittedly knew so little about it that he called it the x (for unknown quantity)-ray. But others quickly found its potential, and within a year or two, it was in wide use. The first x-ray pictures made in Michigan were taken by neither a physician nor a physicist, but by a handyman at the county infirmary at Eloise. He was Stanislos M. Keenan, who possessed the knack for putting together electrical gadgets and who built an x-ray machine with which he took the first pictures on April 26, 1896.[34] The value of his work was instantly recognized, and for some time thereafter all local x-ray work was done at Eloise. Dr. Louis J. Hirschman recalled that around the turn of the century he would take his patients on the interurban cars out to Eloise to have them photographed by Keenan.[35]

Soon doctors began either to build or buy x-ray machines which they installed in their offices, and the results they obtained were highly encouraging. One of the first recorded uses of x-ray in Detroit was to locate the position of two revolver bullets which a Mrs. George Puyton fired into her head in a suicide attempt. She was taken to the office of Dr. P. M. Campbell, 25 Washington Boulevard, and x-rayed. An exposure of eight minutes clearly revealed the location of the slugs, enabling a surgeon to operate—with what results is not known.[36]

Harper acquired its first equipment in 1901, when Dr. H. R. Varney was listed on the staff as the "skyographist," skyography being a term then used for x-ray. Varney was a dermatologist and, according to Hirschman, used his machine to treat skin diseases.[37] He must have been fairly successful because in 1902 a local newspaper carried an item which stated that "x-rays are destroying cancers at Harper Hospital Clinic. . . . The power of x-rays seems almost limitless, and their use for destroying cancer will give hope to thousands who suffer with the dread malady." [38] In the Hospital's annual report for 1902, Varney was listed as "radiographist and radiotherapist." In 1903, the report of the "skyographist" showed 389 "treatments," 17 "radiographs" taken, and 22 "fluoroscopic examinations made." The chief of staff, Dr. Carstens, reviewing the record, promised that "this line of treatment will undoubtedly be very much increased." [39] The promise was made good; 1,718 x-ray treatments were given in 1904, with 44 radiographs, and 63 fluoroscopic examinations made. [40]

Then, in 1909, Harper's x-ray work came under the direction of an acknowledged master of the art, Dr. Preston M. Hickey. Appointed to the staff as a house physician in 1892, immediately following graduation from the Detroit College of Medicine, Hickey first interested himself in surgery and pathology. In 1909, he was made roentgenologist at Harper. Hickey proved to be a scientist of unusual ability, and is today recognized as one of the truly great pioneers in the field of roentgenology. He served in World War I as consulting roentgenologist to the Army Medical Corps in France. Soon after his return from France in 1920, he resigned from the Harper staff to become head of the department of roentgenology at the Medical School of the University of Michigan. [41] In 1925, it was stated that Dr. Hickey "is responsible for the development at Harper Hospital of what is recognized as one of the finest and most complete x-ray departments of any hospital in the world." [42] Apparently Dr. Hickey purchased his own equipment which was installed in the Hospital and operated on a "concession" basis. At least, the trustees reported in 1915 that "Dr. P. M. Hickey has agreed to bear all the expense of maintaining the x-ray department and further agreed to put in the additional equipment." [43] After Hickey left Harper in 1922, Dr. W. A. Evans became chief of the division of roentgenology, with Dr. Lawrence Reynolds associate roentgenologist. The concession arrangement was carried on under Evans, until his death in 1940; after that, Reynolds and others took over as Lawrence Reynolds and Associates, an enterprise which continued under that name after Reynolds' death in 1961.*

A new machine, capable of delivering 280,000 volts and permitting two treatments at a time, was installed in 1922. The Hospital announced upon acquisition of this equipment, used for deep therapy, that

. . . the results which have been obtained with the more intensive radiation treatment justify the hope that the profession has now an effective therapeutic measure for the cure of at least *some* of the different types of carcinoma. [44]

Two years later, there was a complaint that "the Hospital is losing an opportunity in not carrying on cancer research."[45] Dr. Evans saw deep therapy as a means of providing "decided relief" for cancer sufferers and anticipated further growth of that type of work. His prediction was borne out in 1933 when Harper obtained a 1,500,000 volt capacity machine, the largest ever installed in North America up to that time. The cost was $50,000.[46] Some years earlier, in 1911, Harper received a $100,000 legacy from the estate of Charles S. Chase.* This money was to be devoted to cancer research, and was known as the Chase Cancer Research Fund. A decade later, the trustees tapped this fund for $10,000 to purchase the Hospital's first radium.[47] Then, on January 17, 1947, Harper moved into the atomic age when it obtained isotopes from the Oak Ridge, Tennessee atomic energy plant. These have been used for investigation of thyroid metabolism and physiological functions.

All of this departmentalization, specialization, new techniques, and scientific equipment resulted in a marked decrease in the average stay of a patient in the Hospital. Back in the 1880's, a patient entering Harper might reasonably expect to remain three weeks or longer. But in 1951, that had materially changed. It was stated in the trustees' minutes,

> It is worthy of note that the average stay of a patient in this Hospital is 7.5 days. This is the shortest average stay we have been able to find in hospitals of comparable size throughout the country, indicating that, in spite of the apparent shortage, our beds are being utilized to the fullest extent.[48]

While Harper was undergoing these many changes and advancements, it also maintained a constantly rising educational level. As in other hospitals, the development of the intern service at Harper is comparatively recent. Originally, the young doctors, who were added to the staff to gain practical experience, were called "house physicians" or members of the "house staff." Gradually, they began to be divided into "seniors" and "assistants," the former being comparable in position to the residents, the latter to the interns. The difference was in the fact that the house juniors, comparable to present-day interns, just joining the staff after one or two years, and sometimes less, of formal medical school education, were, unlike interns, full-fledged physicians and surgeons, licensed to practice. Not until 1890 was something like the present residency system established at Johns Hopkins. It was soon followed at Harper. The number of "house staff assistants" (they continued to be

20. DR. LAWRENCE REYNOLDS — Few men possessed a wider range of interests than Dr. Reynolds, scientist and bibliophile. A native of Alabama, he became an internationally known radiologist. He joined the Harper staff in the early 1920's and served as chief of staff and chief of the department of radiology. For 17 years prior to his death in 1961, he was a member of the Detroit Library Commission. *courtesy Harper Hospital*

21. DR. PLINN F. MORSE — A man of "encyclopedic knowledge," Dr. Morse directed the Hospital's laboratory and research department for 45 years. In the field of pathology, he gained wide recognition, not only as a scientist, but also as a teacher. *courtesy Harper Hospital*

22. Exterior, Base Hospital No. 17 — Harper's World War I unit left Detroit on July 13, 1917 for duty at American Base Hospital No. 17 at Dijon, France. It returned in March, 1919.   *courtesy Harper Hospital*

23. Interior, Base Hospital, No. 17 — Hundreds of Allied soldiers received treatment at Base Hospital No. 17 in Dijon, France. Emily A. McLaughlin, who served as principal of the Farrand School for Nurses from 1913-1927, is seen in the center; Harper nurse Mamie Du Paul is shown in aisle at right next to Dr. Angus McLean, who commanded the Harper unit.   *courtesy Harper Hospital*

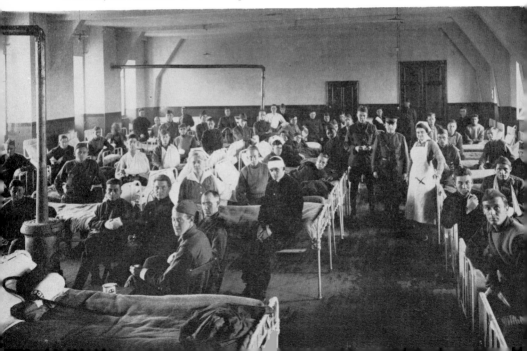

called that at Harper until about 1909) appointed for one year continued to increase as the Hospital grew.

Back in the early days of the army barracks, there were but one or two, and even these were not always subject to annual appointment, but stayed on for indefinite periods. In 1899, there were four juniors and one senior, and in 1900 an additional "assistant" was appointed. Regularly thereafter, the house staff grew each year by one or more appointments, until in 1909, eleven interns were named. That was the first year in which the term "intern" was officially used, although for three or four years prior to that time, the designation was sometimes applied, but informally. Beginning in 1902, externs were designated as such, the list usually supplying the following year's "interns" or house physicians. In 1905, an experiment was tried. Half of the new additions were appointed for two years. This procedure was followed intermittently until 1911, when the one-year term became permanent policy. By 1916, when the new Hudson pavilion was open and departmentalization had become a way of life at Harper, there were thirty-seven interns. In 1924, the intern service—residents and interns—totaled fifty. It is interesting to note how far Harper had departed by that time from limiting its house staff to Detroit College of Medicine graduates. That policy was changed in 1891 to admit "outside" interns. In 1924, nine of the fifty appointees were from Canadian schools. Of the others, seventeen were from the University of Michigan; three from Harvard; two from Northwestern; and only five from Detroit College of Medicine. Other medical schools represented were Johns Hopkins, Ohio State, Rush, Pennsylvania, Boston University, Syracuse, Illinois, Indiana, and Vanderbilt. In 1962, there were 28 interns and 77 residents appointed to the staff.[49]

In 1922, Dr. J. W. Vaughan stated it was his belief "that Harper Hospital is now turning out surgical interns better prepared to serve the public than is the case with any other hospital."[50] Granting the accuracy of that claim, there was room for further improvements. A new state law became effective in 1923, requiring a budding physician to spend one year as an intern after a four-year medical school course, in order to obtain a license to practice in Michigan. In order to adapt to what became known as "the fifth year law," Harper expanded its training.[51] "A program has been laid out to give these young physicians a complete course in all branches of medicine, as required by law," the Hospital announced. "We have established connections with the Herman Kiefer Hospital, which will give us facilities for training these young men in internal medicine and obstetrics to a much greater extent than our limited facilities in these fields will allow." [52] Clinical facilities were also used at Children's Hospital.

"The interns have access to all private as well as staff cases including Out-Patient," the Hospital *Bulletin* said in describing the Harper internship.

The junior intern takes all histories and does the routine physical examination on each patient at time of admission. He does his own routine hall laboratory work and acts as second assistant at all operations and as first assistant at many owing to the preponderance of surgical work at Harper.

To conform with the Michigan State Law which requires a rotating service for the Junior year in medicine, surgery, pathology, obstetrics and gynecology, the intern service at this institution is arranged so that the first year men rotate on these services. Each man receives approximately six months on surgery, four months on medicine and pathology, and two months on obstetrics and gynecology. The services at Harper Hospital include surgery, medicine, obstetrics and gynecology, eye, ear, nose and throat, urology, proctology, orthopedics and X-ray. The services at the Herman Kiefer Hospital give obstetrics, tuberculosis, diphtheria, scarlet fever and mixed infections. The services at Children's Hospital of Michigan include medicine (infants and two services of older children), surgery, orthopedics, and eye, ear, nose and throat.[53]

Professional education did not end with the interns. In 1922, Dr. George E. Frothingham proposed an extension course for "some" interns to train them in specialties under the direct supervision of the chiefs of the various departments.[54] Dr. Max Ballin took up where Frothingham left off and, as chief of staff, agitated for regular postgraduate courses which he was successful in getting started in November, 1923. At that time Dr. Freund conducted a month-long review of diagnostic and therapeutic methods in internal medicine. These classes were conducted daily from 8:30 A.M. to noon. Similar courses for practitioners were given in early 1924 in surgery under Ballin, and in eye, ear, nose, and throat by Frothingham.[55] Ballin considered the results to have been so successful that in April, 1924 he recommended the establishment of a postgraduate school on a permanent basis as a means of keeping "the real hospital standard of Harper at its proper level." [56] No hospital, Ballin stated later, "fulfills its full function unless every reasonable attempt is made to use its facilities for promoting the progress of medicine and surgery." [57] The courses begun in 1923 continued through 1925 when, despite there being more applicants than could be admitted to the courses, the program gradually died. The reason, it was explained, was because of lack of time on the part of the department chiefs and others to whom responsibility for conducting the courses was given. In time the idea was revived, but it was conducted under the auspices of the state's medical schools in co-operation with professional societies.

A teaching arrangement of great significance was made in 1953 when Wayne University's College of Medicine, which had its origins at Harper as the old Detroit Medical College, returned to the fold, and the Hospital once more became a teaching unit for undergraduates. This plan was being discussed in 1936 and was approved then in principle by the medical staff and the trustees. Considerable thought also was given at that time to an affiliation for postgraduate teaching.[58] Not until 1953, however, was approval definitely given to an association with Wayne for the training of residents and interns. The director was authorized to proceed with the necessary arrangements, and the plan was spelled out in some detail when the trustees adopted a resolution, stating in part: [59]

Recognizing that the Medical Staff of Harper Hospital and the faculty of the College of Medicine of Wayne University have in their respective areas traditionally upheld the highest standards in medical care, education and research, and believing that the best interests of the community they serve lie in a close collaboration of the two institutions . . .

it was agreed that the dean of the college would become a member ex-officio of the executive committee of the medical staff, and the director of the Hospital a member ex officio of the college's administration committee. The administration committee also was to be given the right to review applicants for appointment to the medical staff.[60] This agreement, although never rescinded, was not followed to the letter, according to Dean Gordon H. Scott, of the college. Later, close collaboration in other areas, he stated, made strict adherence to the terms of the resolution of 1953 unnecessary. The intent of the resolution, however, was observed. The affiliation took real form in 1958 when a forty-two-bed teaching ward in internal medicine was set up in the Hospital under the supervision of a full-time Wayne faculty member. Since then, clinical resources at Harper have been increasingly at the disposal of the medical school.[61]

Another important educational program is the dietetic internship, conducted by the Dietetics Department. One of the earliest in the United States, the first class of three was graduated in 1932. In 1946 the Hospital also initiated an administrative residency program for hospital administrators. George E. Cartmill, who in 1963 was the Hospital's director, was the first administrative resident under this program.

Finding itself thrust into the new industrial age in the early part of the twentieth century, Harper Hospital discovered that it had new responsibilities to the community as a whole. This realization brought about service innovations, one of which was the creation of a Social Service Department. Social service as a professional function had its genesis in a paper, read at a staff meeting by Dr. Channing H. Stiles, attending physician to the Out-patient Department, October 18, 1912.

It seems to be the consensus of intelligent opinion that hospital social service is the next logical step in our effort to cure and prevent all kinds of disease. . . . The work for the clinic patient is only begun when the diagnosis has been made and prescription filled. A large number of these patients are partially or wholly illiterate; still greater number are careless and utterly fail to appreciate the importance of strictly carrying out the instructions of physicians or nurses. Many have home surroundings which make the following of such instructions a virtual impossibility. In view of all this it is most desirable that the worker shall be in attendance at our clinics to investigate the homes of the patients, acquaint herself with their needs, and acquire an influence over them which would insure their deriving the utmost benefit from the help which we have been able to extend to them.[62]

This program, as outlined by Dr. Stiles, also included investigation of home and family finances in an effort to determine what part of the cost of treatment, in and out of the hospital, a patient might be expected to bear.

The Stiles paper was discussed by the executive committee of the Medical Board and by the trustees, both separately and jointly. As the plan first unfolded, the Hospital was to either take over or co-ordinate the work of agencies already existing, with the financial support of the United Charities, forerunner of the United Foundation.[63] After nearly a year of consideration, however, the plan narrowed itself down to one which would service only Harper. The trustees on October 16, 1913, hired Miss Alice H. Walker as director of Social Service.[64] Miss Walker was a Farrand Training School graduate nurse who had done postgraduate work in Chicago. The department opened for business January 1, 1914 in the Buhl Memorial Building. There were few such hospital departments in existence at the time. One of them was at Massachusetts General Hospital. As a prototype, it was carefully studied by Harper, whose own department was modeled after it. For three years, the Social Service Department was wholly supported by the Hospital; in 1917, along with the Out-patient Department, it was included in the Detroit Community Union (another United Foundation predecessor) from which part of its support thereafter derived.[65]

So important did the Social Service Department become under the direction of Miss Walker, that in 1925 its annual report stated that

. . . the assistant superintendent of the Hospital is the medical director of the dispensary, but the management of the clinics has been delegated largely to the Social Service Department.[66]

Organization of the Department is rather different from the regulation form in that three distinct types of service center in the Social Service office —first, social casework for the hospital wards and the out-patient departments; second, the administrative work of the dispensary and third, the nursing service in the dispensary.

From time to time, the department further broadened its scope of activity. In 1926, in connection with the medical staff, a branch of the dispensary was opened and for some years supported at the Dodge Community House, a social service center in Hamtramck.[67] The department also served a highly useful educational function. Co-operating with the social service schools of the University of Michigan and Wayne State University, it provided the field work training for students.

The department underwent some reorganization in 1946 when Miss Walker retired. She was succeeded by Miss Merle Draper, who reported that

. . . with the increasing appreciation by modern medicine of the part played by social and emotional factors in the treatment of illness in all groups of patients, it seemed time that the department look toward better integration into the total hospital program. . . . The new director was relieved of responsibilities having to do with out-patient administration. . . .

The name of the department at that time was changed to Department of Medical Social Service, and more emphasis was put on giving service to the admitting department of the Hospital.[68]

In 1963, all of Harper Hospital's social service work was provided by the Rehabilitation Institute under contractual arrangement. The Institute also took over Harper's physical and occupational therapy. At the same time, Harper agreed to provide the Institute with certain services such as laundry and employee dining room facilities. The Rehabilitation Institute, Inc., which is wholly separate from the Hospital, was built on property adjoining Harper in 1957.

An expanding economy, mushrooming population, and an inflationary trend, which sent living costs spiraling upward after World War I, made it expedient to stay well, to keep out of hospitals where the bed shortage, particularly in Detroit, already was acute. These new conditions led to the establishment of diagnostic clinics which, in the case of Harper, was hailed as "a distinct step forward in the progress of this hospital." [69] It was a plan

. . . to make the resources of our Hospital widely available for a moderate charge to persons who do not belong in the free clinic and yet find regular hospital and professional charges a heavy burden.

The fact is that this group of persons comprises from 60 to 70 per cent of our total population,

the Hospital pointed out.[70]

Discussion at the staff and trustee level regarding a diagnostic clinic began about 1917, but the war prevented anything being done about it. The matter was brought up again early in 1921 by Dr. Freund, who pointed out that a few cases had been sent to Harper "for examination, opinion and treatment." Most of these cases were war veterans, referred to Harper for diagnosis by the Marine Hospital which "sent many of their more difficult cases." Soon thereafter a staff committee was appointed to examine the question of creating a diagnostic clinic. The report was favorable; the trustees gave their sanction; and on September 15, 1921, the clinic was officially opened. The announcement pointed out:

Only patients referred by physicians or surgeons will be received. A few small wards have been set aside for the accommodation of these patients.[71]

All facilities of the Hospital and its staff of specialists were made available under this plan, which included a complete physical check-up and examination, with all of the routine tests. There was a flat charge of $25.00 for this service, plus $3.50 a day for a ward bed.[72] The referring physician, usually a general practitioner and family doctor, was permitted to be present at the examination, but whether he was there or not, he received a complete report of findings and recommendations for treatment.[73]

Describing the clinic's work, the *Detroit Journal* reported as follows:

Once a patient has been sent to the clinic, a complete examination will follow, involving x-rays, Wassermann test, dental, eye, ear, nose and throat examination, etc., the services of the hospital's entire staff of specialists being at the patient's disposal. . . . This system brings within the reach of the individual of moderate means medical service which would otherwise cost upward of $150.[74]

This service not only benefited patients, but also built good will for the Hospital. After less than a month of operation, Director Hamilton told the Board of Trustees that "the Diagnostic Clinic is now an established fact. . . . From reports received, the outside physicians are very much pleased with the Clinic." [75]

Five years later, in 1926, cautious feelers were put out concerning a plan "for establishment of a general diagnostic service" available to any individual on personal application. Such a patient, admitted to a private room, would be "assigned to a group" for examinations.[76] This idea was not favorably received by the staff, either when it was first proposed, or ten years later when it was revived in somewhat different form by Dr. Freund who asked the Board of Trustees "what their attitude would be toward doing health examinations for various organizations at a blanket fee." He was told to work out all the details, put them on paper, and submit them formally.[77] What Freund had in mind was the type of diagnostic service then being given by some other hospitals, including Ford in Detroit and the Mayo Clinic in Rochester, Minnesota. Detroiters, particularly, were much interested in the Ford arrangement, and it was undoubtedly to divert attention back to Harper that prompted Freund's exploratory inquiry. Again, the matter lay dormant until 1938 when Dr. George Kamperman raised the question of an "extension of the diagnostic service," and reported that the consensus of staff opinion was against it.[78] Trustee Fred T. Murphy, himself a physician, stated that he was surprised that anyone considered favorably the acceptance of any diagnostic patient without referral from a physician. However, he added, the feeling of the staff need not be the determining factor in what was done. The decision would be based on whether or not the proposed extension would be of service to the community. Dr. Edward Spalding,* a spokesman for the staff opposition, stated that a diagnostic survey should be run as an individual affair by the physicians, and not as a hospital function.

> For years physicians have been building up their reputations, the most valuable thing they possess, and now they are being asked to merge this into the hospital.[79]

In the end, the staff prevailed, as it usually did in such matters. At least nothing more was done until 1943, when the board recognized a new economic factor—the need of preventive measures for the industrial-managerial class. The preservation of the health of business and industrial leaders was considered a social and economic necessity. Their know-how was relied on to keep local industry at a high level. It was to these men that the nation looked for production leadership in wartime. And it was on their gifts that the Hospital relied for its continued support.

In 1943, Director Hamilton reported to the trustees on the success of the recently-established clinic "for check-up of key men in various industrial organizations such as the Murray Body Company and the Briggs Manufacturing Company." [80] The popularity of the Executives' Diagnostic Clinic, as it was called, is indicated by the fact that 1,525 examinations were made in 1950, and in 1951, the number increased to 1,884.[81]

Chapter 18

FROM BRUSH STREET TO DIJON

Harper Hospital,
in a sense, was a "war baby," the institution taking form to meet the medical needs of the Civil War. From that time on, the Hospital boasted of a most honorable military tradition. Four times, altogether, Harper responded to the nation's call in times of emergency. On April 27, 1898, upon the outbreak of the Spanish-American War, the Board of Trustees sent a letter to Governor Hazen S. Pingree offering the facilities of the Hospital.

Harper Hospital having been originally a government hospital for the care of soldiers during the late rebellion, it seems meet and proper to the Board of Trustees that they should tender at this time the services of the Hospital, free of any charge, for the care and treatment of any Michigan soldiers and sailors at Island Lake Camp, on Board the *Yantic,* or en route, who are disabled, either through sickness or accident, and cannot be properly cared for with the facilities that you have at hand. Any such, presenting proper credentials, will be received at the Hospital at any time, or the ambulance will meet them at any of the depots if the superintendent is notified in season; and we also offer to sterilize and prepare any dressings and bandages that may be required while in camp.[1]

This offer was accepted and Harper became what might be termed an unofficial infirmary for the members of the state troops training at the mobilization center near Brighton. There is no record that the number of cases sent in was large, but patients are known to have been treated.

Unlike in later wars, Harper was not called upon in the Spanish-American War to organize and staff base or general hospitals. While many of the personnel saw service of one kind or another, it was on an individual, volunteer basis, with the single exception of the nurses. Several of the doctors volunteered, men such as Andrew P. Biddle, who served as surgeon for the Thirty-first Michigan Volunteer Infantry, and Victor C. Vaughan, surgeon for the Thirty-third. Some served as contract surgeons in various military hospitals, while still others, patriotically motivated, joined the armed services. Even members of the Board of Trustees rallied to the colors: Trustee Russell A. Alger was secretary of war during the conflict, while Joseph Stringham and Divie B. Duffield, both of whom later became trustees, were in the navy.

But the real story of Harper's participation is found in the records of the Farrand Training School. It was the Harper nurses who did most to represent the Hospital. Before hostilities broke out, the Farrand Alumnae Association * offered the services of its members to the surgeon general. A Hospital Corps Committee was set up through the offices of the Daughters of the American Revolution. It served as a recruitment agency and sent out a call for graduate nurses. Farrand responded immediately, and Henrietta Morrison became the first Harper nurse volunteer. She was assigned to a military hospital at Chickamauga, Georgia.[2]

Late in August, a call was received by Governor Pingree for nurses to staff a temporary hospital at Camp Wykoff, Montauk Point, Long Island, New York. Men stricken with fever, dysentery, and other tropical diseases were being sent there from Cuba. Sixteen Harper nurses immediately responded, and within a matter of hours were en route to New York, chaperoned by Hazen S. Pingree, Jr. Their arrival in New York occasioned much attention in the press of that city. One newspaper commented that "a more buxom and altogether agreeable lot of young women has not been in this town for many a day."[3] The Montauk Point hospital closed after about three weeks. Volunteers then were sought to go to Puerto Rico, and several of the Harper nurses responded. They worked in Ponce and San Juan for several weeks under undescribably bad conditions, and almost all of them sooner or later succumbed to the same tropical diseases that laid the soldiers low.[4]

Meanwhile, events were stirring in other parts of the world. In the Orient, American troops were fighting in the jungles of the Philippines in what became known as the Filipino Insurrection. Again came the call, and a nursing contingent, with several young ladies from Harper, shipped out. One Farrand nurse, Janet D. Mitchell, was transferred from the Philippines to Nagasaki, Japan, where a United States hospital had been established to care for Boxer Rebellion casualties. The work of the Farrand nurses received a glowing commendation from the army surgeon general. Of the seventy graduates of Farrand resident in Detroit in 1898, twenty-five responded to the calls for trained nurses. Among them was Miss Emily A. McLaughlin who was to render distinguished service in a later war.[5]

Back in Detroit, Harper felt the effects of the campaigns in the far corners of the earth. In 1898, it was reported that the increase in the number of soldier patients combined with a shortage of nurses taxed to the utmost the Hospital and the training school; yet, there seems to have been enough volunteer service and community interest to overcome the main obstacles. When the men of the Thirty-first Michigan, many of them fever-ridden, returned to Detroit with their disabled, they were met at the station by a string of J. L. Hudson Company delivery wagons, converted into ambulances, to transport the sick and wounded to Harper. Arranged by Trustee J. L. Hudson, those wagons all bore Harper Hospital signs in large letters. Many of the men were cared for at Harper under contract with the state at the rate of one dollar per day.[6]

By the measurement of years, the respite from war after the conflict with Spain was brief. Before very long, Harper was being called upon again to furnish its facilities and skills for the care of the battle wounded. On June 28, 1914 in Serajevo, Serbia, a town few Detroiters had ever heard of, a wild-eyed revolutionary student shot and killed Archduke Francis Ferdinand, heir to the throne of the Austro-Hungarian Empire. Within a month, Europe was in flames, and what went into the history books as World War I had begun. Before long, the United States was embroiled.

But Harper, represented by a detachment of nurses, went to war before the nation did. At the call of the Red Cross, two Farrand nurses went overseas in December, 1914, to work in the Balkans under conditions so bad they are almost impossible to describe. Another nurse, Matilda Kreuger, who had been principal of the training school from 1907 to 1913 was in charge of all nurses in this unit which was based at Salonika, Greece.[7] Later, as the war was prolonged, the call went out for doctors to assist the French and British, and some from Harper, including Drs. Henry R. Carstens, A. E. Catherwood, and Bruce C. Lockwood, worked in British military hospitals. That was prior to America's entry into the war.

While Americans kept a wary eye on developments in Europe, they were having their troubles nearer home. Unsettled relations with Mexico caused a punitive force under General John J. Pershing to be sent across the border in 1916, and various military units, including the Michigan National Guard, were mobilized and sent to Texas. Harper nurses went with them, as did one or two doctors, attached as medical officers to National Guard units.[8]

The Mexican affair was, in a sense, a training exercise for what would follow. By 1915 and 1916, far-sighted Americans knew it was almost inevitable that the United States, sooner or later, would have to enter the European war on the side of the Allies. In 1916, the American Red Cross began its preparations, and on July 5 of that year, the Harper trustees agreed to organize on paper a base hospital, eventually designated Base Hospital 17.[9] The following April, the United States declared war on Germany and began to mobilize. Base Hospital 17, the Harper unit, received its orders within a matter of days. Dr. Angus McLean, with the rank of major, was the chief medical officer, and by May 28, he had his unit organized and ready for whatever duty it might be assigned. The initial contingent of Harper doctors on its roster, twenty-one in all, included such well-known staff members, besides McLean, as Preston M. Hickey, Henry N. Torrey, Roland Parmeter, Louis J. Hirschman, and George E. McKean.[10] Others were soon added, including the assistant director, Thomas K. Gruber, who was given the post of adjutant. Colonel H. C. Coburn, a regular army officer, was placed in overall command. Harper nurses, too, were included in the unit under Emily A. McLaughlin, as chief nurse. The first contingent of Harper nurses numbered thirty-two, although ten more soon were added.[11] About the same time, a second base hospital, number 36, was being organized by the Detroit College of Medicine. It was commanded by Dr. Burt R. Shurly and was joined by several Harper staff members and nurses. By June 25, 1917, Dr. McLean, now a lieutenant colonel, reported to Washington that Base Hospital 17 was organized and ready for orders.

Meanwhile, the Hospital itself was foreseeing problems as its staff was depleted, and as it faced the then unanswered question of what additional burdens would be placed upon it in caring for both civilian and military patients. In June, 1917, space in the Buhl building was offered for physical examination of recruits, and the staff members entering military service were assured they would do so under leave of absence.[12] A month later, Superintendent Hamilton, who would himself before long don a uniform, was instructed to look into the possibility of obtaining an appropriation from the government to build an additional unit on the grounds to take care of returned soldiers.[13] Harper began to take on a warlike appearance, heightened on May 15, 1917, when the skeletonized unit formed ranks on the south grounds of the Hospital and, with a large crowd in attendance, was presented with its colors.[14] Orders finally came, and the unit left Detroit for Allentown, Pennsylvania, where it arrived July 4, the nurses proceeding to New York.[15] On Friday, July 13, 1917, the entire unit boarded the U.S.S. *Mongolia* in New York, landing at Plymouth, England. Disembarking in that historic port, it traveled by rail to Southampton and was ferried across the English Channel to Le Havre. From there it moved directly to Dijon, where it arrived July 29, 1917, the fourth American hospital unit to be assigned to duty with the American Expeditionary Force.[16]

For the Harper personnel, Dijon was a far cry from the red brick hospital building on John R Street in Detroit. The unit took over a French hospital housed in an ancient chateau-like structure, which once had been a boys' school. It was a four-storied, ell-shaped building which had been equipped by the citizens of Dijon out of their own spare household articles. It had a bed capacity of only 75, which was soon expanded to 1,800 by the addition of 14 wooden barracks. Base Hospital 17 was the first American unit in Dijon except for a detachment of bakers, and the burghers took the Yanks to their hearts. One of the first things the hospital staff had to do was clean up the town through a public health project. In the end, that effort paid off, because Base Hospital 17 had comparatively few cases of tetanus among the wounded.[17]

At first, Base Hospital 17 had few patients. To keep the staff busy, three operating teams were organized and sent close to the front where they manned advanced dressing stations. Others, both doctors and nurses, were detached and sent to help out in other military hospitals. Time hung heavy, and to relieve the tedium all kinds of entertainment was devised. At Christmas, Dr.—now Captain—Hirschman donned a makeshift Santa Claus costume and played the same role he had customarily filled in peacetime for the student nurses at the Farrand Training School.

In time, large-scale drives erupted along the fronts which the hospital was intended to serve, and by summer of 1918, it was flooded with casualties of the battles of Chateau-Thierry, the Argonne, and St. Mihiel. Its patients were both French and American soldiers. Before long, it had to expand to 2,000 beds, all of which were filled. It was said to have been the largest of the American military hospitals.[18]

Back in Detroit, Harper Hospital was having its troubles, brought about by shortages of food and coal. There was an insufficient number of doctors and nurses to handle the added duties imposed upon them. A night clinic for venereal patients, particularly women, was opened in April, 1918. Facilities were provided for the examination of Air Corps candidates,[19] and, from time to time, physicians and surgeons were called away to help out in emergencies in other domestic camps and cantonments.

Some of the medical men were uncomfortable in uniform and Clark D. Brooks,* writing from Camp Custer, expressed a rather common disenchantment with military life.

Some life. The first few days I was here, I saluted everything from privates, and even saluted myself in the shaving mirror. My arm had the St. Vitus' dance. Now I can tell the colonel from the corporal—that's about all.[20]

In 1918, a new crisis arose when the influenza epidemic swept the country and much of the world. More doctors and nurses were taken away from Harper to tend the sick in the army camps, contingents going to Camp Custer, Michigan; Camp Grant, Illinois; and Camp Dodge, Iowa. The Hospital faced a serious situation; the epidemic attacked civilians as readily as it did the soldiers and sailors.[21] "As the influenza epidemic is spreading in the country," said the trustees' executive committee, "the question of what the hospital policy should be was referred to the superintendent and Executive Committee of the Medical Board for action as to isolation, care of these patients, etc."[22] The epidemic continued into 1919, and the trustees considered the advisability of erecting temporary barracks because so many patients were seeking admittance. By that time the war was over, but the shortages were not. The trustees were prompted to ask the surgeon general to send the supplies of Base Hospitals 17 and 36 to be stored at Harper, to be used in the emergency.[23] Influenza cost Harper its only war casualties. Three nurses died: Mabel Ragan, attached to Base Hospital 17; Pansy M. Birch, at

Camp Dodge; and Irene Parr, at Camp Grant. Nurse Ragan was buried at Dijon with full military honors.[24]

But all things come to an end—even wars. The armistice was signed November 11, 1918, and the thought uppermost in the mind of every American in France was to get home as quickly as possible. Unfortunately for Base Hospital 17, its patients did not immediately recover with the firing of the last shot, and it was not until March, 1919 that the unit finally returned to the United States, landing at New York. It arrived by train in Detroit on March 11. Many of the doctors had been detached. Some had come on ahead. Colonel McLean remained behind to serve as physician to President Woodrow Wilson during his peace mission to France. A few of the Harper nurses also stayed in Europe, helping with rehabilitation work in the war-ravaged and famine-ridden areas of Rumania, Bulgaria, and Czechoslovakia.[25] But most of them came back in a body, several wearing foreign decorations. With them was the contingent from Base Hospital 36. They were given a warm public welcome, including a reception by Mayor Couzens at the City Hall.[26]

Couzens was said to have been much moved by the appearance of these dedicated women and remarked that there should be some suitable memorial to their services. Dr. Hirschman, who was on hand, and overheard what Couzens said, suggested a municipal university. According to Hirschman, Couzens, who was not college trained, snorted that there were already "too damned many universities." [27]

But very soon there was another suggestion, this one made by Dr. Freund who was Couzens' physician. As much interested in Harper as was Couzens himself (the mayor was still a trustee at this time), Freund proposed a new nurses' home. The idea appealed to Couzens, and the result was his donation of the funds to build McLaughlin Hall. The gift was a valuable one. The Swain building had long been overcrowded. As far back as 1916 the trustees had deplored "the lack of accommodations for nurses." They pointed out that having nurses housed in three different places—the Swain building, the Richmond Terrace, and the John R building—"makes supervision and necessary discipline exceedingly difficult." They acknowledged then that they were "looking into the matter of a new nurses' home." [28]

According to the recollections of James Deming Smith, the treasurer of the Hospital, Couzens sold back to Henry Ford his stock in the

Ford Motor Company about the time he decided to build a new home for the nurses. He gave a block of stock to the Hospital, but it was not immediately used. His fellow trustees thought it would increase in value if it was held. Finally, Couzens demanded to know whether or not they intended to proceed with the building.[29] If not, he would withdraw his offer. That stirred up the necessary action, and on March 9, 1921, the ground was broken, the first spadeful of sod being turned over by Miss McLaughlin.[30]

The site selected was on John R Street, at the head of Orchestra Place. This was south of the Hospital and the Swain building. Albert Kahn, the architect, visualized the structure as "the most fitting [war] memorial idea yet conceived. To the young women living within its portals it will be an ever-present reminder of the service and patriotism of their courageous associates in the Harper Overseas Unit." It was planned to be six stories in height, with accommodations for 285 nurses. Kahn promised that every effort would be made to obtain a residential, home-like atmosphere.[31] Work progressed rapidly, and in February, 1922, the home was partly occupied, although the official dedication and opening was held May 10. The total cost was said to have been $535,000.[32]

"Of the Italian Renaissance type," the *Detroit News* described it, "built of brick and trimmed with limestone . . . a six story structure shaped like an inverted U, surrounding a 75 foot court. The rear overlooks sunken gardens and tennis courts. . . ."[33] The first floor had a large reception hall, a spacious living room with a library opening off it, a business office, an apartment for the superintendent of nurses, and rooms for nurses working in admitting, Social Service, and Out-patient departments. The north wing's first floor housed the administrative quarters of the training school, with a lecture hall, two classrooms, and a laboratory. The floors above were given over mostly to sleeping rooms, some single, some double. Each of the living floors had a kitchenette. The basement provided the recreational facilities with an auditorium and gymnasium which could be thrown together to form one large hall, suitable for dances and banquets. There were also a kitchen, laundry, sewing rooms, and storage space.[34] If all of this appeared overly luxurious, it was still lacking one thing. Kahn's original plans provided for a swimming pool, but Couzens put a stop to that, with an expression of his personal philosophy. The girls who would live in the building, he said, would be from ordinary homes and would not be accustomed to such frills as a swimming pool. He declared,

It has been my observation that the chief cause of unhappiness in this world is having to do without luxuries that have come to be regarded as necessities. People can stand almost anything better than having to accept a lower scale of living. For that reason, no person should improve his standard of living until he can be fairly certain he can hold it the remainder of his life.[35]

The trustees, gratefully accepting Couzens' gift, showed their appreciation by naming the building Couzens Hall, but the philanthropist would have none of that. At the trustees' meeting on May 29, 1922, it was recorded that,

. . . Mr. Couzens requested that the motion by the board at its meeting of February 15, 1922, naming the nurses' new home "Couzens Hall" be rescinded. Mr. Couzens suggested that the nurses' home be called "McLaughlin Hall" and on motion duly supported, it was so named.[36]

In the immediate prewar and postwar periods, the number of hospital beds failed to keep up with Detroit's population growth. In an article describing the city's lag in 1920, the *Detroit Saturday Night* pointed out that "with a million people inside its borders, Detroit has only 3,556 hospital beds available for the care of its sick and maimed, one bed for every 281 inhabitants." This is a ratio of three and one-half beds per thousand of population, a ratio which put Detroit eighth in a list of the nation's leading cities—far behind such places as Boston, Cincinnati, Kansas City, and Minneapolis. "Nearly 100 patients a day, on the average, are turned away from Detroit's hospitals because of lack of beds," said the *Saturday Night*.[37]

No one was more aware of this situation than the medical staff of Harper. It was stated in the *Harper Bulletin* for April, 1924,

In Detroit at this time, we seem to have reached the peak in a shortage of hospital beds. Good! you may say, more business than can be handled! No, it is not good, it is terrible! A reflection upon responsible people who comprise our city. Except in emergencies it is necessary at Harper Hospital to wait four or five days for a hospital bed. This problem can be solved only by people of wealth—those whose great understanding and sympathy is with humanity.[38]

In 1924, the combined resources of the John R (or, as it was soon to be called, the Harper) building and the comparatively new Hudson pavilion were 450 beds. If Detroit needed more beds, the Harper trustees were more than eager to provide their proportionate share. All that was needed for expansion was money. In February, 1924, the trustees' executive committee recommended to the board

. . . that a joint committee consisting of members of the Board of Trustees and of the Medical Executive Committee be appointed to study plans and formulate a policy for the future development of Harper Hospital, number of departments, and the number of patients in each department.[39]

The matter must have been thoroughly mulled over because it was not until the following October 23 that the trustees' executive committee reported that it had held a "general round-table discussion." Out of it came a recommendation to the board that the Hospital be expanded to 650 beds. Of these, 200 were to be for medicine, 275 for surgical cases, 100 for obstetrics and gynecology, and 75 for eye, ear, nose, and throat. It also was decided that the entrance to the Hospital be changed from John R Street to Brush. These proposals meant a new building, fronting on Brush. It was to be a private-room pavilion, while the old Harper building would be turned over to staff cases. Dr. Hamilton, the director, was instructed to see Albert Kahn, the famous architect, although it was specified that the Hospital reserved the right to call in any consulting architect of its choice. The expansion plans included the rearrangement of the operating rooms and the removal of the amphitheater.[40]

Kahn not only was willing to accept the commission, but he also suggested that a committee made up of members of the Board of Trustees, the Medical Board, and the director be appointed to work with him in an advisory capacity. This was done, and the next few months were devoted to preparatory planning, but the intent of the board to go ahead with a new building was unmistakable. The quarterly *Bulletin,* issued early in 1925, stated there was much enthusiasm among the staff at the announcement of the intended construction of a new unit on Brush Street which would enable the Hospital to care for 650 patients.[41]

When it is realized that entrants to the Hospital other than in emergencies must necessarily be admitted from a waiting list, the great need for more beds can be readily understood.

During the period of preliminary planning, a Y-shaped building was discussed, but on June 16, 1925, the executive committee declared it favored "a straight building on Brush Street, and the superintendent was instructed to have the building staked out on the lot for inspection by the executive committee. . . ." [42]

Once the plans had been given approval, the money started to come in. Dr. Ballin announced the first major donation, $125,000 for the new operating rooms. It came from Mrs. Alfred G. Wilson, the former Mrs. John Dodge. [43] The estimated cost of the new building was $2,300,000, including $225,000 for equipment. Obviously, this money had to be raised by public subscription from friends of the Hospital, so in November, 1925, a fund-raising campaign was organized. A committee was appointed consisting of Trustees Murphy, Boyer, R. H. Webber, Schlotman, Browning, Oscar Webber, and Dr. Ballin. These men already had been busy soliciting support, and at the trustees' meeting at which he was made a member of the fund committee, Dr. Murphy read a letter from a donor whom he did not identify, offering a donation of $500,000 provided $1,000,000 was raised in other pledges by February 1, 1926. [44] This meant that a substantial amount was in sight before the fund-raising drive had started. Confident that the goal would be reached, the trustees proceeded to create a building fund of $2,000,000 by issuing bonds, secured by a trust mortgage to the Detroit Trust Company, covering several leasehold estates in the endowment fund. The bonds were to be retired by subscriptions. The Detroit Trust Company was made fiscal agent to receive the subscriptions, donating its services. Early in the spring of 1926, the campaign was officially launched. [45] The call for subscriptions stated:

The appeal has been made, the necessity for more hospital beds is unquestioned. Detroit—throbbing, bounding Detroit—bows her head and steps down from her commanding position of commercial supremacy into the twilight zone of business failure; she neglects to provide adequately those simple means whereby her people can help themselves.

It was not a question of charity, the appeal pointed out, but of providing beds for the average citizens

. . . who comprise the cogs in this great, mad, money-making machine. . . . Detroit cries out in distress for her people. . . . No beds are available. A small disaster would blacken Detroit's name before the world. You may be struck down today in Detroit's wild traffic, and rushed to our congested city hospital. First aid is rendered, and your family ask your transfer; an appeal to some one of our reputable institutions is made—and the reply: "We are sorry, but not a bed available." [46]

This was undistilled emotionalism, but it had its effect on the minds and hearts of Detroiters. Two hundred and twenty-nine individuals and business concerns pledged a total of $2,118,077.75 of which $2,100,872.75 was collected. This was practically accomplished by the fall of 1927 when R. H. Webber reported to the trustees that additional pledges of $300,000.00 were still needed. Albert Kahn made one of the most welcome contributions of all in November, 1927, when he informed the trustees that he had been able to scale down his original cost estimates from $2,300,000.00 to $2,217,000.00. To the fund-raisers, that was like finding $83,000.00.[47] Most of the pledges were fairly large, indicating that reliance had been placed upon Detroiters of wealth. The subscription list which has been preserved includes such well-known names as Clarence H. Booth, Walter O. Briggs, Fred M., Henry M., and Leo Butzel, Mr. and Mrs. Roy D. Chapin, A. T. Crapo, Harry B. Earhart, Mrs. Edsel Ford, Ossip Gabrilowitsch, Frank J. Hecker, Mr. and Mrs. Richard P. Joy, Alvan Macauley, Peter J. Monaghan, C. A. Newcomb, Jr., William A. Petzold, Horace H. Rackham, Mr. and Mrs. Benjamin Siegel, Mr. and Mrs. C. B. Van Dusen, Sidney D. Waldon, and Mr. and Mrs. Henry Wineman. The trustees, of course, were generously represented, with the largest single pledge—$500,000.00—coming from Mr. and Mrs. Richard H. Webber. Dozens of members of the Harper staff were on the list, some of them for sizeable amounts. Among the contributors from business and industry were Chrysler Corporation, Detroit Edison, *Detroit News,* Dodge Brothers, Inc., Fisher Brothers, General Motors, Hudson Motor Car Company, James Vernor Company, and National Twist Drill & Tool Company.[48]

Before all the pledge cards had been turned in, the bids were called for, and on June 7, 1927 the general contract was awarded to Bryant & Detwiler. Dr. S. S. Goldwater, of Mt. Sinai Hospital, New York, an authority on hospital planning, was paid $1,000 for consultant services.[49] All this was done under the immediate supervision of a trustees' building committee of which Oscar Webber was chairman, and W. R. Farrand, Joseph Boyer, and John A. Bryant were members. Considering the size of the building and all that was involved, the work progressed at a remarkably fast pace. It was June, 1927, when the work was begun, and by the following February 22, Dr. Hamilton made the encouraging report that construction was progressing very rapidly. Oscar Webber added that contracts for furnishings had been let. Five weeks later the main topic for discussion by the trustees was when to hold the formal opening. It was decided that the public would be invited to inspect the Hospital on May 16, and the patients would be moved in on Monday, May 28. From the time of the ground-breaking until the Brush Street building was ready for use, less than eleven months had elapsed.[50]

The city press was given a preview and was as laudatory as it had been when it looked at the Harper building on John R Street in 1884. The new eight-story Brush unit was described as "a hospital of innovations." The *Detroit Free Press* said:

> The new unit of Harper is odorless, soundless and its operating rooms may be called shadowless. . . . There are no creaking doors. There are none of the usual hospital smells. There are no colors or lights that will excite the eye. In its service, its cuisine and its general aspect it can truthfully claim to rival any modern hotel.
>
> There are 450 beds in the new unit. This, with the 200 available in the Hudson Memorial unit, will make a capacity of 650. Historic old Harper, which faces on John R Street, will be closed to patients and used in the future as a general service building. The new one, facing on Brush Street, is a model of pleasantness and efficiency.
>
> Whether the visitor starts at the top or bottom, he will be amazed at the complete modernity of the institution. In the basement there is a laundry, perhaps the most efficient of its kind in Detroit. On the top floor, the eighth, he will find operating rooms that are equipped with a heatless, glareless and shadowless light. All the operating rooms have a natural north light.[51]

The *Free Press* was particularly intrigued by the obstetrical department where babies were kept behind panes of vita glass, and new fathers were given a waiting room with "a telephone in it that you can call up and tell the world." Even the mothers were not overlooked. They would be "particularly pleased" by their surroundings and the facilities for their care. "The kitchen service is amazingly efficient. It is able to feed the entire unit in 30 minutes." If the press descriptions ran heavily to adjectives, they were, in this instance, excusable. The Brush building was the last word in hospital planning and construction. At the time, there was probably nothing to surpass it in the United States. The wards and private rooms were so arranged that the same types of cases could be kept on one floor, facilitating multiple nursing. Each room had its own toilet and most of the facilities for the patient's care in his room. The first floor had a spacious and attractively appointed lobby and efficient administration office layout.[52]

There was one other important matter which, in the description, fortunately was not overlooked. "The staff today," said a Harper brochure, "contains many names that are outstanding in the medical profession, and in that respect, too, it measures up to the traditions of Harper staffs in the past." [53]

A few weeks after the Brush building was in use, the trustees turned their attention to remodeling the old Harper unit, appropriating $47,000 for that purpose. The major change contemplated was to provide living quarters for house employees and an expanded educational department for student nurses. There were revisions and additions to the Hospital since the opening of the Brush building. From time to time conversion of some single to double rooms increased the bed capacity from 650 in 1928 to 701 in 1963. The remodeling of the old power plant in 1951 resulted in room for the laundry and excellent library quarters. In 1952, with funds supplied by the Greater Detroit Hospital Fund, the Murphy building, located between the Harper and Hudson buildings, was completed. Used for offices and providing quarters for such needful activities as some of the diagnostic services, this building was named in honor of Dr. Fred T. Murphy, a trustee from 1920 to 1947.

With funds contributed by the Ford Foundation, members of the board, and others, an emergency suite and ambulance drive were added in July, 1957. Located on the south side of the Hospital, with the entrance from Brady Street, the emergency suite consisted of an admitting lobby, two treatment rooms, examining cubicles, two wards accommodating seven patients, service and x-ray rooms, and a discharge lobby. The cost of this installation was $250,000.

Chapter 19

FROM DEPRESSION TO WAR

It was fortunate
that Harper Hospital was able to erect and pay for the Brush building
when it did. Had the modernization of the Hospital been delayed two
years, it might never have been built, and Harper might have slipped
into the category of a second- or third-rate institution—if it had survived
at all. It so happened that just seventeen months after the Brush building
was opened, the worst economic depression of the modern era spread a
paralyzing blight across the land. It was ushered in by the stock market
collapse of October 24, 1929, although the signs of impending trouble
had been evident for a long time. The trouble was that the United States
and most of the Western world were living in a dream of unreality in
which everyone was wildly speculating, and in which everyone thought
he was becoming rich. From the pinnacle of false, paper prosperity, the
country plunged within days to the depths of despair. The lines of eager
stock market speculators shifted from the brokers' offices to the bread
lines. Factories and businesses closed, and unemployment mounted.
No place was hit harder than Detroit, and as real estate and investment
values shrunk, sometimes to the vanishing point, institutions which
existed on endowments and the largesse of charitable-minded people
found themselves in dire straits. Harper Hospital was no exception.

Harper had known economic panic and depression before. The
panic of 1893 hit the Hospital hard. In the annual report covering that
year, it was stated:

Early in 1893 a movement was inaugurated to secure an adequate endowment, but the panic coming on put a stop to it. Depression in business
led to close economy on the part of people in general, greatly reduced the

number of paying patients and left many private rooms vacant. It is not possible to vary the expenses of the hospital from day to day to correspond with the varying number of patients.[1]

Nevertheless, the panic of 1893 was of comparatively short duration, and recovery was speedy. A year later the gloomy clouds had lifted to the extent that the Hospital was able to report that

. . . the year 1894 proved a notable one. . . . It opened with anxiety and closed with confidence as to its future. It is now assured that it will be able to do more of the charitable work for which it was in part established than has been possible for it to do in the past.[2]

Too much credit cannot be given a dedicated, hard-working staff, both professional and lay, for a willingness to accept sacrifice in time of stress. It was outstanding men on the Medical Board who, in 1893 as in the later depression, brought in enough business to keep things operating. This was recognized in 1911 by President J. L. Hudson who credited Drs. J. H. Carstens, E. L. Shurly, and H. O. Walker with making it possible for Harper to keep its doors open in the bad times of the early 1890's. "Had it not been," he said, "for the unswerving loyalty, the intense devotion and the medical and surgical skill of these three gentlemen, Harper Hospital would have gone out of existence." [3] The same kind of tribute, after recovery from the Great Depression of the 1930's, could have reasonably been paid to their successors—such men, to name a few, as Ballin, Freund, Brooks, Kamperman, Morse, and Hirschman.

Harper, around the time of World War I, was becoming a big business. Its endowments were substantial, its income largely being derived from mortgages and rents on the various properties it owned. Heavy investments had been made, first, in mortgage real estate bonds. Looking after financial affairs required closer attention than the trustees were able to give. As a result, the Detroit Trust Company was designated fiscal agent for the trust funds, and for a while—from 1916 to 1920— it even acted as corporate treasurer.[4]

The full impact of the depression was not felt immediately by the Hospital. Instead, it took the form of a creeping paralysis. Gradually, bonds were defaulted, mortgagors fell behind in their payments, forcing foreclosures, and lessees negotiated for lower rentals which, of necessity, usually were granted. In October, 1931, the trustees discussed with deep concern the losses to the general endowment fund from the sale of first mortgage bonds. They ordered a more careful scrutiny of the investment portfolio, and decided in the future to put more of the funds in listed bonds instead of mortgages. At the same time, they ordered a careful watch for economies in operation.[5]

On February 14, 1933, the depression hit its low point when Governor William A. Comstock proclaimed a bank holiday, closing all Michigan banks. Less than a month later, President Franklin D. Roosevelt extended the holiday to the entire nation. A severe financial crisis was the result, and the Harper trustees met in emergency session to determine what measures should be taken.[6] Unfortunately, sickness did not take a holiday, and while banks could be closed, hospitals could not. But patients had no cash with which to pay their bills; Harper could not pay its employees and suppliers. With Detroit banks closed, some never to reopen, there was no ready channel of credit. Detroit paid its municipal workers and creditors in scrip, and Harper eagerly accepted this when it could get it.

Funds were deposited and withdrawn from a safety deposit box by Richard H. Webber for the Board of Trustees and J. D. Smith, the treasurer, who recalled, "We did our banking out of a tin box." [7] Wages were reduced three times, and a large number of employees, particularly those who lived in the Hospital, received no wages at all. They were given board and room which put them in a preferred class, compared to many people. As much of the Hospital as possible was closed temporarily. No one entered Harper or any other hospital except in case of dire need. In July, 1933, conditions were a little better and the trustees took up the matter of paying wage arrearages. The superintendent was authorized to pay up to twenty-five per cent when he felt that could be done. It was the start of a catching-up operation.[8]

One of the tragic victims of the depression was the Farrand Training School for Nurses. It was supported, not by Hospital funds, but by gifts from interested people. That source suddenly dried up through the necessity of financial belt-tightening. At the end of 1932, the trustees held a special meeting to discuss the school's plight, but were unable to find any immediate solutions.[9] Meanwhile, the spring classes, beginning with that due to enter in 1931, had been omitted. In May, 1933, after the banks had closed, the Training School Committee reluctantly recommended that that year's September class also not be admitted. That meant, in effect, the closing down of the school after those students who had already been admitted were graduated. The last class was "capped" May 16, 1935, and thereafter there was no more Farrand Training School.[10]

The trustees did not give up immediately nor did the friends and alumnae of Farrand. Meeting in May, 1935, about graduation time, the board discussed reopening as soon as possible, but took no further action. In 1936, the trustees expressed the belief that conditions had so far improved that the school could be reactivated by funds obtained through private subscription, and moved that it be reopened on September 1, 1937.[11] Before that happened, however, Mrs. Gretter appealed to Senator Couzens in Washington for help.

It has been a burden of thought with me that you, who have proven your interest in nurses and nursing in many ways, but particularly by your munificent gifts for the building and equipping of Nurses Homes, would be open to an appeal for the pressing need that is now facing the Farrand Training School for Nurses.

The incomparably beautiful and useful building you have provided has been a great factor in furthering the prestige and standing of the School which its founders established fifty years ago, with the expressed purpose of creating a high order of nursing for Harper Hospital and for the community at large.

That aim should be maintained, and we have faith that an endowment will be forthcoming for such a laudable objective.[12]

The senator's reply was not encouraging.

I do have a feeling that a willing horse should not be overdriven. It seems that in view of all the money I have spent in behalf of nursing service, there should be people in the great City of Detroit who would be desirous of preventing what you call "a great calamity" to the Farrand Training School for Nurses. However, I am exceedingly busy and because of bad health, I expect to leave here at the end of the week for Detroit and, at least for the time being, I will have to suspend consideration of the matter. I would like to see somebody else take up the work, but if you are unable to get anyone, I am not averse to reconsidering the matter next fall.[13]

He did not reconsider the matter. Instead, when the nurses' school reopened in 1937, it was no longer the Farrand School, but the Harper Hospital Training School for Nurses—an integral part of the Hospital, supported by Hospital funds. The decision that each diploma should carry the note that the school was originally founded as a memorial to Dr. David O. Farrand provided the only link with the past.[14]

One of the by-products of the depression was the emergence of a militant labor movement. Nowhere was its effect felt more than in Michigan, where the automobile industry became tightly organized, or in Detroit, which prior to the 1930's had been a traditionally "open shop" town. All that changed, and Harper Hospital could not have claimed status as a part of the Detroit community had it, too, not been the target of an organizing effort. Prior to 1941, Harper had never experienced any serious labor troubles, but in that year, it was twice hit by walkouts on the part of non-professional employees protesting the dismissal of two workers. At that time no particular attempts had been made to unionize the Hospital's personnel. Accordingly, the strikers were not well organized and the walkouts were of only a few hours' duration each.[15] But the incidents did serve as warning signals, and the management of the Hospital took steps to forestall an organizing drive by bringing its personnel policies into line with those in private industry. On May 19, 1941, for instance, the Board of Trustees voted to set aside $1,000 per month to build up a special reserve to provide pension benefits for eligible retiring employees.[16] In 1947, the trustees petitioned Congress to exempt all non-profit hospitals from compliance with the Wagner Labor Act, the Wages and Hours Act, and similar federal legislation. The Hospital's appeal was based largely on the argument that unionization of the non-professional staff and the obligation to negotiate labor contracts could only result in increased hospital rates and higher cost of medical care for the public.[17]

As early as 1937, the United Hospital Workers Union was established in Detroit. Affiliated with the American Federation of Labor, this union was an offshoot of the Hotel, Restaurant Employees and Bartenders International Union. Its eight-point objective included union recognition as bargaining agent, a forty-eight-hour, six-day week and "reasonable" wage increases.[18] This was aimed at all hospitals, not just Harper, and in time the employees of the county and municipal hospitals were organized. Not until May, 1948, was the move made against the private hospitals, and Harper was given the distinction of being the first on the organizing list. In anticipation of this, Superintendent E. Dwight Barnett unfolded a new personnel program on April 20.

In an announcement to all employees, he stated that he had been authorized by the trustees to inaugurate a forty-hour week for all employees beginning May 1.[19]

On May 21, however, an AFL organizer called on Barnett and delivered a copy of a letter which had been sent to the State Labor Mediation Board. This letter claimed that a dispute existed between the Hospital and some employee groups, and that Harper was guilty of unfair labor practices as a result of refusing to recognize the union as the channel for grievances and as an agent for negotiation. Barnett replied that that was the first he had heard of any grievances, or that any of Harper's employees were members of the union.[20] This dispute went on through the summer, the Hospital refusing to recognize the United Hospital Workers, or to agree to an election for the purpose of permitting the employees to designate a bargaining agent. Barnett, speaking for the trustees, reiterated that Harper was a charitable institution, that it regularly ran a deficit which had to be made up by contributions, and that, unlike the ordinary business, it showed no profits from which higher wages, determined by bargaining, could be met. Barnett stated in a circular to all employees, dated June 1,

Your Board of Trustees and the Medical Staff firmly believe that a hospital is no place for unions. Unions imply the right to strike, and strikes have no place among the critically ill. A strike in a hospital is a strike not against a business institution making a profit, but against the general public. The dangers to the lives and welfare of patients resulting from a hospital work stoppage cannot be over-emphasized.[21]

Many Harper employees had joined the union, and appeals such as Barnett's were to no avail. The Hospital would not yield, so on November 8, a strike was called, and 380 of Harper's approximately 900 non-professional employees walked out. Picket lines were formed in front of the Brush and John R entrances, and police details were sent to the scene to prevent disorder.[22] For the moment, the normal hospital routine was upset. There were 455 patients registered at that time. To take care of them, nurses, students, interns, doctors, and volunteers pitched in, operating the kitchens, running elevators, and doing all sorts of unaccustomed chores. The Out-patient Department closed for one day, and only emergency cases were admitted to the Hospital. Within twenty-four hours, however, the Hospital had recovered its aplomb and prepared a counterattack. Barnett threatened to "shut the place down"; the trustees firmly declared they would not recognize a union under any circumstances, and a warning was issued to the effect that all strikers failing to report for work on Monday, November 15, would be fired.

There were a few instances, during the next few days, of picket line roughhousing, but the police kept things well under control. A few public-minded citizens sought to bring both sides together, but it was suspected by the Hospital authorities that their good will offers were based largely on the premise that the trustees would negotiate. This they had no intention of doing. There were acrimonious charges and counter-charges, aired in the press, but generally public support was on the Hospital's side. After a few days, the picket lines dwindled to only a handful of bitter-enders, and Harper openly solicited and signed up job applicants. By Monday, many of the strikers had either returned to work or indicated a desire to do so. On Tuesday, November 16, final letters of dismissal were sent to about 212 of those who were still on strike, notifying them they would be paid off on the nineteenth.[23] New employees from the list of job applicants went to work, and by November 20, the newspapers announced that Harper was back to normal. The walkout continued as far as the union was concerned until February 12, 1949 when the State Labor Mediation Board ruled that it was officially over.[24] Harper Hospital had won a victory such as few other Detroit organizations, public or private, could boast of. Although it never recognized a union of its employees, the Hospital did take steps to improve relations with its employees, establishing a wage scale and other benefits which, it claimed, compared favorably not only with those in effect in other hospitals, but in private industry in the community as well.[25]

Of more significance to Harper Hospital than an abortive strike was another depression-born phenomenon, the development of prepaid hospital care. Generally known as Blue Cross, this method of paying in advance for hospital service was established in 1939 in Michigan, partly through the help of Harper. Years before Blue Cross was thought of, Harper Hospital authorities evidenced deep concern over rising hospitalization costs. After World War I, prices of commodities and services began to move upward at a steady rate. Hospital and medical costs were no exception.* Harper's concern, particularly for those in the large middle-income group, was revealed in the following discussion of the problem in 1924.

The poor, and people of very moderate means, have available to them hospitalization and medical care practically without limit; but that great middle class of self-respecting and enlightened people, whose pride and modest income prevent their acceptance or even being considered for charity, are the ones who are suffering under the present economic conditions. It is this class who are deserving of consideration and sympathy. A man in this class must pay for his loved ones' care, an average of $52.50 a week for a room, to which must be added where a major operation is performed $15 for the operating room, and $4 for the very necessary laboratory work, totalling $71.50 for the first week.

Under the ordinary circumstances the services of the hall nurse are amply sufficient, but frequently a special nurse is necessary, which adds, in the case of but one nurse on twelve-hour duty schedule, $42 more, and $10.50 a week for board, making a total of $124 for the first week's hospitalization. The second week which is figured without the operating room and laboratory charge adds $105 more. In extreme cases, it is occasionally necessary to employ a special night nurse, which adds $105 more for the two-week period, bringing the total cost to $334.[26]

The situation was much worse five years later when the depression came. People, who under ordinary circumstances would go to a hospital, were discouraged from doing so by high costs. With high unemployment and shrinking incomes, patients, who had no alternative except to go to the hospital, were unable to pay and were uncollectible. Harper, like most hospitals, faced a critical situation because a high percentage of the cost of operation was supplied by patients' fees.[27]

The solution was being cautiously worked out in Dallas, Texas, where in 1929 a school teacher thought of getting a group of his associates to pay a monthly fee to the Baylor University Hospital, in return for which they could claim hospital service when they needed it. This plan, beginning on a very limited scale, proved so successful that other groups joined together under the same arrangement. The idea attracted attention and began to spread across the country. Within three years, prepaid hospital service was in effect in a dozen states. In almost every instance, the plans were organized by the hospitals themselves, working through their state associations.[28]

Prepaid hospitalization was well established, then, by the time the

Michigan Hospital Association, meeting in Marquette in June, 1938, laid the groundwork for a plan in the Wolverine state. The idea was endorsed by the Detroit District Hospital Council on August 18, 1938, and a committee was appointed to work out the details and arrange the financing. Harper's director, Stewart Hamilton, was a member of that committee, and proved to be such a driving force that he was selected to be one of the incorporators of the Michigan Hospital Service, originally called the Michigan Society for Group Hospitalization. At its first meeting on December 12, 1938, Hamilton was elected vice-president, and named a member of the executive committee of the board of trustees.[29]

Thus, Harper was well represented at the beginning of the movement in Michigan, and can claim considerable credit for its initial success. Probably through Hamilton, the Harper trustees became interested, and on October 3, 1938 they agreed to "join in organizing a group hospital service plan among the hospitals of Detroit and Michigan," and pledged financial help in getting it started.[30] The initial support consisted of $10,000 raised by Harper, Ford, and Grace Hospitals, plus an additional $5,000 loaned by R. E. Olds and Joseph Gleason, both of Lansing. On January 6, 1939, when the organizational groundwork had been laid, the Harper trustees

. . . decided that the Hospital would be willing to go along with the other hospitals in the plan as soon as the legal technicalities were ironed out and the agreements were in form acceptable to Harper Hospital.[31]

These conditions were easily met, and on March 17, 1939, Michigan Hospital Service, popularly known as the Blue Cross plan, opened for business with 53 Detroit and Michigan hospitals participating. To give the plan wider acceptance, a sponsoring committee was appointed in May. Harper again was well represented with Standish Backus, Joseph M. Dodge, Dr. Fred T. Murphy, and Joseph B. Schlotman, all Harper trustees, on the committee.

Michigan Hospital Service, despite some early ups and downs, was a success from the beginning. Simply stated, enrollment was by groups, usually representing employees of a business, industry, labor union, or, as in some cases, social organizations. Eventually, provision was made for limited enrollment of individuals. Fixed rates were charged, these sometimes being shared by employer and employee, and a schedule of benefits—meaning hospital services—was set up. This marked the difference between Blue Cross and hospital insurance. The former returned services only; the latter paid benefits to the policy holder. Blue Cross paid the hospital directly, remittance for about 90 per cent of all charges being made twice each month, subject to adjustment. The payments were made out of the total contributions of members, often in the form of payroll deductions. Under this arrangement, Michigan Hospital Service became a super collection agency for the member hospitals. The original service benefits were for 31 days. Later, this was expanded to 120 days, and, in time, benefits of up to 365 days became possible under certain arrangements. The subscriber's contract could cover himself and his family. One strength of the plan was that administrative expense was held below 5 per cent, and although rates were increased several times since 1939, the percentage of each subscriber's dollar allocated for administration remained constant.

The advantages to Harper, as to almost all hospitals, were felt almost immediately. With their bills, or at least most of them, paid in advance, people began once more coming to the hospital, despite the lingering effects of the depression and the soaring living costs which accompanied World War II. Harper no longer faced the difficulty of collecting its bills. They were all but guaranteed. In a community such as Detroit, where Blue Cross participation was high, uncollectible accounts were said to run less than one per cent, against about eight per cent in other communities. In 1963, it was estimated that sixty per cent of Harper's patients were Blue Cross members. The greatly reduced cost factor in collecting bills on an individual basis, resulting from this high participation, proved an important economy for the Hospital.[32]

Although Blue Cross was state-wide in scope, Harper Hospital has played an important part in its operations. After helping to get it started, Dr. Hamilton served on its board of trustees as a hospital representative until his death in 1945. He was succeeded by Dr. E. Dwight Barnett, who was not only a trustee from 1946 to 1952, but also served as vice-president of the board from 1947 to 1948, and as president from 1949 to 1952. When he resigned as Harper's director to go to Columbia University, George E. Cartmill, the new director, went on the board. Among the trustees representing the Michigan State Medical Society was Dr. William S. Reveno. He became a member of the original board in 1939, and was still serving in 1963, having the longest unbroken

24. DR. HUGO A. FREUND — An internist and diagnostician, Dr. Freund made major contributions toward firmly establishing Harper's department of medicine, and modernizing its intern and resident programs. His colleagues credited him with being one of the first to bring the electrocardiograph to American medicine.
courtesy Irving Katz

25. PRESENTING THE COLORS TO GENERAL HOSPITAL No. 17 — In July, 1942, just before its departure for active service in World War II, General Hospital 17 (the Harper unit) received its colors in a ceremony on the Hospital grounds. Shown are (center) Dr. Stewart Hamilton, Harper Hospital director; and receiving the colors are (left) Col. Henry R. Carstens, commanding the unit, and Coral Bremer, chief nurse.
courtesy Harper Hospital

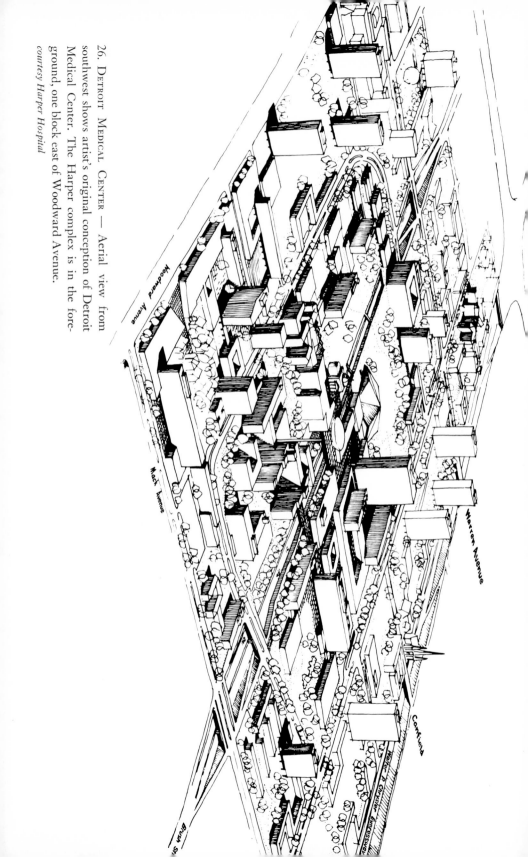

26. Detroit Medical Center — Aerial view from southwest shows artist's original conception of Detroit Medical Center. The Harper complex is in the foreground, one block east of Woodward Avenue. *courtesy Harper Hospital*

service of any member. Although not officially representing Harper, Dr. Reveno's long association with the Hospital as a member of the staff certainly provided still another strong link between Harper and Blue Cross.

The United States had barely recovered from the depression when it was involved in a new crisis in which Harper Hospital was called upon to do its share. Out of the dark lowering war clouds, which covered most of the earth, came Japanese planes on the morning of December 7, 1941 in a bombing attack on Pearl Harbor. Again, the United States was at war.

World War I had taught its lesson about the need for preparedness. The weapons of that war had hardly cooled off before a new medical officers reserve corps was being organized, and the *Bulletin* of November, 1923 was urging members of the Harper medical staff to join.[33] A few months later, on February 13, 1924, the trustees executive committee approved a recommendation of the Medical Board that Dr. Henry R. Carstens be appointed commanding officer of Base Hospital 17 which, after demobilization in 1919, remained as a paper organization.[34] Later in 1924, the Harper unit's designation was changed to that of General Hospital 17; Carstens was in command, with forty officers with reserve status under him.[35] In March, 1940, following the outbreak of war in Europe, the surgeon general inquired whether the affiliation between Harper and General Hospital 17 was still in effect as far as the Hospital was concerned. Stewart Hamilton assured him that it was and that Harper "is most anxious to continue the World War tradition of Base Hospital No. 17, a record which goes back even further, for this institution functioned as a military hospital during the Civil War." With that assurance, the surgeon general requested the trustees to establish formally the Seventeenth General Hospital, "the staff to be recruited from the staff and personnel of Harper Hospital." [36]

Two months after the Pearl Harbor attack, the active organization of the Harper unit was ordered. Miss Coral Bremer, a graduate of the Harper Hospital School of Nursing, was appointed chief nurse, and she began immediately to assemble a staff of 100 nurses. Meanwhile, Colonel Carstens was organizing a medical staff, consisting of 56 medical and dental officers, all of them drawn from the Harper staff. The unit was officially activated July 15, 1942, and was ordered to Fort Custer, Michigan, where it remained until August 24, when it proceeded to Camp McCoy, Wisconsin. At McCoy, the Harper unit received the rest of its personnel and equipment and began a period of intensive training which included operations of the Camp McCoy station hospital.[37] Early in July, 1943, the Seventeenth General was placed on alert, and on July 21 it left Wisconsin for Camp Patrick Henry, an embarkation center near Norfolk, Virginia.

On July 30, the unit aboard the "Empress of Scotland" sailed from the United States, landing at Casablanca, French Morocco, on August 6. The Seventeenth General remained in camp near Casablanca for about six weeks. In mid-September it moved to Oran where it was assigned to a staging area at Ain-el-Turck. This was during the period of the Allied invasion of Sicily and the Italian mainland. The fighting in this campaign was fierce; Nazi resistance was desperate, and casualties were running high. The Seventeenth General was more or less marking time in North Africa, waiting to begin the role for which it was organized and trained. The wait was not a long one. Every available medical facility was needed, and on October 24, 1943, the Harper unit received the call and was moved to Naples where it remained for the duration.[38]

The facilities with which the Harper doctors and nurses found themselves provided made war, if not a pleasure, at least something to be endured. They were assigned to a new, modern hospital which had been constructed during the Mussolini regime in 1938–39. Known as the "Ospedele Grande," part of it was being used by a British hospital group; the Harper unit took over its section from the Ninety-fifth Evacuation Hospital. Wrote Miss Bremer,

> The hospital which is the newest of the Naples Municipal Hospitals is situated on the northwestern outskirts of the city, about three and one-half miles by road from the center of the business district. The buildings are located "on the hill" about 900 feet above the bay level, facing the east and commanding a magnificent view of the city and harbor, with Mount Vesuvius in the background. The complete hospital grounds cover an area of about 65 acres, and is surrounded by a stone wall. The main administration building with an impressive portico and containing only offices and a huge auditorium, faces on the street. Immediately behind this building are four modern hospital buildings. Farther to the west are located a power house, a laundry, a kitchen building, a mortuary and an isolation hospital building.[39]

The Seventeenth General occupied the administration, the contagious, and one of the hospital buildings. These provided space for 1,450 beds, but the flow of battle casualties, as the fighting raged up the Italian boot, soon made it necessary for the Harper outfit to increase its beds to 2,500 by erecting tents and temporary "hutments" on the hospital grounds. The unit received its first patients—538 of them—from the Ninety-fifth Evacuation Hospital, beginning November 11. From that time, the Harper personnel were busy, handling mostly battle casualties. In June, 1944, the busiest month, there were 1,392 operations performed. In the first year in the hospital the total number of operative cases was 10,047. According to Colonel Carstens, the hospital had 34,000 admissions during its stay in Naples. While most of these were battle casualties, there were a substantial number of medical cases, too. A good deal of jaundice was treated, and the hospital was designated as the tuberculosis center for the area.[40]

Colonel Carstens called the hospital a "show case," although there were some drawbacks. The water supply was uncertain, and the local electrical current was completely unreliable. On one occasion, Nazi bombers mistakenly took the hospital for a harbor installation and attacked. Fortunately, the damage was small, and there were no American casualties, although the British neighbors suffered some.[41] In spite of handicaps and dangers, the personnel were able to maintain standards which were a credit to the mother hospital back in Detroit. When supplies were inadequate, as was often the case, the shortages were overcome by improvisation. A lack of rubber sheeting was taken care of by requisitioning from the navy a blimp which had been shot down. Cut up, the salvaged material provided all the rubber covers for mattresses and operating-room use that were needed. A piece of ground adjacent to the hospital was commandeered, and civilians were hired as gardeners, with the result that fresh vegetables were available. During the early part of 1944, the nurses and doctors had their first introduction to penicillin, and at one time a daily average of 250 patients was receiving the new drug. High nursing standards were maintained, and Chief Nurse Bremer boasted that "not one bed sore was permitted to start in this hospital." [42]

At long last, V-E Day arrived, and the work of the hospital drew to an end. Some of the personnel, including younger doctors, were detached and given orders to go to the Pacific. While they were still at sea, Japan capitulated, and they returned to the United States, arriving there before the older men—much to their disgust—left Naples. The Seventeenth General was deactivated in Naples October 25, 1945, but some of the staff, including Colonel Carstens, did not return home until January, 1946.[43]

World War II, as far as Harper was concerned, was not exclusively a Seventeenth General venture. Many of the staff, nurses and doctors, saw service with other units. The war also saw the Hospital engaged in civil defense activities, with preparations made for such possible emergencies as might be caused by enemy action. First aid instruction was given to employees, and the buildings were prepared for emergency use, with blackout and blast protection measures being taken. By May, 1942, the trustees were worrying about a manpower shortage, a situation which grew progressively worse. Dr. Hamilton reported the difficulty in obtaining enough nurses, and a shortage of domestic help made it hard to operate the Hospital smoothly. The result was that from time to time floors or parts of floors had to be closed. The situation was in some measure alleviated by volunteer workers, some of whom were trained as nurses' aides.[44] Valuable assistance also was rendered by American Red Cross workers and Gray Ladies. This type of volunteer service, and the interest in the Hospital which it generated, developed in the postwar period into the Harper Hospital Auxiliary which in 1962 claimed a membership of 320 women. The Auxiliary, formally organized in 1951, engaged in a diversity of activities and services, devoted both to patients and to fostering good community relations.[45]

Chapter 20

THE MEDICAL CENTER—
A DREAM COMES TRUE

The immediate postwar
years were devoted to getting the Hospital back to normal as quickly
as possible. The strong administration of Richard H. Webber, president
of the Board of Trustees, which began in 1918 when he succeeded Joseph
Boyer, continued until 1961. In that year he resigned the post in favor
of Ray R. Eppert, head of the Burroughs Corporation. Eppert, in whom
was maintained the Harper tradition of interest and leadership in a
wide range of community affairs, went on the board in 1951. The postwar board was strengthened by the addition of Andrew W. Barr, Robert
Bryant, Arthur H. Buhl, Jr., Robert B. Semple and Joseph A. Vance, Jr.
Buhl represented a family association of one hundred years, while
Joseph L. Hudson and William M. Joy as board members also continued a family tradition of inestimable value to Harper.

The later additions to the board were not, in all cases, replacements
for men who had died or resigned. As on another earlier occasion, the
added responsibilities of trusteeship, resulting from the need to provide
community service on a continually broadening base, created the necessity for more representation on the board. As a result, a new bylaw
was adopted June 19, 1950 which permitted the board membership to
be increased from fifteen to a maximum of thirty.[1] A few months earlier,
it was noted that the original thirty-year term of incorporation, granted
in 1863, had been renewed October 9, 1893 for another thirty years. That
extension ran out, with no new reincorporation. It was held unnecessary
because of state laws which contained perpetual existence provisions.[2] On
February 14, 1950, the original name, The Harper Hospital, was officially

changed to Harper Hospital.[3] Dr. Stewart Hamilton, the Hospital director, died December 18, 1945 after nearly forty years of association with Harper. His successor was Dr. E. Dwight Barnett, who served until January 1, 1952 when he resigned to take a position with Columbia University as director of its Institute of Administrative Medicine. When he left, the long-standing policy that the directorship be held by a medical man was abandoned, and the post went to George E. Cartmill, who previously had served as treasurer.

Nearly two decades passed since the last great war ended, but in the intervening years Harper Hospital remained a vital, vigorous, and dynamic institution. From its beginning, marked by a row of wooden military barracks and wards, Harper became an aggregation of buildings, of warren-like corridors confusing to all but the initiated. Sprawling over an area of eight and one-half acres, these buildings had been added as the need for them arose. A look at the ground plan suggests a utilization of space dictated by necessity, rather than a long-range plan.

The old red brick Harper building, facing on John R Street, no longer was the hub and nerve center of the Hospital, although in outward appearance it remained virtually unchanged. Once it housed almost all of the activities and functions of an integrated hospital. In 1963, its first floor, where old soldiers once found refuge, had been converted largely into offices. The upper floors were occupied by clinic rooms, laboratories, classrooms, and personnel quarters. Its basement was a storehouse. Beside it, the Buhl Memorial Building continued to serve as the Out-patient Clinic, the entire structure being given over to that purpose. The Gray operating pavilion, once the pride of Harper and the admiration of the medical world, was converted into maintenance workrooms and shops, except for two or three rooms which were turned into laboratories.

Behind the Harper building was the new Murphy building, largely given over to the x-ray department, the school of nursing, an auditorium, and, again, a group of laboratories. Jutting off from it was the Hudson pavilion. Its first floor was full of x-ray equipment. On the second was the department of ophthalmology; the third was occupied by medical and surgical beds, the fourth by the department of orthopedics. On the fifth floor was the neurological center under the direction and supervision of the Wayne State University College of Medicine. On the sixth floor was the pediatrics department.

The Center building, which connects the Harper and Brush buildings, contained the medical records, the library, and some x-ray facilities. The upper floors—second to sixth—had medical and surgical beds; the seventh, the pathology labs; and the eighth, operating rooms. The Brush building had the administration offices on the first floor, north wing, with the psychiatric department at the opposite end. The second, third, fourth, and fifth floors were given over to medicine and surgery; obstetrics was on the sixth; delivery rooms and gynecology were on the seventh, with operating rooms on the eighth. McLaughlin Hall continued to serve its original function as the nurses' home.

After World War II, the people of Detroit took a long, hard look at their town, and were not pleased by what they saw. The city had grown old and, in many parts, ugly. There were said to be 8,000 acres that had deteriorated into slums, and the blight was concentrated largely within the central area. The section around Harper Hospital was badly run down. City Planner Charles A. Blessing characterized the district which included Harper, Grace, Woman's, and Children's Hospitals as "among the most deteriorated acres." [4]

Nancy Martin's stately grove behind old Harper, the beautifully shaded streets, the fine mansions along Woodward, and the comfortable, middle-class homes on the neighboring side streets—all were long gone. In their place was a jungle of decayed stores, dilapidated houses, and teeming apartments. It all added up to a section where the crime and disease rates were high and delinquency was spawned. The surroundings made a sordid setting for a great hospital. The situation became critical. As the interior of the city declined, many of the families who were better off economically moved to the outskirts and suburbs. They, too, had need for medical service, with the result that new, modern hospitals were built on the city's periphery. Although Harper and its neighboring hospitals continued to provide the best and most advanced type of care, their futures became increasingly uncertain.

The answer seemed to lie in a program of rehabilitation, and this suggested the creation of a great new medical center, incorporating all the existing facilities in the district, plus the relocation of the Wayne State University College of Medicine from its downtown site in a blighted area. The dream of a medical center for Detroit had long existed, particularly in the minds of those interested in the medical college who recognized that the need for more clinical and teaching material could only be filled by a closer association with a large hospital or group of hospitals. Actually, the medical center idea can be traced back to 1932 when the Detroit Common Council, reflecting the interest in such a project by the Wayne County Medical Society and the Wayne medical school, adopted resolutions favoring it. Five years passed, and the program was revived in a series of articles in the *Detroit News,* pointing both to the interest in and the benefits which would be derived from a medical center. In one of these articles, it was stated that future plans for the school included

. . . development of graduate medical education and research activity. On these hinges the possibility of making Wayne University College of Medicine a truly great contributor to the health of the people of Detroit and to medical science of the world. . . .[5]

In all of these early, and somewhat vague discussions, the medical school was the axis upon which the larger medical center concept revolved. The idea was pressed by Dr. Edgar H. Norris, then the medical school dean. He finally persuaded the Board of Education in 1942 to direct David D. Henry, president of the University, to develop plans for the establishment of a Medical Science Center in connection with the University. A Medical Science Center Committee was appointed. It was composed of civic leaders including Wendell W. Anderson, chairman; George R. Fink, of Great Lakes Steel Corporation; Charles T. Fisher, Jr., financier; Ormond E. Hunt, of General Motors; George W. Mason, of Nash-Kelvinator Corporation; and Fred M. Zeder, of Chrysler Corporation. Their first concern was to obtain a new and modern plant for the medical school, then housed in antiquated and inadequate quarters near Receiving Hospital.[6]

In 1943, this committee published a report which it claimed was based on three years' study. The report stated that Memorial Park, between Jefferson and the Detroit River at Burns Drive, had been made available for school facilities, including a University hospital to be built with funds largely appropriated by Wayne County. The preliminary architect's plan included, besides school and hospital buildings, such adjuncts as dormitories, a nurses' home, an Institute of Biological Studies, recreation facilities, a library, a Center for Continuation Study, and an Institute of Industrial Health.[7] Here was a full-blown medical center plan. But it was on too grandiose a scale, well beyond any visible means of successful financing. The fact that the city and its people were, at the moment, deeply involved in World War II made fund-raising for the time being virtually out of the question.

Attention shifted to a new and better site within a year. New plans were discussed. These would locate the College of Medicine and a 350-bed hospital in the Art Center district, using a 53-acre tract bounded by Warren, Brush, Ferry, and Hastings—the project to cost an estimated $21,500,000. It is significant that in considering this location, mention was made of the advantages inherent in the college's proximity to Harper, Grace, Woman's, and Children's Hospitals. On November 22, 1943, the Board of Education gave its approval to this site, and nothing more was heard about Memorial Park as a medical center.[8] For the next three years, the Art Center location was definitely "it." The proposed University hospital was to care for indigent county patients; its construction was to have been financed by a $2,000,000 grant by Wayne County, with the approval of the state legislature. The other buildings were to be paid for by funds solicited from the public. This scheme hit a snag in 1946, when it was discovered that postwar building costs far exceeded 1943 estimates, that the legislative enabling act was defective, and the postwar adjustment period was not conducive to fund solicitation.[9]

In 1949 occurred what may be regarded as the first breakthrough when Congress passed the Federal Housing Act which included the important provision for urban redevelopment. This was an acknowledgment, at the federal level, that the older American municipalities could not by themselves cope with community deterioration and growing slums. The problem was a national one, not something peculiar to Detroit. Urban redevelopment was intended to restore old neighborhoods through a process of rebuilding. With subsequent amendments, the Urban Renewal Act permitted cities to condemn slum areas, both industrial and residential. The municipalities would pay one-third of the cost; the federal government would supply two-thirds of the money. Once condemned, the blighted property would be cleared, and slum buildings razed. The land then would be offered for resale to private developers who would rejuvenate the cleared areas under favorable financing arrangements supported by the government.

Detroit was quick to see the advantages of this program. The city already had embarked upon development of a civic center in an attempt to revitalize its downtown business district. Community leaders, both in and out of government, joined in this enterprise with enthusiasm and money. The results were encouraging. At the same time, it was realized that to add a high polish to the central business district would avail little if the outer edges remained slums. That was why the concept of urban redevelopment was eagerly accepted by Detroit, and plans were quickly formulated to take advantage of it.

By 1953, these plans began to take shape in the form of a redevelopment program on Detroit's lower east side, known as the Gratiot Redevelopment Project. Wayne's College of Medicine, which had made no progress in the Art Center area, now began to eye the Gratiot sector. Here was, or soon would be, available land, close to Receiving and Memorial Hospitals and the Kresge Eye Institute. These three institutions, it was felt, could be utilized as a "university hospital," and steps were taken to go ahead with a Medical Science Building and a neuropsychiatric institute as the nucleus of a medical center. But the Citizens Redevelopment Corporation turned down the plan to convert fifteen acres of the Gratiot project into a Wayne medical campus. The land was needed, it was felt, for large-scale residential development. The result was that the medical school was placed on a new site on Rivard Street, east of the Gratiot area. And although Wayne had a new medical science building, the dream of a medical center was far from being realized.[10]

Meanwhile, the trustees of Harper Hospital were casting speculative eyes on the possibilities of urban redevelopment. Members of the board, particularly the Webbers and Ray R. Eppert, were fully aware of the possibilities the federal program offered through their membership on city committees formed for the purpose of rejuvenating the downtown area. What could be more logical, they asked, than to apply the methods being used for the rebuilding of other neighborhoods to their own.

A meeting of representatives of Harper, Grace, Woman's, and Children's Hospitals was held August 19, 1954 in the office of Harper's director, George E. Cartmill. A report of that conference was made in a letter from Cartmill to Ray R. Eppert on August 30, 1954. The group, according to the letter, discussed the general plight of the area hospitals and concluded that unless there could be rehabilitation in the near future, these hospitals were threatened with the alternative of moving from the area or becoming community hospitals, unable to continue their educational and scientific functions. Discussing the cost of the alternative of moving, Cartmill pointed out that the four hospitals had a book value of $23,000,000, but replacement would be in excess of $50,000,000. He suggested that the investment represented by the institutions was greater than the assessed valuation "of all taxable property" within an area bounded by Kirby, Hastings, John R, and Mack.

The implication was that rehabilitation not only would preserve institutions in the area, but would restore taxable values. It was pointed out that renewal of the neighborhood would produce housing attractive to desirable tenants, such as doctors and other professional people, who would find it advantageous to live near their work. It was at this point in the letter that the possibilities of a medical center were cited as beneficial to the Wayne medical school and as the salvation of the hospitals. The location was superior to any other in the community, or for that matter, anywhere else. Cartmill declared,

> The famous Columbia-Presbyterian Center in New York can boast of but 1,100 beds [the Detroit area already had 1,700], with none of them presenting any more potential for fine medical care or teaching than is presented among these four hospitals in Detroit.[11]

Eppert took this letter to Mayor Albert E. Cobo who gave it his endorsement, and at his suggestion, it was laid before the City Planning Commission. This led to formation of a Medical Center Citizens Committee of which Eppert was made chairman, and which included representatives of the other hospitals and the College of Medicine. The Cartmill-Eppert letter was used "as a summary for the benefit of the presidents of each of the hospital boards involved in the spring of 1955." In April, 1955, Richard H. Webber, then president of the Harper board, called a meeting of the area hospital representatives and Dean Gordon H. Scott, Dr. Norris's successor, and out of that gathering came not only final agreement on the medical center concept, but also a decision to move ahead in a co-ordinated effort.[12]

Meanwhile the Medical Center Committee had begun work in 1954, and by the following year it had received sanction for its plan. In fact, the sanction was enthusiastically given by the federal government, according to Eppert, because it involved something more than refurbishing a down-at-the-heel slum district. It called for the creation of a whole new area, and as a result, the project was placed high on the federal priority list. A talented architect and planner was retained by the committee in June, 1955, and the whole project began to take shape on paper.

The medical school enthusiastically joined forces with the hospitals. In July, 1956, Dean Scott of the College of Medicine hailed the project, stating:

There is no question but what the Detroit Medical Center . . . with several hospitals using the same equipment could cut medical expenses. This is inevitable when hospitals need such apparatus as cobalt units, artificial kidneys, and other modern equipment.

The projected location of the school near the hospitals obviated the need of a new Wayne State University hospital.[13]

In March, 1960, a total site of 236 acres was confirmed, and the Federal Housing and Home Finance Agency approved temporary loans of $7,000,000 for development of the area. In July, 1960, plans were announced for construction of a new Medical Research Building for the medical school at a cost of $4,000,000, the work to be started in 1962. It was expected that the entire Medical Center, which was to be developed in stages, or phases, would taken ten years to complete. In 1961, Wayne's Board of Governors decided to move all of the medical school's facilities into the Medical Center, and received permission to use the $250,000, originally appropriated for an addition to the downtown school, for planning purposes.[14]

To go back a step, the Medical Center Committee had retained Anthony J. J. Rourke, M.D., of New Rochelle, New York, an authority on hospital planning, to study the medical center possibilities. Dr. Rourke's report was made in March, 1960. In it he stated "the ingredients for a medical center of national significance are present, or potentially available, in Detroit." Applied specifically to the midtown area under consideration, Dr. Rourke offered a long list of recommendations. Included was one that the Wayne State University College of Medicine be located in the center, that a medical library and research center be built, both in or near the school, and that the existing downtown buildings be used as part of an expanded mental health center. The hospitals in the area would retain their separate identities. Children's Hospital, however, would be replaced by a new hospital to which the others would assign all their pediatrics cases. The old Children's would be converted into a mental retardation institute.[15]

Several recommendations applied to Harper. Dr. Rourke suggested that, while the present Harper and Grace Hospitals be retained as independent institutions, a new facility to be called the Grace-Harper Medical Center Hospital, of about 600-bed capacity, be built. To it would be assigned surgical, surgical specialty, and obstetrical services, with all other adult services going into the old hospitals. The Grace-Harper unit, he stated, should be under the administration of a new board of trustees, made up of Harper and Grace trustees, and staffed by physicians having full- or part-time faculty appointments in the College of Medicine. All parts of Harper and Grace built prior to 1912 would be demolished, and Dr. Rourke urged demolishing the Buhl building. All the schools of nursing would be consolidated and housed within present Harper buildings.

Other recommendations included a new municipal receiving hospital of 500 beds, the old one to be turned over to the mental health center, relocation of the University of Detroit's dental school in the new center, and centralization to the greatest possible extent of such services as laundry and maintenance. Dr. Rourke's plan for the Medical Center development also included provision for housing, commercial development, and parking.

Using the Rourke report for guidelines, if not for a blueprint, all interested parties stepped up their activity. On April 20, 1961, the Detroit newspapers reported that the Metropolitan Detroit Building Fund would raise $2,300,000 to acquire land in the area, and another $1,840,000 for a new building for Children's Hospital. Eppert pointed out at this time that Wayne State University would not get a new hospital, but would have the benefit of more than 2,000 beds in several hospitals at a saving of millions in tax money, which could be used in other ways to advance medical teaching.[16]

The Medical Center area had been divided into four sections. The first section, bounded by Woodward, Mack, Hastings, and East Alexandrine, encompassing a 58-acre area immediately around Harper Hospital and including the original Nancy Martin and Military Park lots, was condemned for $7,040,234, in a verdict handed down on March 1, 1962. Condemnation proceedings on the second section, immediately north of Harper, were scheduled to begin in April, 1963. On November 20, 1962, ground was broken at East Alexandrine and St. Antoine Streets for the Wayne State University's Medical Research Building which, it was announced, had been completely financed for $3,050,000, plus $900,000 for equipment. With the land condemnation and the start of construction of the first building, the Medical Center moved from the dream stage into one of reality!

At the same time the story of Harper Hospital shifts from history into the future. And what is that future likely to hold? The answer probably lies in what the Medical Center evolves into. Harper Hospital was not quite ready, in 1963, to give full endorsement to the Rourke report. No one could say, with certainty, that a Grace-Harper unit would be built, or that the older Harper buildings would be torn down and replaced by modern structures. Funds were not immediately in sight to do these things, nor were there plans to start a subscription drive. But the Medical Center concept was accepted, and the long-range view was one of optimism, not only for Harper's prospects, but also for better medical service generally in Detroit. "The modern medical center of the last half of the Twentieth Century," stated Dr. Rourke, "will find all disciplines needed for patient care, education and research." [17]

The Medical Center, with its enlarged clinical and educational resources, would contribute, in the never-ending fight for better health, to the graduating physicians who would serve all sections of the metropolitan area and to the trained specialists who would have available the "fruits of research and development." It would provide the expensive facilities for diagnosis and care, the continuing educational programs for the family physician, and the trained professional and technical personnel in the health services and research, the report stated. Dr. Rourke maintained,

There is no conflict of interest between a medical center development and the orderly development and expansion of hospital facilities in the periphery of large cities. . . . Each, then, has a specific and different primary charge from its community, which, when properly related, complement and supplement each other.[18]

The role of Harper Hospital in the Medical Center, according to one staff member, will be an enlarged sphere of usefulness. Specialization will be carried even further; Harper will serve the peripheral hospitals, receiving from them "the tough cases." This will be possible because of the educational, clinical, and research advantages gained from the pooling of experience and facilities. There have been those who have expressed the fear that, as Harper is absorbed into the Medical Center, it may lose its identity, its time-honored and traditional community status.

More than forty years ago, when the Hospital was passing through a critical stage, the Board of Trustees stated, in letters to each member of the staff, what the trustees conceived to be Harper's functions. These were:

First, the care of the hundreds of patients that are entrusted to this institution each day.

Second, the training of that splendid body of nurses who are later to minister to the suffering of our people.

Third, the further education of the young doctors who serve each year as internes.

Fourth, the developing skill and ability of the members of our staff through the care of our patients, through the clinics, and through the daily association and conference, one with another.

Fifth, the contribution to medical science made possible by our laboratories and our department of research.[19]

These are high and noble precepts. They have been followed and adhered to for a hundred years. That they will be as closely followed in the days to come is a matter of no doubt. The Harper tradition of service to humanity is too deeply rooted to permit of anything else. And as long as they continue to be adhered to, Harper Hospital's prospects for the years ahead appear to be as bright as its past years have been glorious.

Through its early relationship with the FIRST PRESBYTERIAN CHURCH, Harper Hospital can claim roots which go deep into the history of Detroit. Because the church was, in a sense, the sponsor of the Hospital, some of its early social and cultural lineage was transferred to Harper.

Prior to the influx of American settlers which really commenced after the War of 1812, Detroit was a predominantly French Catholic town, despite the long period of British occupation from 1763 to 1796. But Americans, mostly from the eastern states and Ohio, began to give Detroit a Yankee flavor which had become quite pronounced by 1815 or 1816. Up to that time the only church serving the area was Catholic St. Anne's. The Protestants, arriving in increasing numbers, had no place of worship until 1818 when a small Methodist church was built near the River Rouge on the southwest outskirts of the town.

Following the fire of 1805, when the lots were redistributed, St. Anne's was given a new parcel of land upon which to build. The Presbyterians, apparently the most numerous Protestant sect, petitioned for ground upon which to build, but the Governor and Judges rejected the petition on the ground that they had no authority to recognize a denomination or sect. They recognized only two religious groups—Catholics and Protestants. In 1816, the latter proceeded to form the First Evangelical Society of Detroit, taking in all Protestants, including Presbyterians, Episcopalians and Methodists. About this time, the Rev. John Monteith, a twenty-eight-year-old graduate of the Princeton Theological Seminary, was sent to Detroit by the American Board of Commissioners for Foreign Missions. He conducted services in the old Council House which stood on the site of the present Mariners' Church. Under the leadership of Governor Cass, H. J. Hunt, and James Abbott, arrangements were made for Monteith to remain in Detroit as the Protestant minister at a salary of $800 a year.

In 1819, Monteith went East and raised $1,122.24 for the building of a church in Detroit. Government officials, recognizing a Protestant, rather than a denominational group, permitted a church to be built in 1825 on the east side of Woodward Avenue between Congress and Larned Streets. About this time the First Evangelical Society changed its name to the First Protestant Society. While it was outwardly non-denominational, it was really Presbyterian. Within a few years, the Episcopalians and Methodists built their own churches on the north end of the same lot. The First Protestant Society then became, in name as well as in fact, the First Presbyterian Church. The original church was occupied until 1834, when a larger building replaced the old one. The latter was sold to the Catholics, moved to Cadillac Square, and became Trinity Church.

On October 1, 1838, the Rev. Dr. George Duffield became the fifth pastor, counting Monteith as the first, of the First Presbyterian Church. He has been called "possibly the most famous pastor the church has ever had."

On January 10, 1854, the church was destroyed by fire and because the neighborhood around lower Woodward Avenue was changing from residential to commercial, it was decided to rebuild farther uptown. Meanwhile, in 1849, the Jefferson Avenue Presbyterian Church and, in 1855, the Fort Street Presbyterian Church were built. The proceeds from the sale of the Woodward Avenue lot were divided among the three churches.

The new site for the First Presbyterian was on Gratiot at the corner of Farmer. Today the property forms part of the J. L. Hudson Company department store. There was ample money for rebuilding, the First Presbyterian having been from the beginning the home church of many of the wealthiest and most influential Detroit families.

Dedicated September 9, 1855, the new First Presbyterian was of brick construction with a graceful, towering steeple. Its dimensions were 70 by 100 feet, with a seating capacity of 700—slightly less than its former building. Originally it had galleries on three sides, but these were removed in 1862. The cost of the new structure was $40,000. While awaiting its completion, the congregation met in the State Capitol at Griswold and State Streets.

The Farmer-Gratiot church continued in use for several years as Detroit's "blue-stocking" church. But eventually, the expanding city outgrew it, and it became a typical downtown parish. Because its members were moving farther out Woodward, it was decided to follow, and on the first Sunday in May, 1891, the congregation occupied the present First Presbyterian Church at Woodward and Edmund Place, only a short distance south of Harper Hospital.

Reference: *One Hundredth Anniversary Celebration—First Presbyterian Church, 1818–1918* (Detroit, 1918).

DR. GEORGE B. RUSSEL was noted equally as a successful physician and industrialist, and the combined roles gave him stature as one of Detroit's leading citizens of the nineteenth century. Born in Philadelphia about 1816, Russel was graduated in 1836 from Jefferson Medical College in his native city. Prior to that he had studied, probably as an apprentice, under a doctor in Lancaster, Pennsylvania. In 1836 he went to Detroit, then a frontier military post, most of whose citizens were of French heritage. At the age of twenty, he began a general practice and was soon recognized as a leader of the medical profession in Detroit. Besides his town practice, Dr. Russel "rode the circuit," regularly visiting patients on the Canadian side of the Detroit River from Amherstburg to Belle River. On the American side, he rode from Trenton to Mount Clemens and Romeo, to Royal Oak and Birmingham, to Farmington and Dearborn. For many years Dr. Russel lived in a brick house that he built at Fort and Shelby Streets, adjoining what remained of old Fort Shelby.

He was in Detroit during three cholera epidemics and gained much experience in treating that plague. Smallpox also was prevalent, and he was looked upon as an expert in treating that disease. During a smallpox epidemic in 1837, he was serving as the town's health officer. A band of Indians was encamped along Connor Creek, a few miles northeast of the city. Accompanied by an interpreter, Dr. Russel visited the camp and in 24 hours vaccinated 700 Indians. It was said that although they were exposed to the disease, not one of them contracted it.

Around 1850, Dr. Russel's attention began to turn to business and industry, and he established, or helped to establish, a concern which manufactured railroad equipment and was the predecessor of the American Car & Foundry Company. As noted in the text, he also operated a steam ferry boat service between Detroit and Windsor. Despite his other business affairs, Dr. Russel never forsook medicine, but continued to practice almost until his death. One account credits him with having influenced Walter Harper and Nancy Martin to give their property for the founding of the Hospital. While, as an original trustee, Russel assuredly had an important part in the Hospital's origins, there is no evidence that he was the motivating force as far as the Harper-Martin benefactions were concerned.

On August 24, 1903, Dr. Russel was knocked down by a bicycle as he was crossing the street. Before he could rise, he was run over by a wagon. As the result of the injuries, he died August 31, 1903 at the age of eighty-seven.

Reference: *Medical History of Michigan*, I, 228–29, 710; Farmer's *History of Detroit*, pp. 50, 218, 646, 917; *Journal of the Michigan State Medical Society*, 1902–03, I and II, 476–79.

Several Detroit families have been closely identified over the years with Harper Hospital, but none influenced it more, or had more to do with its founding, its early growth, and the development of its community character than the DUF-FIELD FAMILY.

The first decade of Harper Hospital's existence is almost the story of the exertions of the REV. DR. GEORGE DUFFIELD, for many years pastor of the First Presbyterian Church. In his successful efforts to obtain a general hospital for the care of the sick and poor which early Detroit so badly needed, Dr. Duffield was ably assisted by his family, particularly his son, DIVIE BETHUNE DUFFIELD, who was recognized as one of the city's most able attorneys.

The account of Dr. Duffield's relations with Walter Harper and Nancy Martin, which led to the establishment of the original endowments in 1859, has been given elsewhere in this volume, and needs no further discussion.

The Rev. Dr. George Duffield was born in Strasburg, Pennsylvania, July 4, 1794. He was educated at the University of Pennsylvania; then he entered the theological seminary of the Reformed Presbyterian Church of New York. Licensed to preach in 1815, he accepted a pastorate at Carlisle, Pennsylvania, which he served for nineteen years. Two years followed at a church in Philadelphia, and then he moved on to the Broadway Tabernacle, New York. In 1837 he was called to the First Presbyterian Church, Detroit, where he filled the pulpit for the rest of his life. In 1817 he married Isabella Graham Bethune, the daughter of Divie and Joanna Bethune.

George and Isabella Duffield raised a family of five sons and a daughter. All of the children, with the exception of George Jr., the eldest, and William W., were involved either directly or through their descendants in the destiny of Harper. George Jr. followed his father into the clergy and is best remembered as the author of the rousing hymn, "Stand Up, Stand Up for Jesus." It was said of the father, and is equally applicable to many of his descendants, that "the labors of no other one man have contributed more to the moral stability and progress of Detroit."

Dr. Duffield's third son was DIVIE BETHUNE, a name, incidentally, which recurred in succeeding generations. Divie Bethune was born in Pennsylvania, August 29, 1821; attended Dickinson College, Livingston College, and Yale. At one time, he, too, considered entering the ministry and studied for a while at the Union Theological Seminary. He finally decided upon the law and was admitted to the bar in 1843. Like so many of the Duffields, he was always interested in civic affairs and was city attorney, United States commissioner, a member of the Board of Education, and one of the founders of Detroit's public library system. The account of his services to Harper Hospital is in this book; as counsel and secretary to the Board of Trustees he rendered valuable aid. Some sources credit him with having as much to do in obtaining the Harper-Martin endowments as his father.

The fourth son of George and Isabella Duffield was SAMUEL P. DUFFIELD, born at Carlisle, December 24, 1833. He attended the University of Michigan and then entered the medical school at the University of Pennsylvania, but bad eyesight caused him to withdraw. He decided to become a chemist and studied in Germany. After his return in the 1860's, he operated a drug store in Detroit. He was still determined, however, to become a doctor, and after directing the chemistry laboratory for the Detroit Medical College, he finally obtained an M.D. degree from that school. He was an early member of the Harper Hospital staff and may be considered its first pathologist and director of research. He established a chemical laboratory in partnership with Hervey Parke which became the Parke, Davis and Company. Samuel Duffield died in 1916.

Divie Bethune Duffield's oldest son, GEORGE, whose name frequently appears in these pages, became one of Detroit's best-known physicians, and during most of his professional life he was on the Harper staff. He was born in Detroit, April 28, 1859 and was a graduate of the Detroit College of Medicine (1882). He began practice with his office in his father's home and later was associated with Dr. Henry A. Cleland at State and Griswold. Dr. Duffield specialized in internal medicine, became an authority on the use of antitoxin in diphtheria, and in his later years developed a strong interest in pathology. He died November 12, 1919.

The second son of Divie Bethune Duffield was BETHUNE, born November 28, 1861. He attended the Michigan Military Academy at Orchard Lake and the University of Michigan. He was admitted to the bar in 1885 and with his father formed the legal firm of Duffield & Duffield. Married to Eliza Steele Muir, Bethune Duffield was an influential and prosperous citizen, holding directorships in several major enterprises. He was a member of the Harper Hospital Board of Trustees from 1892 until his death, November 24, 1929.

The only daughter of the Rev. Dr. George Duffield was ISABELLA, named for her mother. She was born in 1830 and, on April 6, 1852, married Dr. Morse Stewart, a prominent young Detroit physician. The charitable impulses of the Duffields found expression in Isabella Duffield Stewart who, as it has been noted, was credited with influencing Nancy Martin into giving her property to Harper Hospital and of joining her husband in persuading other members of her family that Detroit needed a hospital more than it needed a vocational school. Mrs. Stewart was an organizer of the Home for the Friendless, the Detroit Association of Charities, and the Women's Christian Association. She was particularly remembered for her charity work on the home front during the Civil War. She died May 27, 1888.

Reference: Farmer's *History of Detroit*, pp. 666–68; The George Duffield Papers, Burton Historical Collection; Clarence M. and M. Agnes Burton, eds. *History of Wayne County* (Chicago-Detroit, 1930), III, 201, 275–78; V, 471; Burr, *Medical History of Michigan*, II, 256; *One Hundredth Anniversary Celebration, First Presbyterian Church 1818–1918* (Detroit, 1918); *Detroit Advertiser and Tribune*, July 9, 1868; *Detroit News*, November 25, 1929.

For more than seventy years the name of the FARRAND FAMILY was almost synonymous with that of Harper Hospital. One of the original trustees bore the name, as did the first real medical chief of the Hospital.

JACOB S. FARRAND and DAVID O. FARRAND were half-brothers, the sons of Bethuel Farrand. Bethuel, a native New York stater, moved to Detroit in 1825 to install the city's first water works. Jacob was born at Mentz, New York, May 7, 1815. The family moved to Ann Arbor where Jacob spent his boyhood, clerking in a drug store and, at the age of thirteen, carrying the mail on horseback between Ann Arbor and Detroit. In 1830, he settled in Detroit, working in the Rice and Bingham drug store and soon becoming a partner in the business. In 1845 he established his own business on lower Woodward Avenue. After several partnership changes, the firm evolved in 1860 into the well-known house of Farrand, Williams & Company, pharmaceutical manufacturers and distributors.

Jacob Farrand's interests were many. He was called "a real tycoon," being involved in banking, insurance, and utilities. He still found time to participate in a wide range of civic activities. He was deputy collector of revenue for the Port of Detroit, military secretary to the governor, elder of the First Presbyterian Church for thirty-five years, member of the Board of Water Commissioners, alderman, president of the Common Council, police commissioner, school inspector, and member of a committee which planned construction of a new city hall.

He was deeply interested in religious, educational and benevolent affairs, serving as president (1878) of the Presbyterian Session; treasurer, Detroit Evangelical Alliance; secretary, Detroit Young Men's Temperance Society; president, Detroit Home and Day School; trustee, Eastern Asylum for the Insane; president, Wayne County Bible Society; president, Detroit Society for Sabbath Observance; commissioner, Presbyterian General Assembly, both for the United States and Canada; delegate, Pan-Presbyterian Council held in Edinburgh, and Detroit's receiving agent for the American Board of Commissioners for Foreign Missions. Not to be overlooked was the fact that he was an original trustee of Harper Hospital and president of its board from 1884 until his death on April 3, 1891.

Of no less importance to Harper Hospital was David Osburn Farrand. Born in Ann Arbor, April 23, 1838, he was graduated from the University of Michigan, then studied in Germany, and returned to the United States to take a degree in medicine at the College of Physicians and Surgeons in New York. The Civil War broke out about that time, and Dr. Farrand immediately offered his services. He was assigned to several hospitals, including St. Mary's and Harper, which he served for awhile as medical director when it was under military auspices. He held the rank of brevet captain. After the war, he was one of the principal staff members of the Hospital, helping in its transition from a military to civilian institution. In private practice he was associated with Dr. Zina Pitcher, dean of Detroit's medical men.

Like his brother, Dr. Farrand's range of interests was broad. He was president of the early Board of Health, surgeon for the police department, and surgeon-in-chief for the Michigan Central Railroad. He was deeply interested in education, both medical and lay, and it was a fitting tribute that Harper's school of nursing, toward the establishment of which he worked, should have been named in his honor. Dr. Farrand died at the age of forty-five, on March 18, 1883.

Jacob Farrand's son, WILLIAM R. FARRAND, carried on the family's traditional association with the Hospital. He was born September 9, 1853, and at the age of seventeen entered his father's business. A few years later, he became a partner in a firm manufacturing organs and ultimately became sole proprietor of the Farrand Organ Company. Under his supervision was built the pipe organ used at the Chicago Exposition of 1893, which was later installed at the University of

Michigan. Farrand disposed of his interest in the company and in his later years devoted himself to the real estate and insurance business.

He was a member of one of the volunteer fire companies; president of the Police Commission; president of the Wayne County Sunday School Association; member of the Public Lighting Commission, the Board of Education, and the state legislature. He was a member of the Harper Board of Trustees from 1891 until his death in 1930.

Reference: Clarence M. and M. Agnes Burton, eds. *History of Wayne County* (Detroit-Chicago, 1930), III, 396, 697; V, 449; Burr, *Medical History of Michigan*, II, 237; *Harper Hospital Bulletin*, II, First Series (June, 1891), 1; *Detroit Medical Journal* (February, 1909), p. 47; Farmer's *History of Detroit*, various references, see index; also miscellaneous material, Harper Hospital Archives.

On July 22, 1934, RINGLING BROTHERS-BARNUM & BAILEY CIRCUS began a three-day showing in Detroit. On the evening of July 22, four of the show's 1,450 employees reported sick and their ailment was diagnosed as possible typhoid fever. They were immediately sent to Harper Hospital, where the diagnosis was confirmed for three of the patients. Public health officials were alerted, and on July 23 and 24, the rest of the employees were examined for fever or other suspicious symptoms, and an additional 70 persons were hospitalized at Harper. The show moved to Flint where it opened on July 25, and 7 more individuals were sent back to Harper. Of the 77 admitted in these 2 latter groups, 54 were proven typhoid cases. Six of them died in the Hospital. During succeeding days, other members of the circus personnel were hospitalized in Lansing, Kalamazoo, and Fort Wayne, Indiana.

The outbreak of this epidemic alarmed Detroit, and health authorities prepared for the worst. City, state, and federal health forces were mobilized to determine the source of the disease. Investigation led to the conclusion that the infection originated in Ohio where the circus had performed prior to visiting Detroit. It was the opinion of investigators that the typhoid came from polluted drinking water, although the community in which the initial infection was picked up could not be exactly determined. It was pointed out that the World War I veterans, of whom there were many with the circus, showed a high degree of immunity due to having received vaccine in the service. Those who suffered disproportionately were performers, such as clowns, acrobats, and trapeze artists, who refused to be vaccinated, fearing it would interfere with their muscular activities.

Immunization, together with improved sanitary regulations in the commissary, checked further spread of the disease. Prompt isolation in Harper Hospital of those stricken was credited by the Detroit Department of Health with possibly having stopped the epidemic from spreading throughout the city.

Unfortunately for Detroit's circus lovers, one of the precautionary measures taken when the first cases were discovered was to halt the sale of food and drink to the public. Thus, there was no pink lemonade, cotton candy, or peanuts which are so much a part of a circus.

Reference: *City Health*, IX, No. 1 (Bulletin, Detroit Department of Health [January-July, 1935] 19 ff.

THEODORE A. McGRAW, M.D. was a member of another of those dynasties which so strongly influenced the destiny of Harper Hospital. Dr. McGraw's father,

ALEXANDER C. McGRAW, one of the original Harper trustees, operated a shoe store and factory at 171 Jefferson Avenue and was recognized as one of Detroit's leading merchants. Active in civic affairs, he was president of the Detroit Mechanics' Society (1841–53); vice-president of the Detroit Medical College (1885), and a juror in the famous railroad conspiracy case in 1851. His residence was at 418 Jefferson Avenue. He died November 2, 1893.

Dr. Theodore McGraw was born in Detroit, November 4, 1839. After graduation from the University of Michigan, he went to Germany to study medicine and was later graduated from the College of Physicians and Surgeons, New York. In 1863, Dr. McGraw entered the Union army as acting assistant surgeon, serving in hospitals in and around Chattanooga. In March, 1865, he became a member of the staff of Major General J. H. Wilson and accompanied him on the famous cavalry raid through Alabama and Georgia. Left behind in charge of a field hospital, he was captured by General Nathan Bedford Forrest.

After the war, he established a practice in Detroit, with his home and office on East Jefferson near Riopelle. One of the leaders in the founding of the Detroit Medical College, he served it as professor of surgery and as president. He became nationally recognized in his profession and was vice-president of the American Medical Association and president of the American Surgical Association. In 1905, the University of Michigan conferred an honorary degree upon him in recognition of his services as an educator and scientist. He was a member of the staffs of Harper and St. Mary's for nearly forty-five years. Dr. McGraw was regarded as "a doctor's doctor," an eloquent and convincing lecturer, and a philosopher who once remarked that " 'Given up by the doctors' is the stock in trade of quacks, impostors and cultists." Dr. McGraw married Miss Alice Simpson in 1866. In 1914 he retired from active practice and died September 6, 1921. His son, Dr. Theodore A. McGraw, Jr., also was a member of the Harper staff, further cementing the family relationship to the Hospital by marrying the daughter of Dr. Howard W. Longyear.

References: Farmer's *History of Detroit* (various references, see index); *The Leucocyte* (October, 1921); *Bulletin of the Wayne County Medical Society* (October 10, 1921); and the Theodore A. McGraw Papers, Wayne State University Archives.

For almost the entire period of its existence, Harper Hospital has relied upon the BUHL FAMILY for direction and support. Buhls were members of the Board of Trustees for forty-five years, and the family was still represented on the board in 1963 by Arthur H. Buhl, Jr., who was elected in 1951. Even when the board roster did not contain the Buhl name, the Hospital was, in each of four generations, the beneficiary of the family's philanthropy.

FREDERICK and CHRISTIAN BUHL, brothers, went to Detroit in 1833 from their native Zelienople, Pennsylvania. Of German ancestry, Frederick was born in 1806 and Christian four years later. In Detroit they established an outstanding record of business success, public service, and philanthropy. The two brothers formed the firm of F. & C. H. Buhl at the northwest corner of Jefferson and Griswold. They engaged in the manufacture and retailing of fur hats, caps, and gloves. Frederick made the hats; Christian bought the furs from the Indians and trappers and handled the selling end of the business. Eventually, they became affiliated with the successor to the American Fur Trading Company, originally founded by John Jacob Astor.

In 1855, Christian Buhl formed a partnership in a hardware business, which ultimately led to a successful manufacturing and distributing enterprise. The family acquired Detroit property, much of which was retained. In 1963, Buhl interests included manufacturing, hardware and appliance distribution, finance and property management.

Frederick Buhl was elected alderman in 1845 and served a term as mayor in 1845–46. He was vice-president of the Fire Department Society, one of the founders of the Board of Trade (predecessor of the Board of Commerce), director of the Michigan State Bank, and a co-founder of the Detroit National Bank. One of the original members of the Harper Hospital Board of Trustees, he served from 1859 to 1884 when, for reasons of health, he resigned. He played a major part in the financing and building of the old Harper building on John R Street. Frederick Buhl died in 1890.

Christian Buhl was no less a personality than his brother. He was equally interested in matters involving civic affairs, and he too was mayor of Detroit, in 1860–61. He was a member of the Harper board from 1887 until his death in 1894. The Buhl out-patient building was the gift of the Buhl family in memory of Theodore H. Buhl, the son of Christian.

In 1912, Theodore's son, ARTHUR H. BUHL, SR., was elected a member of the Board of Trustees. He held that post until 1920.

Reference: Farmer's *History of Detroit,* numerous citations, see index; Clarence M. and M. Agnes Burton, eds. *History of Wayne County* (Chicago-Detroit, 1930), III, 222; *Harper Hospital Bulletin,* V, First Series (February, 1895), 96; *One Business, One Family, One Hundred Years* (centennial publication, Buhl Sons Company, Buhl Land Co. [Detroit, 1955]).

CHARLES STUART TRIPLER is one of the most interesting figures in Michigan medical history. He was born in New York City, January 10, 1806. As a youth, he was apprenticed to an apothecary, and learning the business stimulated an interest in medicine, with the result that he entered the College of Physicians and Surgeons. Upon graduation he entered the army as assistant to the surgeon at West Point. In the following years, he was stationed at various army posts and served three years with the troops during the Seminole Indian War in Florida. In 1836 he was sent to Detroit. At the outbreak of the Mexican War, he accompanied troops from Michigan to Mexico where he saw considerable campaigning and where he was placed in charge of the army's general hospital in Mexico City.

Following that war, he again served at several posts on the western frontier, and in 1854 he was placed in charge of the Department of the Pacific with headquarters in San Francisco. At the outbreak of the Civil War he was post surgeon at Newport Barracks, Kentucky. In 1862 he was assigned to the Army of the Potomac as medical director. In the shuffle of commanders during the early and unsuccessful—from the Federal standpoint—campaigns, Tripler was removed, and at his own request was reassigned to Detroit, which by that time he regarded as his home. It was while he was on this duty that he became interested in establishing the army general hospital in Detroit which became Harper Hospital. During 1865, he headed the Department of Ohio which included Michigan. His headquarters were at Cincinnati. After the war he returned to Detroit, although he remained in the army. Army surgeons were permitted to see private patients, which explains why he was on the Harper Hospital staff in 1866 when it became a civilian hospital. He did not long survive, however, dying of a malignancy at Cincinnati,

October 20, 1866. A devout churchman, he was a lay reader in the Episcopal church and a vestryman for various parishes in places where he was stationed during military service. He was buried from St. John's Episcopal Church, Detroit. His grave is in Elmwood Cemetery.

Tripler General Hospital, Honolulu, well-known to hundreds of GI's during and after World War II, was named in his honor.

Reference: Tripler Papers, Wayne State University Archives.

Harper Hospital owes a great deal to COL. GEORGE W. LEE, Civil War quartermaster at Detroit, under whose direction Harper Hospital was built for military purposes in 1864. Colonel Lee was an industrious and conscientious officer, always willing to co-operate with the Board of Trustees. He helped materially in effecting the transfer of the Hospital and its equipment from military to civilian status after the war.

Born in Chenango County, New York, in 1812, Colonel Lee settled at Howell, Michigan in 1836. For several years he was a farmer, later becoming a successful merchant and newspaper publisher. He was one of the founders of the Republican party "under the oaks" at Jackson in 1854 and was a presidential elector in 1860, casting his ballot for Abraham Lincoln. For several years after the war he was Indian agent for Michigan. He died at Ypsilanti, June 8, 1882.

Reference: *History of Washtenaw County*, II (Chicago, 1881), pp. 1217–18; *Lansing Republican*, June 14, 1882.

In pressing the Federal authorities so hard for a military hospital for Detroit, DR. JOSEPH TUNNICLIFF was not motivated entirely by altruism. Being a politician, he had his eye on election returns. A Michigan hospital, it appeared to his practical mind, would give medical care to the wounded, and it would also be filled with properly appreciative voters in uniform.

Shortly before the crucial 1864 national and state elections, Tunnicliff called Governor Austin Blair's attention to the fact that there were hundreds of Michigan convalescents in the hospitals around Washington. He thought it would be a good idea if they could be given thirty-day furloughs beginning about October 12. That would get them home in time to cast their ballots. "This would give great encouragement and tone to the Union home vote," he observed. "Too bad Harper Hospital isn't completed, but even if that is finished in October as anticipated, it can't hold a tenth part of them."

Reference: Dr. Tunnicliff to Gov. Blair, September 3, 1864, in the Austin Blair Papers, Burton Historical Collection.

FRANK GROSS was born March 8, 1846 in Portage County, Ohio, but spent most of his life in Michigan, in or near Grand Rapids. He enlisted at Grand Rapids, September 8, 1862 for three years in the Sixth Michigan Cavalry. Following his discharge from Harper Hospital in 1865, he returned to his home at Laphamsville (now Rockford) Michigan where he was a farmer. His service record describes him as five foot six inches tall, light complexion, blue eyes, and dark hair. He married Ruth Amelia Upson, March 20, 1873, and they had two children. Gross retired prior to 1915 and lived in Grand Rapids where he died May 6, 1917.

Reference: *Michigan Adjutant General Reports*, Michigan State Archives, Lansing, Michigan.

Some of the dissension referred to in the text, which troubled the staff, may have stemmed from the trustees and their families, particularly the Duffields and McGraws. Each clan may have felt it possessed an overlordship where Harper Hospital was concerned. While this feeling did not break out into open antagonism, evidences that it existed are unmistakable. DIVIE B. DUFFIELD had great hopes that his son, DR. GEORGE DUFFIELD, would be made superintendent of the Hospital. The younger Duffield was made assistant resident in 1881, and in that junior capacity, he viewed the work of DR. THEODORE A. McGRAW with rather lofty disdain. "McGraw removed a spleen weighing from 19 to 22 pounds from a man Monday and the man lived three hours and died of nervous shock—Scientific murder, I call it," George Duffield wrote to his brother, BETHUNE.

The following year George spent studying abroad, while his father and mother pulled strings at home to get him a top staff position at Harper. From belittling remarks, it is apparent that Dr. McGraw appeared to the elder Duffields as the obstacle to their son's ambitions. "Dr. Gailey [the superintendent in 1882] is hoping the Faculty will let him put out his sign and Dr. Farrand [David O.] promises to use his influence, but Dr. G. fears McGraw will not consent," Mrs. Duffield wrote George. A few days later she described an operation performed by Dr. McGraw in which the patient died. "And worse still," she commented, "the operation revealed that the Dr. had made a mistake in his diagnosis. . . . I shall not have as much faith in him as before."

Later in 1882, when George Duffield was about to return from Europe, his father wrote that he had talked with J. S. Farrand "as to yourself in connection with the new Harper Hospital. He said there was no one he would so like to see at the head of the new Harper as you, and if Dr. Gailey should want to leave, as he heard he might . . . he would be glad to do what he could to secure you the position."

But unfortunately for young Dr. Duffield's hopes, Gailey was not ready to give up the superintendency, and to the shock and horror of the Duffields, George was offered his old post as assistant resident, "and without any salary."

"I would not consent to have you come back from Continental schools to take an inferior position of that sort," wrote the outraged Divie B. The father told the Hospital officials that he preferred to have George start independent practice, adding that "I believed you to be a better physician today than ⅔rds of those now practicing." He concluded his letter to his son with the flat injunction that if a subordinate post at Harper should be offered, "your mother and myself wish you to peremptorily decline any such offer if made."

Reference: Duffield Papers, Burton Historical Collection.

Not all of the original Harper buildings were torn down in the summer of 1884 after the opening of the new Hospital. One of them, built for the Detroit College of Medicine between two of the original pavilions, was sold to an enterprising Detroit businessman and moved to a new location at 3513 Beaubien, near Eliot. The two-story structure, with its ornate windows, elaborate friezing, and columned porch, was occupied by the Medical College from 1868 to the fall of 1883. After its removal, the building was used successively for small manufacturing businesses, by a storage company, two groceries, two gospel halls, a restaurant, and during the past fifty years as a rooming house. Although the elegant cupola and the porch have been removed, the roof brackets, the flat gable, and the round top windows remain as they were ninety-five years ago. The building was discovered by Professor Leslie L. Hanawalt in 1962 in his research on the history of Wayne State University.

PERPETUAL FREE BED endowments were a natural outgrowth of the Free Bed Fund. Free Bed Fund benefits, determined at a fixed weekly rate, ran out when the subscription was used up. To an extent, then, the fund was a form of prepaid hospital care, anticipating Blue Cross. The Perpetual Free Bed Fund, on the other hand, continued to provide service in perpetuity.

The first Perpetual Free Beds were endowed by J. S. Farrand. He contributed $6,000, the income from which was to maintain two beds, one in his name and one in the name of his wife. For a while thereafter, $3,000 was the accepted rate for support of a bed in perpetuity. Donors were given handsome certificates, having somewhat the appearance of stock certificates, acknowledging the contribution and stating that

. . . the donor is entitled to the privileges of a free bed in a ward in the Hospital with power to devise the same. In default of such devise such free bed shall become the sole property of said Hospital and its successors, to be maintained, however, under the above name [of the donor] as a Free Bed in Perpetuity.

It was soon found that $3,000 was not a sufficient endowment, and the price began to go up. In 1889, about six years after the original Farrand subscription, Hiram Walker paid $15,000 for two perpetual free beds. In 1900, the trustees announced that a free bed endowment was not acceptable at less than $10,000. Two years later, the Detroit Teachers Association was asked to pay $12,000, it being pointed out that "such endowments now earn only five per cent." However, the trustees finally, although reluctantly, accepted $10,000 from the teachers.

James E. Scripps, founder and proprietor of the *Evening News* (now the *Detroit News*) insisted that a bed endowed in perpetuity should be precisely that, regardless of the possibility that the donor himself might not be perpetual. In a letter dated April 30, 1889 to S. M. Cutcheon, president of the Harper board, relative to a $5,000 bed endowment for the benefit of his paper's employees, Scripps stated:

While the life of the incorporation now engaged in the publication of the *Evening News* in the city of Detroit is limited to 30 years, the newspaper will, without doubt, continue in existence for five times that period, or even longer. There will also probably be printers in Detroit as long as it continues a city. For the benefit of the editors, reporters, printers, pressmen, clerks and all other persons employed in the printing and publishing of the *Evening News,* and in the event of their not requiring the benefaction then of the printers of Detroit generally, I desire to endow a perpetual free bed in Harper Hospital, provided that it can be done in such a way that irrespective of the life of any individual or corporation, the benefits contemplated may be perpetual so long as the said newspaper continues in existence or printers practice their calling in Detroit.

This was agreed to by the trustees and Scripps' $5,000 was accepted.

On June 10, 1889, Cutcheon reported that since January 1 of that year he had obtained subscriptions totaling $111,500 for perpetual free beds from the following: J. S. Farrand, A. C. McGraw, J. L. Hudson, R. A. Alger, Hiram Walker, E. J.

Penniman, C. H. Buhl, William H. Elliott, C. A. Black, Simon J. Murphy, Eleanor J. Swain, James E. Scripps, Frederick Buhl, William A. Moore, and George F. Moore.

Reference: *Harper Hospital* (Detroit, 1886), p. 78; Harper Hospital Trustees' Minutes 1883–93, pp. 146, 151–54; 1897–1913, pp. 65, 88.

A recluse and, apparently, somewhat of a miser, JAMES THOMPSON won no popularity contests among his neighbors. His "peculiarities of disposition and erratic temperament often made trouble," it was said after his death in 1881. Known locally as "Scotch" Thompson, he was born in Ayrshire, Scotland, about 1803 and emigrated to the United States in 1834. Originally a printer of calico in Kilmarnock, he worked at that trade in Philadelphia before settling on a farm close to the Macomb-Lapeer county line. He lived there until 1876, when he moved into the village of Almont. His chief interest was the breeding and raising of fine horses for which he gained a wide reputation. It was said that he was "something of an artist and poet, inclining to the terrible in imagination and description."

Reference: *History of Macomb County* (Chicago, 1882), p. 764.

There are individuals who seemingly amass fortunes for the express purpose of giving their money away to benefit mankind. WILLIAM KIEFT COYL was such a man. He looked upon success as a trust. Born in New Haven, Connecticut, February 13, 1808, he was the son of a sea captain who lost his life in the War of 1812. Coyl grew up on a farm, receiving only a limited education. As a youth, he moved to Canandaigua, New York, where he learned the trade of manufacturing farm implements. About 1832 he went to Michigan, locating in Birmingham where he married Jane Bell, helped lay out the town, and is said to have produced the first iron plows made in Michigan.

Within a few years he moved to Detroit, becoming a merchant and hotel keeper. He operated the Checker Store on Woodbridge, just west of Woodward. The place took its name from the alternate black and white squares with which the front was painted. Later he moved to the Woodward-Campus Martius location, conducting a produce and forwarding business. He is credited with making the first shipment of meat from Detroit to the East coast.

William Kieft Coyl was ardently interested in education and has been called the "father of Detroit's public school system." As ward assessor and school inspector, he personally supported the city's first free school, held in rooms above his store. He paid the teacher's salary out of his own pocket. He was also a generous contributor to Miss Sarah Hunt's Seminary for Young Ladies. The only elected public office he held was membership on the Board of Estimates.

Coyl had six children, three of whom—two boys and a girl—grew to maturity. He invested heavily in Iowa lands, and his sons settled there. Both enlisted when the Civil War broke out. The elder, William H., became lieutenant colonel in the Ninth Iowa Infantry and died in 1866, the result of battle wounds. The younger, Samuel, was with the Sixth Iowa Cavalry, serving on the western plains against the Indians. Alkali dust infected his eyes, resulting in total blindness. Samuel Coyl died in Detroit in 1893, leaving a substantial estate and bequeathing a large part of it to St. Luke's Home and Hospital.

JEAN COYL, described as a beautiful woman of much grace and charm, attended Albion College and after graduation either attended or taught at Canandaigua, New York. She returned to Detroit, however, to serve her father as secretary and business confidante until his death in 1883. Aware of his desires regarding the disposition of his estate, she managed it ably, even to the extent of denying herself some of the necessities of life. She died at the age of fifty-five. A photograph of her as a young girl of about seventeen was copied as a portrait by the celebrated Detroit painter, Percy Ives, on commission from the Harper Hospital Board of Trustees after her death.

References: Silas Farmer, *The History of Detroit and Michigan* (Detroit, 1889), II, 1136; *Harper Hospital Bulletin*, V, First Series (February, 1895), 93; *Detroit News-Tribune*, November 4, 1894; March 16, 1895; and April 26, 1896.

The first and for many years the only woman member of the Harper Hospital medical staff was HELEN FRANCES WARNER, M.D. Born in Vermont in 1842, she was the daughter of William Warner, president of the Detroit Bridge & Iron Works. William Warner was a close friend of Dr. George Russel, and it may have been through the latter's influence that Dr. Warner received her staff appointment.

She graduated from the old Detroit High School, was a member of the first class to graduate from Vassar College, and in 1872 became the first woman to graduate from the medical school of the University of Michigan. She joined the Harper staff soon thereafter, serving until about 1899 when she retired because of poor health. She died October 23, 1905. Thousands of Detroiters of an earlier generation knew the Warner family through Dr. Warner's sister, Harriette Anna Bishop who for many years was on the faculty of old Central High School.

The second earliest known woman staff member was DR. HARRIET A. GERRY, a native of Ypsilanti and daughter of Dr. Ruth Gerry, said to have been one of the country's pioneer medical women. Dr. Harriet Gerry attended the state normal school at Ypsilanti and took her medical degree at the University of Michigan in 1883. She entered practice in Port Huron, but soon went to Detroit as assistant to Dr. E. W. Jenks. She was appointed gynecologist on the Harper staff in 1897, but developing tuberculosis, she soon went to Arizona. She died in Detroit in March, 1899.

Other early women staff members were DR. FLORENCE HUSING, listed as consulting physician in 1908, and DRS. EVA M. FINN and FLORENCE CHADWICK, the latter a pediatrician. Their appointments dated from 1921.

Reference: Burr, *Medical History of Michigan*, II, 384; *Harper Hospital Bulletin*, X, First Series (June, 1899), 13; XVIII, First Series (February, 1908), 179; I, Second Series (July, 1921), 7; I, Second Series (December, 1921), 5.

JOHN KNOX GAILEY, M.D., born in Sterling, New York, went to Michigan as a child and grew up in Birmingham. He graduated in 1874 from Michigan Agricultural College (now Michigan State University), after which he studied medicine with Dr. David O. Farrand. In 1877 he received a medical degree from New York University. After spending two years as a mine surgeon in the Copper Country of Michigan's Upper Peninsula, Dr. Gailey studied general surgery for thirteen months in Europe. In 1880 he was made home surgeon and superintendent of Harper Hospital with the privilege of conducting a private practice, which soon became large and lucrative. Dr. Gailey died in Detroit in 1928.

Reference: Burr, *Medical History of Michigan*, II, 556.

By any standards which may be applied, LYSTRA EGGERT GRETTER stands out as one of the most remarkably able and effective women in Detroit's long history. Mrs. Gretter was born in Canada, September 3, 1858, the daughter of Dutch and Swiss parents. Her father, a doctor, served in the Civil War, and after peace was restored he moved to Greensboro, North Carolina. When she was nineteen years old, Lystra Eggert married John B. Gretter, a four-year veteran of the Confederate army. He died a few years after their marriage, and Mrs. Gretter moved to the vicinity of Buffalo, New York. Faced with the necessity of supporting herself, she enrolled in 1886 in the Buffalo General Hospital Training School for Nurses, from which she graduated two years later.

At that time the Farrand Training School was seeking a new principal. Even before her graduation, Mrs. Gretter was recommended for the position, so outstanding was her training record. She accepted the post which she filled for the next nineteen years, and in doing so materially advanced the profession of nursing, not only in Detroit, but throughout the United States.

Mrs. Gretter combined outstanding administrative talent with the characteristics of a true teacher. Under her, the training of nurses changed from a system of apprenticeship to a sound educational program aimed at the highest professional standards. She revised and devised a curriculum at the Farrand School which eliminated much of the "scullery maid" drudgery of nursing training, replacing it with technical and academic education of a high order.

So imbued was she with the ideals of nursing as a profession that in 1893 she was instrumental in drafting the Florence Nightingale Pledge which to the nurse is what the Hippocratic Oath is to the physician.

The Florence Nightingale Oath was first administered to the Farrand graduating class of 1893, and since it has been generally adopted as the climax of "capping," or graduating exercises in training schools all over the world. While Mrs. Gretter was assisted in preparing the original draft, it is universally conceded that the spirit behind the words of that noble pledge is hers.

Mrs. Gretter was always an innovator and originator. It was she who revised the long work day of student nurses from twelve hours to eight in order to provide time for study and recreation. Lacking text books, she wrote her own manuals of instruction, many of which are preserved in the Harper Hospital Archives.

In 1907, Mrs. Gretter relinquished her post at Farrand to become superintendent of the Detroit Visiting Nurse Association which she helped organize. Among her other professional contributions was her part in organizing the Farrand Training School Alumnae Association, and securing adoption of a registration, or nurses practice, act. She was influential in creating the Detroit Council on Community Nursing. She also is credited with persuading schools of higher learning to broaden their curricula in the field of nursing science. In 1920, the Farrand Alumnae established a scholarship in her name and honor, and in 1937, Wayne State University conferred an honorary degree upon her. She retired as head of the Visiting Nurse Association in 1923. Mrs. Gretter died April 30, 1951, survived by a daughter, Mrs. John C. Dodds, wife of a prominent Detroit physician and long-time member of the Harper Hospital staff.

Reference: Helen W. Munson, R.N., "Lystra E. Gretter," *American Journal of Nursing,* 49, No. 6 (June, 1949). Not to be overlooked are the voluminous files of Mrs. Gretter's correspondence, scrapbooks, and other pertinent documents in the Harper Hospital Archives.

The story about DR. JOHN HENRY CARSTENS and the lighted cigar becomes more plausible in connection with another incident related by his son, DR. HENRY R. CARSTENS.

"I had occasion to go to the Hospital one day to see my father," Colonel Carstens stated, "and upon arriving, I noticed his Cadillac, an early four-cylinder job, parked near the John R entrance with the engine running. I thought that was strange, and as I went up the steps, the old man came out the door. I asked him why he hadn't switched off the ignition.

" 'It wasn't worth the trouble,' replied the elder Carstens. 'I only had one appendectomy, and that damn car is so hard to crank.' "

Dr. Henry Carstens was born December 19, 1888, attended Detroit schools, the University of Michigan (1909), and Detroit College of Medicine (1911). After two years' study in Germany, he began practice in Detroit as an internist. Soon after ending his military service in World War II, he retired and in 1963 resided in Birmingham, Michigan.

As another example of the interlocking relationship of persons prominently identified with Harper, it might be noted that DR. LOUIS J. HIRSCHMAN married the daughter of J. H. Carstens. Dr. Hirschman, the son of Dr. Frederick Hirschman, a mine surgeon, was born August 15, 1878 at Republic, Michigan. Dr. Louis J. attended Detroit College of Medicine where he later became professor of proctology. He was editor of the *Harper Hospital Bulletin* from 1906 to 1910. In 1963 he was living, retired, at Traverse City.

After Dr. J. H. Carstens had become established as one of Detroit's leading surgeons, he built a splendid house at Woodward and Mack. The house, constructed of striking green marble, quarried in Maryland, was a show place and landmark. His colleagues, passing by, would observe that "each of those stones represents an ovarian cyst." The elder Carstens retired from active practice in 1911, being honored on that occasion by a banquet attended by medical leaders and civic dignitaries. He died August 13, 1920.

Reference: C. M. Burton, *The City of Detroit, Michigan 1701–1922* (Detroit-Chicago, 1922), IV, 898; *Harper Hospital Bulletin*, V, Third Series (June, 1942), 50; XVII, Third Series (September-October, 1959), 263; Burr, *Medical History of Michigan*, II, 870.

By a short flight of imagination, THE GRACE HOSPITAL's origin can be traced to Harper Hospital. It came into being as a homeopathic hospital partly because homeopaths were not permitted to practice at Harper.

In 1869, Amos Chaffee, a wealthy and prosperous Detroiter, donated a lot for a hospital, but as nothing was immediately done, the land reverted to him. In 1886, the homeopathic physicians of Detroit felt the need for a hospital. A number of prominent people, including Chaffee, John S. Newberry, and James McMillan, felt favorably toward homeopaths and lent their support. Chaffee donated the building site at Willis and John R. A board of trustees was elected, including D. M. Ferry and Frederick Buhl, both of whom served as Harper trustees also. A medical staff was appointed and The Grace Hospital was opened as a homeopathic institution in 1888.

Within ten years, efforts were made to admit allopaths or "regulars" to the staff, stirring up quite a controversy. The latter won out, however, and in 1901 Grace became a "dual" hospital, open to practitioners of both schools of medicine. In June, 1913, Grace opened a convalescent home or branch on West Grand

Boulevard and in 1941 opened its new branch, known as the Northwest Unit or new Grace Hospital, on Meyer Road at West Seven Mile.

Reference: *The First Fifty Years—The Grace Hospital* (Detroit, 1938); Harper Hospital Scrapbook I, p. 2; *Detroit Journal*, August 22, 1901; Burr, *Medical History of Michigan*, II, 604–06.

Had it not been for the influence, the leadership, and the generosity of J. L. Hudson and members of his family, particularly his nephews, Richard H. and Oscar Webber, Harper Hospital would undoubtedly be an institution of decidedly different character and lesser importance than it is. It is quite possible that, without the support of Hudson and his nephews, the Hospital might not even have survived to observe its one hundredth anniversary. For more than seventy-five years, it is fair to say, Hudsons and Webbers exerted a dominant and guiding influence over the affairs of the Hospital. To a very great degree their association has been responsible for Harper's identity as a civic institution.

Joseph L. Hudson was born in Newcastle-on-Tyne, England, October 17, 1846. He was the son of Richard and Elizabeth Lowthian (a sturdy Northumbrian name). There were seven children, four sons and three daughters. Joseph's brothers were Richard, Jr., James B., and William. His sisters included Mary Eleanor who married Joseph T. Webber.

The family migrated first to Canada, then to the United States, about 1855. They lived in Grand Rapids, Pontiac, and then Ionia, where the elder Hudson was a clothing merchant, ultimately in partnership with his son. In 1877, Joseph moved to Detroit where, after four years of association with Christopher Mabley, he established his own store on Campus Martius. In 1891, he moved to Gratiot and Farmer, the old site of the First Presbyterian Church. Periodic expansion resulted in the huge downtown department store which became world-renowned as a great merchandising enterprise.

J. L. Hudson never married, but nevertheless he became head of his family. He established stores in Toledo, Cleveland, and Buffalo which were managed by his brothers whose merchandising genius was comparable to his own.

Hudson's name quickly became synonymous with everything that was progressive and in the best interests of Detroit. He gave money away with an open hand for public purposes, but he always gave it wisely. Moreover, he was willing to devote his personal energies to worthwhile causes, and these qualities led to his election in 1887 to Harper's Board of Trustees, of which he became president in 1901. He retained that post until his death July 5, 1912 while on a visit to England. During the period of his stewardship, Harper not only expanded, but also weathered some grave crises which threatened its stability.

In 1912, Hudson's nephew, Richard H. Webber, was elected a Harper trustee, and in 1925, the latter's brother, Oscar, became a member of the board. Both were born in Ionia, Richard in 1879, Oscar in 1889. After attending high school in Ionia, Richard went to work as a stock helper in his uncle's Detroit store, and in 1912 he succeeded J. L. Hudson as president of the company, later becoming chairman and honorary chairman. He was made president of the Harper board in 1918, and in that capacity guided the institution through the difficult years of World War I and II and the depression of the 1930's. He relinquished the presidency in 1961, but remained on the board, having the longest tenure of any trustee and president.

Oscar Webber's career closely paralleled that of his brother. He started in the Detroit store as a cash boy in 1903. After graduation from old Detroit Central High School and the University of Michigan, he moved up through the company chain of command, becoming chairman.

The Webber brothers were known to have been among the leading financial contributors to Harper. Always having shunned the spotlight of publicity, despite their interest and participation in public affairs, their philanthropies have never been made a matter of general record.

The fourth member of the family, JAMES B. WEBBER, JR., became a Harper trustee in 1948. He was born in Detroit in 1911, his father, James B. Sr., being the brother of Richard and Oscar. After attending Trinity College and Harvard School of Business Administration, he, too, entered the J. L. Hudson Company business and also displayed great activity in civic affairs. His career, one of great promise, came to a sudden end with his unexpected death at the age of forty-five on August 28, 1956. At that time he was executive vice-president of the company.

To fill the gap caused by the death of James B. Webber, Jr., a namesake and grandnephew of J. L. Hudson was brought into the business in 1956. J. L. HUDSON, JR. was the son of J. L. Hudson II, who was the son of William Hudson, head of the family interests in Buffalo. J. L. Hudson, Jr. (or III) was born at Buffalo in 1931. A Yale graduate, he saw service with the army. During his summer vacations he worked as a stock boy in the Detroit store and eventually became president of the company. He followed the family pattern of community responsibility, serving as a bank director, director and vice-president of the United Foundation, director of the Detroit Symphony Society, and a trustee of Harper Hospital, being elected in 1957.

References: Paul Leake, *History of Detroit,* III (Chicago, 1912), 1186; Reading Room File, Burton Historical Collection; *Detroit Times,* January 28, 1956 and August 28, 1956; *Detroit Free Press,* July 12, 1960.

In 1901 Harper Hospital and its staff were called upon to care for the victims of one of the worst disasters in Detroit history. On the morning of November 26 of that year a boiler explosion rocked the PENBERTHY INJECTOR COMPANY plant on Detroit's Brooklyn Avenue. Several hundred employees were inside the three-story brick building at the time. It was exactly 9:30 A.M. when, without any warning, one of the plant's large boilers exploded with tremendous force. The floors above, laden with heavy lathes and foundry machinery, buckled and the brick walls caved in. Over 150 workers were buried in the rubble, some scalded by the escaping steam and others burned from the flames which followed the explosion. Fortunately, the Abbott Street end of the plant, constructed at a later time, was not damaged, and the employees in this section escaped to safety.

News of the disaster spread rapidly. Firemen rushed to the scene and put out the fires; ambulances from Harper, Emergency, Grace, and St. Mary's hospitals arrived in a matter of minutes to shuttle the wounded to hospitals; physicians from all over the Detroit area responded to the call to assist the injured and dying. Among the first to arrive was Dr. C. G. Jennings from Harper.

The scene was horrible. According to a *Detroit Journal* reporter, the injured were "crying, groaning, writhing in pain from their burns and shock." The cries of men buried in the basement rubble could be heard as workers hurriedly worked to remove the twisted debris. The families of workers milled about attempting to locate their loved ones. Nearby, panic-stricken children at the Houghton School were quieted by teachers after the explosion had shattered the school windows. Some of the children, whose fathers and relatives worked at the plant, witnessed the collapse of the building from their classrooms.

The physicians took charge of the casualties. They sent scores of injured to hospitals in ambulances. Other victims rode to the hospital in wagons, on mattresses donated by local residents. Homes in the area were converted into temporary hospitals to care for those too seriously injured to move. A morgue was set up in a nearby building for the mounting toll of dead. The doctors from Harper and other Detroit hospitals who worked all day and night on the scene were commended for their work by the police, press, and fire officials. A reporter described them as "running to and fro aiding the wounded, soothing the dying." Six of the most critically injured were taken to Harper. When the toll was taken at the end of the day, thirty were dead, fifteen still missing in the debris, and over fifty badly injured.

Detroit barely had time to hospitalize the victims of the Penberthy Injector Company explosion when another tragedy shook the city. At 7:30 P.M., November 28, two fast Wabash trains, carrying a combined passenger load of an estimated 500, crashed head-on near the town of Senaca, Lenawee County, sixty-nine miles west of Detroit. Within a few minutes news reached Detroit of the accident accompanied by an urgent call for doctors. Detroit police interrupted a meeting of the Detroit Medical Society and asked for volunteers. Led by Dr. Angus McLean of Harper Hospital, the physicians boarded a special train bound for the scene of the wreck. They arrived at Senaca at 10:30 P.M. to find the wrecked cars still afire and scores of injured groping about in the darkness. McLean and the Detroit contingent worked through the night to aid the victims. Thirty persons lost their lives and over 200 were badly injured. In both crises, Harper personnel were commended for their prompt help in saving lives of disaster victims.

Reference: *Detroit Journal,* November 26, 1901; November 28, 1901.

ELEANOR J. SWAIN, donor of the Swain Building, was a native of Albany, New York, born July 15, 1818. Her family went to Michigan when she was a child. In 1840 she married Theodore Champion, of Ypsilanti. Following his death, she married Isaac N. Swain, of Detroit, September 1, 1859. Mrs. Swain was charitably inclined, and Harper Hospital was a frequent beneficiary of her generosity. Among her gifts, other than the Swain Building, was the endowment of a free bed in 1889. A semi-invalid in the later years of her life, Mrs. Swain was confined to her home at 1115 West Fort Street where she died, February 11, 1896. Isaac N. Swain, a native of New York State, made a comfortable fortune as a speculator in land in southeastern Michigan. He died at Detroit, April 30, 1880.

Reference: *Harper Hospital Bulletin,* VI, First Series (April, 1896), 97; *Detroit Journal,* May 16, 1896; Farmer's *History of Detroit,* II (biographical edition: Detroit, 1889), 1232.

WILLIAM FRANCIS METCALF, M.D., the stormy petrel of the Harper staff in the early 1900's and the founder of Detroit General Hospital, was described as "an artistic surgeon." But due, apparently, to his volatile temperament, his career never quite managed to equal his potentialities. He became intimate with Henry Ford after performing surgery upon Mrs. Ford. Although he is credited with having interested Ford in becoming one of the backers of Detroit General, the two men soon became estranged. This was attributed to a clash of personalities, each man feeling that he should dominate policy and the direction of the hospital. After the break which resulted in Ford's taking over Detroit General and re-organizing it into Ford Hospital, Dr. Metcalf's prestige suffered, and he was little heard of thereafter. He retired from practice about 1927. Metcalf was born at Picton, Ontario, December 27, 1863 and died at Bayfield, Ontario, October 17, 1935. He was a graduate of the University of Michigan's medical school, class of 1888.

Reference: Ross and Catlin: *Landmarks of Wayne County and Detroit*, Part II, pp. 63–64; also, Ford Archives, Dearborn, Michigan.

Harper Hospital's high standards were maintained and its role in a grow-ing, dynamic community was guided to a very large extent by the administrative capabilities of DR. STEWART HAMILTON.

A native of Detroit, born June 20, 1880, Hamilton grew up in Joliet, Illinois. Following his graduation in 1905 from the Northwestern University Medical School, he served his internship at Harper. He then entered private practice at Painsdale, Michigan, in the Upper Peninsula mining country, after which he re-turned to Detroit. While in the Upper Peninsula he became interested in hospital administration and in 1910 was named medical director at Harper. Upon the death of Dr. Wayne Smith in 1915, he was appointed superintendent. Two years later, the title was changed to director.

Under Hamilton's administration, Harper underwent the greatest expansion program in its history. When he first became associated with the Hospital, it had 180 beds. He saw it grow to more than 600. "The outstanding feature of his in-fluence on the Hospital," wrote Dr. George Kamperman, "has been the ability to maintain the highest quality of medical service to this community through the years, and any effort to lessen the quality of medical care for reasons of expedi-ency met with his immediate disapproval."

Dr. Hamilton died December 18, 1945.

Reference: *Harper Hospital Bulletin*, III, Third Series (December, 1945), 104; George Kamperman, "Memorial to Dr. Stewart Hamilton" (MS in Harper Hospital Archives), 1946.

DR. THOMAS K. GRUBER became one of the country's best known hospital administrators. He was appointed assistant director at Harper in 1915, remaining there until 1919, except for time spent in military service. He was adjutant of the Harper Base Hospital 17. Until 1922 he was superintendent of Highland Hos-pital, Rochester, New York, but returned to Detroit to assume the superintendency of Receiving Hospital. He remained there seven years when he was appointed gen-eral superintendent of Wayne County General Hospital, Eloise. He died while holding that post on August 7, 1949, at the age of sixty-five.

Reference: *Detroit News*, August 8, 1949.

Dr. William J. Stapleton, Jr. recalled that as a young doctor in the early 1900's word began to get around about the remarkable work being performed by a little-known surgeon in a small west side hospital. The young medical men of Detroit went to observe and came away with loud praises for DR. MAX BALLIN. Ballin did not long remain obscure. He soon had an international reputation which, through association with Harper, gave the Hospital added luster.

A German Jew, Max Ballin was born in Nordhausen, Germany, August 13, 1869. He studied medicine at the Universities of Munich, Freiburg, and Berlin, receiving his diploma from the latter in 1892. After a year of service in the German army and four years of postgraduate study, Ballin went to the United States, settling at Leadville, Colorado in 1896. His work there attracted the attention of Dr. Donald Maclean, who persuaded him to go to Detroit. He did so, becoming affiliated with the old Detroit Sanatorium about 1901. In 1906 he became a member of the Harper staff. Eventually he became chief of staff from 1920 to 1928.

Ballin was highly respected as a diagnostician, technician, teacher, and researcher. He was particularly skilled in thyroid surgery, a field in which he pioneered. In 1932, he and Dr. Plinn F. Morse were awarded a gold medal by the American Medical Association for work on parathyroid glands.

A warm, kindly man, Dr. Ballin nevertheless was a strict disciplinarian. One of his associates wrote that he was an early riser who required his associates to be at the Hospital at 7:15 A.M. including Sundays. "Following rounds, he would have office hours even on Sundays and return to the Hospital in the afternoon to see the very sick patients. We were always glad when he made his annual trip to Europe so we could rest from this strenuous routine."

Dr. Ballin died at Detroit on March 3, 1934.

Reference: *Harper Hospital Bulletin,* XVII, Third Series (January-February, 1959), 27 ff.; George Kamperman, "Max Ballin, M.D., An Address Given Before the Staff of Harper Hospital," Friday, March 9, 1934 (Harper Hospital Archives); *Detroit Times,* March 5, 1934.

The work of Drs. Charles G. Jennings and Ernest W. Haass in giving Harper Hospital a position of preëminence in internal medicine was carried on by DR. HUGO A. FREUND famed as an internist and diagnostician. Connected with the hospital beginning in 1909 he was chief of the Department of Medicine from 1927 to 1945.

A native Detroiter born in 1881, Freund attended Central High School, and his graduation from the University of Michigan Medical School in 1905 was followed by intensive postgraduate study in Germany. A captain in the army medical corps in World War I, he soon began to win wide recognition in his special field after that conflict. Along with an enviable reputation as a teacher and administrator, he was highly regarded as a technician. Dr. Plinn F. Morse credited him with being one of the first to bring the services of the electrocardiograph to American medicine and to introduce a new drug, "atophan," in this country, with the result that a new trend was developed in pharmacology, leading to the search for special drugs for particular disease processes. In his later years of practice, Freund gave special attention to arthritic diseases.

In 1917, he was made a member of the Detroit Board of Health, a post he retained until 1930. During that tenure, Detroit experienced an outbreak of smallpox (1923), and largely under Dr. Freund's direction 820,000 citizens were vaccinated, resulting in the prompt suppression of the disease. He also played an important role in development of the city's Herman Kiefer Hospital. Some of his colleagues say his greatest contribution, particularly to Harper, was his organization of the intern and resident program.

A close friend of Senator James Couzens, a Harper trustee, Dr. Freund was given much of the responsibility for administering the Children's Fund of Michigan. In 1936, he was appointed to a four-year term on the Detroit Welfare Commission. In his later years, Dr. Freund was a consultant to the Ford Motor Company on industrial diseases.

Many honors came to him, and his professional associations were many. He was a Diplomat of the American Board of Internal Medicine, a member of the American Association of Pathologists and Bacteriologists and the Central Society for Clinical Research, a fellow of the American College of Physicians, and president of the Michigan Chapter of the Arthritis and Rheumatism Association.

Dr. Freund died December 24, 1952.

Reference: *Harper Hospital Bulletin*, XI, Third Series (January-February, 1953), 3; (July-August, 1953), 111–18; *The Detroit Free Press*, December 25, 1952.

GEORGE A. KAMPERMAN, M.D., was born at Zeeland, Michigan in 1881. After being graduated from the University of Michigan Medical School in 1907, he remained on the faculty until 1912. Then, following a period of study in Vienna, he went to Detroit, joining the Harper staff in 1913. From 1933 until his retirement in 1944, he was chief of staff. After retirement and until his death, his close association with the Hospital continued with membership on the Board of Trustees. In 1958, the University of Michigan conferred an honorary degree upon him.

Active both in professional and civic affairs, Dr. Kamperman was president of the Central Association of Obstetricians and Gynecologists, the American Gynecological Society, the Detroit Academy of Medicine, and a member of the American College of Surgeons. An avid art collector and enthusiast, he was a trustee of the Founders Society of the Detroit Institute of Arts. He died March 30, 1961.

Reference: *Detroit News*, March 31, 1961.

When DR. PLINN F. MORSE died February 18, 1962, his long-time friend and colleague, Dr. Robert Moehlig wrote:

Doctor Morse came to Harper Hospital in 1913 and it was not long before he was the friend and confidant of the internes, residents and attending staff. We soon learned that here was a man with an encyclopedic knowledge—not alone of medicine, but of philosophy, psychology, and the arts. His knowledge of the classics and of the Bible was a revelation to us all. Summarizing Dr. Morse's talents, one can say that here was a man bordering on genius.

Plinn Morse was born in Middleville, Michigan, December 22, 1885 and received his M.D. degree from the University of Michigan in 1909. For the next year he was instructor in pathology. Soon after he went to Detroit, he joined the Harper staff as assistant pathologist, but within a year was named pathologist. For forty-five years he was director of laboratory and research for the Hospital. For his work in pathology and research, he won many honors. Of particular significance was the recognition he gained from work on parathyroid physiology in association with his close friend, Dr. Max Ballin, in 1932.

Morse belonged to a long list of professional and honorary societies, and was a Founding Fellow of the American College of Pathology. He served as a lieutenant in World War I.

Writing Dr. Morse's obituary, Dr. William J. Stapleton, Jr. spoke glowingly of his ability as a teacher and as the author of many outstanding medical papers. He was a profound student of medical history.

Reference: *Detroit Medical News*, LIII, No. 45 (March 12, 1962), 8.

Among the more recent Harper Hospital research projects of outstanding significance was the development of a "mechanical heart" in co-operation with General Motors Corporation. On January 9, 1951, the trustees were informed that General Motors had approached Dr. F. D. Dodrill, of the Harper staff, concerning the device, with the request that space be provided in the Hospital where some of the work could be done. The request was granted, and working as a team, Dr. Dodrill and General Motors technicians perfected the heart which was the first of its kind in medical history to be used on a human patient undergoing heart surgery. The project was aided by the Michigan Heart Association.

On October 17, 1952, the Board of Trustees took official cognizance of the project on the occasion of the public announcement of what had been accomplished. There was a motion of commendation to the Hospital's research department, to Dr. Dodrill and his associates, and to C. E. Wilson, president of General Motors.

The use of the DODRILL-GENERAL MOTORS HEART was designated one of the ten top scientific achievements of 1952. On September 9, 1954, the "mechanical heart" was presented to the Smithsonian Institution, Washington, D.C., as a permanent exhibit.

References: Harper Hospital Trustees' Minutes, 1944–53, January 1, 1951; October 17, 1952; *Journal of the American Medical Association*, CXIV (October, 1952).

Among all the luminaries on the Harper Hospital scene, none has shown more brilliantly than LAWRENCE REYNOLDS, M.D., physician and radiologist who, in the latter field, had an international reputation. Born at Ozark, Alabama, February 11, 1889, Dr. Reynolds was educated at the University of Alabama and Johns Hopkins. Following World War I service, he affiliated with Peter Bent Brigham Hospital, Boston, and at the same time was an instructor in roentgenology at Harvard. While in Boston, he became an associate of Dr. Harvey Cushing who exerted a strong influence upon Reynolds and his career.

Reynolds went to Detroit in the early 1920's and eventually became chief of staff and chief of the department of radiology at Harper Hospital, as well as heading the firm of Lawrence Reynolds and Associates which furnished x-ray service to individuals, other hospitals, and Harper. His interests were broad. Among other things, he was a confirmed bibliophile, and it was to a large extent through his efforts that the Harper libraries were unified. For seventeen years he was a member of the Detroit Public Library Commission, and just prior to his death he donated his valuable private library to the University of Alabama.

Dr. Reynolds was the recipient of many honors, including honorary degrees from the University of Alabama and Wayne State University. For thirty-one years he was editor of the *American Journal of Roentgenology, Radium Therapy and Nuclear Medicine*. In 1957, the city of Detroit awarded him a Citation of Meritorious Service. He was a member of numerous American and foreign professional societies. On the occasion of his death, August 17, 1961, one of his colleagues, Dr. K. L. Krabbenhoft, paid him the following tribute:

As a clinical radiologist, he had no peer. He was ever a source of encouragement, understanding and rare consultative insight in problems both professional and personal. He inspired and guided dozens of young radiologists through their training and into service to doctor and patient.

Reference: Reading Room File, Burton Historical Collection; *Harper Hospital Bulletin*, XIX, Third Series (November-December, 1961), 195.

One of the earliest large bequests was made to Harper Hospital by CHARLES S. CHASE, a Detroit attorney. He left the Hospital $100,000 for a perpetual endowment, known as the Chase Cancer Fund. The money was to be used to support a free bed for a cancer patient and to conduct cancer research.

Chase was born in Vermont, January 8, 1866, but spent most of his life in Detroit. He was a graduate of the University of Michigan Law School (1887). A bachelor with no close relatives, he left the bulk of his estate to Harper. He died July 10, 1911.

Reference: *Detroit Journal,* July 19, 1911.

Detroit's medical profession suffered a tragic and needless loss on November 30, 1953, when a deranged man mistook DR. EDWARD SPALDING for someone else and shot him to death on the street in front of the Professional Building at Peterboro and Woodward.

Possessed of a brilliant mind, Dr. Spalding was a native of Detroit and was educated at Princeton and Johns Hopkins. He served in both World Wars and joined the Harper staff in 1921. In 1924 he became physician on the active staff, division of internal medicine.

Reference: *Harper Hospital Bulletin,* XI, Third Series (November-December, 1953), 219.

Once a member of the Harper Hospital family, always a member! That rule has resulted in professional Alumni organizations which carefully nurture world-wide associations with and continuing interest in the Hospital.

As far back as 1902, a group of medical staff members, occasionally getting together for an evening of shop talk and sociability, formed the Bull Durham Club—a name which referred to a popular brand of smoking tobacco and also, one may suspect, to the general flavor of the conversation. Composed of past and present staff members, the club met periodically in a room in the Hospital set aside for the use of the group. The first officers were Drs. P. E. Moody, president; and H. O. Walker, Donald Campbell, W. F. Metcalf, and W. F. Acker vice-presidents. Other officers bore the titles of Tobacco Tester, Chief Pipe Filler, Chief Torch Bearer, Chief Pipe Story Teller, and Official Tobacconist.

After a few years of such association, it was decided that a more permanent and formal organization should be established, made up of doctors who had served their internships, residencies, or held other staff positions at Harper. Because these men, having served their terms, were scattered throughout the world, and because the number of those eligible became increasingly large, it was thought advisable to form some link which would keep them in touch with the Hospital and with each other.

The result was the organization of the HARPER HOSPITAL ALUMNI ASSOCIATION which grew out of a meeting held May 24, 1909 in the office of Dr. Clark D. Brooks. Dr. Angus McLean was elected president, and the Association agreed to meet twice a year. The first annual meeting was held in the Tuller Hotel, Detroit, October 23, 1909.

About the time of World War I, formal organization of the Association came to an end, and the Harper Hospital Alumni became little more than a mailing list. It was estimated that in 1963 the list, or Association, as it was sometimes still called, contained approximately 2,000 names, including some of the most distinguished ones in modern medicine, both locally, throughout the United States, and in far corners of the world.

The nurse graduates of the Farrand Training School organized their own ALUMNAE ASSOCIATION nearly 20 years before the doctors got around to forming their Association. On November 10, 1892, after 68 nurses had graduated from the school, Mrs. Lystra E. Gretter wrote each graduate, calling a meeting in the Nurses' Library for December 7, 1892 "for the purpose of obtaining the views and opinions of all graduates of the Farrand Training School upon the organization of an Alumnae Association." The result was the founding of the Association on January 4, 1893 for "the mutual protection, improvement in professional work, promotion of fellowship . . . establishment and maintenance of a sick benefit fund, and the establishment of a systematic method of registering." Elizabeth L. Parker, a member of the class of 1888, became the first president, with a membership of 27. Among the various activities of the Association were the organization of a residence club; creation of loan funds, contributions, and donations largely for the benefit of the school and nurses' home; and publication of a directory. It also was instrumental in organizing the Detroit Graduate Nurses Association and the Wayne County Graduate Nurses Association. When the school was renamed the Harper Hospital School of Nursing, the Farrand alumnae designation was dropped in favor of the present name, the Alumnae Association of the Harper Hospital School of Nursing. Out of a total of about 2,400 graduates since the school was first opened, the Association in 1963 had 100 active and 425 associate members. The president in 1963 was Mrs. Margaret Roebuck.

Reference: *Detroit Medical Journal*, II (July, 1902), 498; IX (June, 1909), 230; Agnes G. Deans and Anne L. Austin: *The History of the Farrand Training School for Nurses* (Detroit, 1936), pp. 134–37.

Among the better-known men recently linked to Harper Hospital was DR. CLARK D. BROOKS, an outstanding surgeon. A native of Southfield, Michigan, born in 1879, Dr. Brooks attended school in Birmingham and graduated in 1905 from the Detroit College of Medicine and Surgery. During his entire professional career he was associated with Harper, beginning in 1904 as an extern. He was an intern in 1905–06, senior house surgeon in 1906–07, and a regular member of the staff from that time on. He was associate professor of surgery at Wayne State University College of Medicine. He early became an associate of Dr. Angus McLean, and at the latter's death in 1939, Dr. Brooks was appointed to the Detroit Board of Education to complete McLean's unexpired term. He later was twice elected to the post, thereby carrying out a service to Detroit education which has been a long Harper tradition. Dr. Brooks died May 28, 1956. He left $5,000 of his estate to the Brooks Loan Fund for Interns.

Reference: *The Detroit Free Press*, June 28, 1929; *Detroit Times*, June 7, 1956.

The need for PREPAID HOSPITAL SERVICE is graphically illustrated by a comparison of costs over a period of 95 years. The report of the trustees of Harper Hospital for 1867 stated:

The number of private patients and boarders received during the year, as shown by the Superintendent's report, is 56, making a total of 2,390 days, for which we have received and charged the sum of $1,683.93, being an average of over 70 cents per day.

For the first 11 months of 1962, the overall average cost per patient per day, according to the Director, was $47.50.

HARPER HOSPITAL CHRONOLOGY

1859–1962

1859   Walter Harper announces gift of his estate for the establishment of a hospital for the care of Detroit's indigent sick and poor. February 3.
Board of Trustees of Harper Hospital organized. February 7.
Nancy Martin gives her property for the site of Harper Hospital. March 15.

1862   Surgeon Charles S. Tripler, U.S.A., proposed construction of 200-bed military general hospital in Detroit. October 25.

1863   Governor Austin Blair urged construction of army hospital in Michigan. January 7.
Harper Hospital Association formally incorporated by Michigan legislature. May 4.

1864   Harper trustees approve lease of hospital land to U. S. government for army hospital site. April 9.
Trustees purchased additional five acres on Woodward Avenue for military hospital site. May 18.
Construction of Harper Hospital begun. June 9.
Harper Hospital, consisting of eleven buildings, officially opened. October 12.
Dr. David Osburn Farrand appointed surgeon-in-chief. October.

1865   Harper signed agreement with U. S. Sanitary Commission to accept transfer of soldiers from Detroit Soldiers' Home. December 29.

1866   Harper opens its doors as a civilian hospital. January 2.
St. Luke's Hospital given temporary quarters at Harper. May 3.
Moved to new location in 1868.

1867   Michigan legislature established Michigan Soldiers' Home at Harper. April 11.
Walter Harper died, age 78. August 28.

1868   Civilian patients, for first time, outnumber soldier and veteran patients.
Dr. George B. Russel appointed medical chief of Hospital. July 7.
Served until July 8, 1875.

1868   Detroit Medical College incorporated at Harper Hospital. January 11.
Forerunner of Wayne State University College of Medicine.
Death of Dr. George Duffield, first president of Harper Hospital Board of Trustees, age 74. June 26.
Free dispensary opened. February 1.
Buckminster Wight elected president to succeed Dr. Duffield. July 7.
Dr. A. T. Smith appointed house physician. August 4.
Robert W. King elected to Board of Trustees. December 6.

1869   Harper receives city patients; county patients in 1870. April.
Dr. George A. Foster appointed house physician. May 13.

1870   Harper operates its own farm on Fremont Street.
            Gaslights replaced oil lamps in Hospital. September.

1871   Free bed fund started.

1872   Woman's Hospital and Foundlings' Home given temporary quarters at Harper. April 12. Moved in 1876 to new home.

1873   Dr. Theodore A. Felch appointed house physician. April 1.

1874   Harper barracks building used by congregation of Westminster Presbyterian Church pending completion of new church at Woodward and Parsons.

1875   Nancy Martin died, age 75. February 9.
            Dr. David O. Farrand appointed chief of medical staff. July 8.
            Dr. Howard William Longyear appointed medical superintendent. November 3.

1876 [*ca.*]   Harper acquired first microscope for pathological investigation.
            David Cooper, one of original trustees, died at age of 86. July 27.

1877   Trustees granted annuity of $100 to Mrs. Margaret Latham, daughter of Walter Harper. July 5.

1878   Dr. Theodore A. McGraw performed first Lister spray operation at Harper.

1879   Michigan College of Medicine organized.
            Dr. M. K. Ross appointed resident physician replacing Dr. Howard M. Longyear, resigned.
            Harper Hospital leased grove in rear of Hospital to Recreation Park Association. May 6. Used for professional baseball games.
            Buckminster Wight, one of original trustees, died, age 83. November 28.

1881   Harper received $11,000 bequest from estate of James Thompson, of Almont, Michigan. Also $5,000 bequest from estate of Fanny Davenport Waterman.
            Trustees' committee appointed to study possibility of building new hospital to replace Civil War buildings. March 1.

1883   John R Street opened north of Brady Street in preparation for building new hospital.
            Detroit College of Medicine moved from Harper Hospital to new location on Farmer Street.
            Farrand Training School for Nurses established. First students admitted April 15, 1884.

1884   New hospital building on John R Street formally opened June 19. Patients had been admitted April 12.
            Jacob S. Farrand elected president of Board of Trustees, replacing Frederick Buhl, resigned.
            Miss Emma Hodkinson became first principal of Farrand Training School for Nurses.
            Staff reorganized into medical departments. June 3.

1885   Detroit Medical College and Michigan College of Medicine combined to form Detroit College of Medicine.
            First class of four nurses graduated from Farrand Training School.

1886   General W. F. Raynolds elected treasurer, replacing R. W. King, resigned. January 5.

1887   Trustees authorize free ambulance service for patients.

Children's Free Hospital Association given temporary quarters in Harper until 1891. January 4.

1887 William C. Bagley appointed general superintendent. June 14.

Articles of Incorporation amended to increase Board of Trustees from seven to fifteen. September 19.

1888 Trustees approved erection of contagious building. Harper claims to have been first general hospital in United States to accept contagious cases. March 12.

Outdoor clinic became Harper Hospital Polyclinic. November 12.

First woman, Dr. Helen F. Warner, appointed to staff.

The Grace Hospital opened at John R and Willis.

1889 Mrs. Lystra E. Gretter appointed principal of Farrand Training School. February 1. Held post until 1907.

C. T. Southwick, first full-time pharmacist appointed.

Out-patient clinic building opened.

Harper operates emergency hospital on grounds of Detroit Exposition.

1890 During the decade of the 1890's, Harper became the nation's leading surgical hospital in number of operations performed.

Frederick Buhl, one of the original trustees, died, age 84. May 12.

Harper Hospital Bulletin first issued. June.

Electric lights installed in Hospital.

[*ca.*] Modern residency system adopted.

1891 Jacob S. Farrand, one of original trustees, died, age 76. April 3.

Sullivan M. Cutcheon elected president. July 13.

Harper became first hospital to have eight-hour day for nurses.

A. W. Shaw appointed superintendent.

Hospital staffs emergency station for national G.A.R. Encampment in Detroit. August 3–8.

1893 New power plant built; gift of Trustee Gilbert Hart.

Duffield Cottage erected; provided quarters for nurses and doctors assigned to contagious cases. Gift of family of Divie Bethune Duffield.

Alexander McGraw, one of original trustees, died, November 2.

1893 Swain Home for Nurses opened for occupancy. November 9. Gift of Mrs. Eleanor Swain. Torn down in 1958.

1894 Coyl Endowment Fund willed to Harper in memory of William Kieft Coyl, by his daughter, Jean Coyl.

1897 Telephone installed in Hospital.

1898 Trustees offer facilities of Hospital to Governor Hazen S. Pingree for wounded soldiers and sailors of Spanish-American War. Harper nurses recruited; saw service in Puerto Rico and Philippines.

1899 Michigan adopts medical licensing and registration law.

1901 Rates for "cheapest" rooms increased from $10 to $12 per week.

Harper acquired its first x-ray equipment.

J. L. Hudson elected president of Board of Trustees. January 14.

1902 Medical library established. December 8.

1903 Inside communication system installed. March 9.

Dr. George B. Russel, one of original trustees, died, age 87. August 31.

Cutcheon operating building and amphitheater opened. December 1.

1904 Avery Building for Contagious Diseases opened. Torn down in 1912.

1906   Dr. Max Ballin appointed to staff. January 22.

Property fronting on Brush Street acquired. Provided future site of Brush building. April 9.

Harper adopted modern record-keeping practices.

1907   Miss Mathilda Kreuger appointed principal of Farrand School. September 1.

Frank Moulder appointed superintendent. November 12.

1908   Dr. Joseph Sill, first regular, full-time pathologist, hired.

1909   Reorganization of staff approved by trustees March 9. Became effective early in 1910. Opened way to specialization.

1910   Henry Ford elected to Board of Trustees in April. Resigned in July.

Dr. Stewart Hamilton appointed medical director. August 9. In 1915, became superintendent. Title later changed to director.

1911   Detroit General Hospital built at Hamilton and W. Grand Boulevard. Became Henry Ford Hospital in 1915.

First motor ambulance acquired by Harper.

Chase Cancer Fund established from legacy of Charles S. Chase, Detroit attorney.

1912   Dr. Henry O. Walker, first house physician at Harper in 1868, died. April 5.

J. L. Hudson, president Board of Trustees and major benefactor of Hospital, died, age 66. July 5.

Richard H. Webber elected to Board of Trustees. Still a member in 1963, he had the longest tenure of any board member since the Hospital was founded.

James Couzens elected to Board of Trustees. November 4.

Trustees ban fee splitting by medical staff members. November 4.

1913   Miss Emily McLaughlin appointed principal of Farrand Training School. May 20.

Dr. Wayne Smith appointed superintendent. September 18. Held post until his death in 1915.

Richmond Terrace, corner John R and Martin Place, given to Harper for nurses' home annex. Became interns' quarters 1922. Torn down 1962.

1914   J. L. Hudson Memorial Building opened. Cost $350,000. January 1.

Theodore D. Buhl Memorial Building dedicated. Janaury 1. Gift of Buhl family.

Social Service Department established. January 1.

Solvay General Hospital, Delray, acquired by Harper and renamed Harper West Branch. In 1917, returned to original owners. June 23.

Pediatrics division established under Department of Medicine.

Dr. Plinn F. Morse became pathologist-in-chief; headed Department of Pathology and Research until retirement in 1958.

1915   Detroit Receiving Hospital opened.

1916   Base Hospital 17 organized.

1917   Base Hospital 17 left for duty in France. July 13.

1918   Richard H. Webber elected president Board of Trustees. February 6. Resigned that post in 1961 after longest service of any president. Continued as trustee.

Gray Pavilion, devoted to operating rooms, opened.

1918–19	Influenza epidemic swept country. Harper called on to help in crisis.
1919	Base Hospital 17 personnel returned from France. March 18.
	Division of Radium Therapy and Division of Anesthesia established.
	Trustees voted to make Harper a closed hospital. April 8.
1920	Division of Oral and Dental Surgery established.
1921	Diagnostic Clinic opened.
	Harper acquired its own radium for treatment of cancer. December 14.
1922	Swain Home remodeled for superintendent's residence.
	New power plant built, gift of Trustee Joseph Boyer.
	McLaughlin Hall, new home for nurses given by Trustee James Couzens, dedicated and opened for use. May 10.
1923	"Five year law" adopted by Michigan legislature, requiring four years in accredited medical school and one year internship before a doctor could be licensed to practice. New law made it necessary for Harper to revise its teaching program.
1924	Division of Industrial Surgery established.
	Trustees approve purchase of first electrocardiograph for $700.
1928	Division of Thoracic Surgery established.
	Brush Street building opened. May. Increased Hospital's bed capacity to 650. Later increased to 701.
1930	Division of Psychiatry established.
	American Academy of Pediatrics founded at Harper. June.
1931	Division of Neuro-Surgery established.
1932	Detroit Common Council adopted resolution favoring medical center.
1933	Harper installs 1.5-million volt x-ray machine; most powerful in North America.
1937	Farrand Training School renamed Harper Hospital School of Nursing. Reopened after having been closed for two years because of the depression of the 1930's. January 1.
1938	Harper officials instrumental in organizing Blue Cross in Michigan.
1941	Employees' pension fund set up. May 19.
1942	General Hospital 17, the Harper unit, reactivated for duty in World War II.
	Detroit Board of Education directed David D. Henry, president of Wayne University, to prepare plans for medical center.
1943	Executive Diagnostic Clinic established.
1946	Dr. E. Dwight Barnett appointed director, succeeding Dr. Stewart Hamilton. Resigned 1952.
1947	Division of Cardiology established.
	X-ray Department gets isotopes from Oak Ridge atomic energy plant.
1948	Non-professional employees of Hospital go on strike. November.
1950	"Integrated" library established by consolidation of medical, nurses', and patients' libraries.
1951	Harper Hospital Auxiliary organized.
1952	Murphy building opened.
	George E. Cartmill appointed director.
1953	Harper became teaching unit for Wayne University College of Medicine undergraduates.
1954	Plans for development of Medical Center crystallized at meeting of representatives of area hospitals, held at Harper, August 19.

1958   42-bed teaching ward opened, staffed by full-time member, Wayne State University College of Medicine.

1961   Ray R. Eppert elected president Board of Trustees.

1962   First section of Medical Center area, including site surrounding Harper, condemned under Urban Renewal Act. Demolition of slum buildings in Harper neighborhood started.

Ground broken for Wayne State University Medical Research Building, first construction in Medical Center. November 20.

MEMBERS OF THE BOARD OF TRUSTEES
OF HARPER HOSPITAL

Alger, Fred M.   1910 *; 1912–23 †
Alger, Russell A.   1887–1906
Backus, Standish   1925–43
Barr, Andrew W.   1948–
Black, Clarence A.   1888–? †
Bowen, Lemuel W.   1899–1925
Boyer, Joseph   1906–30; president 1915–18
Browning, McPherson   1922–53
Bryant, John A.   1922–38
Bryant, Robert   1946–
Buhl, Arthur H.   1912–20 *
Buhl, Arthur H., Jr.   1951–
Buhl, Christian H.   1887–94
Buhl, Frederick   1859–84 *; president 1879–84
Candler, W. R.   1895–1909
Carter, David G.   1907–10 ; 1910–12 * †
Cooke, George   1945–56
Cooper, David   1859–76
Cooper, Rev. David M.   1880–88
Couzens, James   1912–24 *
Cutcheon, Sullivan M.   1884–1900; president 1892–1900
Dodge, John F.   1913–20
Dodge, Joseph M.   1936–
Duffield, D. Bethune   1893–1929 †
Duffield, Rev. George   1859–68; president 1859–68
Elliott, William H.   1887–1901
Eppert, Ray R.   1951– ; president 1961–
Farrand, Jacob S.   1859–91; president 1884–91
Farrand, W. R.   1891–30
Ferry, D. M.   1876–87 *
Ford, E. L.   1906–09 *; 1910–42
Ford, Henry   1910–10 *
Glancy, Alfred R., Jr.   1958–
Gossett, William T.   1954–
Green, A. H., Jr.   1906–? †
Hart, Gilbert   1889–1919
Harris, Julian H.   1925–33
Hayden, Martin S.   1963–
Hecker, Frank J.   1887–1927

* Resigned.

† During 1910 there were several elections and resignations of trustees which the hospital records do not satisfactorily explain.

329

Hudson, J. L.   1887–1912; president 1901–1912
Hudson, J. L., Jr.   1957–
Jackson, John Brook   1936–39
Joy, Richard P.   1901–02 *; 1917–30
Joy, William M.   1951–
Kamperman, Dr. George   1945–61
Kanzler, Ernest   1943–
Kelley, Nicholas, Jr.   1953–
Kent, Charles A.   1894–1917
King, Robert W.   1868–97
Kirchner, Otto   1910–20
Ledyard, Henry B.   1887–1901 *
Marshall, Alfred   1943–45
McGraw, Alexander C.   1859–93
McRae, Milton A.   1909–30; president 1912–15
Moore, George F.   1887–93 *
Moore, William A.   1890–1906
Morrow, Thomas F.   1963–
Muir, William K.   1888–92
Murphy, Dr. Fred T.   1920–47
Oxtoby, James V.   1931–40
Russel, Dr. George B.   1859–91 *
Russel, J. R.   1910–32 †
Russell, George   1955–
Schlotman, Joseph B.   1916–51
Semple, Robert B.   1952–
Smith, Jesse M.   1894–99 *
Stringham, Joseph B.   1912–37
Stone, Ferris   1939–45
Vance, Joseph A., Jr.   1945–
Viger, Nathan T.   1939–59
Walker, Bryant   1899–1936
Wallace, Harry L.   1931–41
Wasey, George E.   1893–97
Watkins, James K.   1925–
Webber, James B., Jr.   1948–56
Webber, Oscar   1925–
Webber, Richard H.   1912– ; president 1918–61
Whitney, David, Jr.   1887–1900
Wight, Buckminster   1859–79; president 1868–79
Wright, James N.   1899–1910

Fred M. Alger and John R. Russel were elected to the Board April 12, 1910, and each resigned July 19, 1910. Alger was re-elected in 1912 and served until 1923 when he resigned again. Russel was back on the Board later in 1910. There is no explanation of whether his July 19 resignation was refused, withdrawn, or whether he was re-elected.

Clarence A. Black, David G. Carter, and D. Bethune Duffield, all with several years of prior membership, resigned March 15, 1910. By July 19, 1910, however, each was back on the Board, again with no explanation of what happened. Carter formally resigned again in 1912, and Duffield continued to serve until his death in 1929. About 1913 Black moved to California. There is no record of his having attended any Board meetings after that, and he was no longer listed as a trustee. However, there is nothing in the Hospital records to show that he resigned after leaving Detroit. He died at Santa Barbara, February 13, 1924.

The date of A. H. Green's resignation, if he did resign, is not indicated in the Hospital records. There is no record that he attended a Board meeting after 1914, although in 1921 he was referred to on one occasion as a member. Green died at Detroit in 1947.

HARPER HOSPITAL CENTENNIAL STAFF

Charles G. Jennings
Emery O. Jodar
Ingeborg Krieger
Irving Levitt
Virginia McCandless
Ruben Meyer
John C. Montgomery
William C. Montgomery
Samuel J. Nichamin

Obstetrics and Gynecology
William M. Chavis
Andrew A. Frier
John P. Ottaway
Loren C. Spademan
Robert M. Stewart

Urology
Sherwin J. Lutz

Guy W. Sewell
Julian Stern

Radiology
Robert L. Willis

Anesthesiology
George E. Frederickson
Janet L. Holloway

Ear, Nose and Throat
Wilfred A. Riddell
Richard R. Royer

Ophthalmology
Kirwin H. Stief

Psychiatry
Jacques S. Gottlieb

William H. Grier
Peter A. Martin
Louis A. Schwartz

Oral and Dental Surgery
Michael J. Bucciero
Aris Hoplamazian
Francis G. LeVeque
Alfred L. Rehfield
Albert J. Richards
A. J. Richards, Jr.
S. Irwin Shaw
James H. Teetzel
Robert T. Watts

General Practice
J. Joseph Drake
B. Hjalmar Larsson
Charles L. Tomsu

THE ASSOCIATE STAFF

Teaching and Research
Thomas A. Bruce
John M. Dorsey
John H. Gaeth
John Gilroy
Manuel R. Gomez
David C. Gustafson
John F. Johnson

Harold J. Kullman
Elliot D. Luby
Roderick P. MacDonald
Richard S. McCaughey
Kamran S. Moghissi
Joseph N. Schaeffer
Gordon H. Scott
Elwood A. Sharp

Garfield Tourney
Elmore C. Vonder Heide
Vernon E. Wendt
Charles F. Whitten

Public Health
Joseph G. Molner
Paul T. Salchow

THE ACTIVE STAFF—JUNE 1, 1963

DEPARTMENT OF MEDICINE

Robert J. Schneck, *Chief of Department, Physician*
G. Thomas McKean, *Chief, Section of Internal Medicine, Physician*
Homer A. Howes, *Chief, Section of Allergy, Physician*
Charles J. Courville, *Chief, Section of Dermatology, Physician*
George C. Thosteson, *Chief, Section of Endocrinology and Metabolism, Physician*
Ralph R. Cooper, *Chief, Section of Gastroenterology, Physician*
Arnold R. Axelrod, *Chief, Section of Hematology, Associate Physician*
Abraham Becker, *Chief, Section of Pulmonary Diseases, Physician*

Richard C. Connelly, *Physician*
Alvin E. Price, *Physician*
John H. Besancon, *Physician*
Clarence D. Moll, *Physician*
Thomas H. Miller, *Physician*
Laurence F. Segar, *Physician*
Frank S. Perkin, *Physician*
Louis Jaffe, *Physician*
James J. Lightbody, *Physician*

Sidney L. Adelson, *Physician*
Raymond A. Sokolov, *Physician*
Sidney Miller, *Physician*
Walter L. Anderson, *Physician*
Richard J. Bing, *Physician*
Muir Clapper, *Physician*
Marcus H. Sugarman, *Physician*
Leonard S. Linkner, *Physician*
Louis Carbone, *Associate Physician*

Morton J. Wiener, *Associate Physician*
Lambertus E. Beeuwkes, *Associate Physician*
Herbert Rosenbaum, *Associate Physician*
Harry A. Kashtan, *Associate Physician*
Walter K. Whitehead, *Assistant Physician*
Nancy T. Caputo, *Assistant Physician*
Henry D. Kaine, *Assistant Physician*
John W. Moses, *Assistant Physician*
Meyer A. Gutterman, *Assistant Physician*
Robert H. Hamburg, *Assistant Physician*
John R. Simpson, *Assistant Physician*
E. Newton Rottenberg, *Assistant Physician*
Seymour S. Adelson, *Assistant Physician*
Paul E. Ruble, *Assistant Physician*
Harold Plotnick, *Assistant Physician*
Howard B. Appleman, *Assistant Physician*
Louis E. Pollens, *Clinical Assistant Physician*
Oscar Bigman, *Clinical Assistant Physician*
Dick A. Tarpinian, *Clinical Assistant Physician*
Robert W. Black, *Clinical Assistant Physician*
Norton J. Cooksey, *Clinical Assistant Physician*

Hershel Sandberg, *Clinical Assistant Physician*
William Gibson, *Clinical Assistant Physician*
Karl J. Kessel, *Clinical Assistant Physician*
John D. McGinty, *Clinical Assistant Physician*
Edwin C. Kerr, *Clinical Assistant Physician*
Seymour Gordon, *Clinical Assistant Physician*
Donald W. Visscher, *Clinical Assistant Physician*
Joseph W. Hess, *Clinical Assistant Physician*
Otto H. Hahne, *Clinical Assistant Physician*
Thomas J. Petz, *Clinical Assistant Physician*
Robert A. Barron, *Clinical Assistant Physician*
Gerald C. Timmis, *Clinical Assistant Physician*
Thomas B. Stock, *Clinical Assistant Physician*

SECTION OF CARDIOLOGY

Howard A. Klein, *Chief of Section, Physician*
Frederick B. Watts, *Physician*
Jack M. Kaufman, *Physician*
Jan Nyboer, *Associate Physician*
Robert A. Gerisch, *Associate Physician*

SECTION OF PSYCHIATRY

Z. Stephen Bohn, *Chief of Section, Physician*
Alexander H. Hirschfeld, *Physician*
Frank A. Cellar, Jr., *Physician*
Ben Marks, *Physician*
Russell T. Costello, *Physician*
Irving B. Shulak, *Associate Physician*
Robert B. Clarke, *Clinical Assistant Physician*

SECTION OF NEUROLOGY

John S. Meyer, *Chief of Section, Physician*
Raymond B. Bauer, *Clinical Assistant Physician*

DEPARTMENT OF SURGERY—JUNE 1, 1963

William S. Carpenter, *Chief of Department*

SECTION OF GENERAL SURGERY

Paul J. Connolly, *Chief of Section, Surgeon*
Harold B. Fenech, *Senior Surgeon*
William S. Carpenter, *Surgeon*
Edward H. Lauppe, *Surgeon*
Clifford D. Benson, *Surgeon*
Luther R. Leader, *Surgeon*
Maurice P. Meyers, *Surgeon*
Benjamin W. Stockwell, *Surgeon*
George Moriarty, *Surgeon*
James W. Lasley, *Surgeon*
Hugh M. Fuller, *Surgeon*
John H. Buell, *Surgeon*
Henry J. VandenBerg, Jr., *Surgeon*
Donald R. Hagge, *Surgeon*
Alan P. Thal, *Surgeon*
Prescott Jordan, Jr., *Surgeon*
John C. Tulloch, *Associate Surgeon*
Earl G. Merritt, *Associate Surgeon*
Gaylord S. Bates, *Associate Surgeon*
Lyndle R. Martin, *Associate Surgeon*
Schayel R. Scheinberg, *Associate Surgeon*
Warren O. Nickel, *Associate Surgeon*
Alexander J. Walt, *Associate Surgeon*
Lyle Jacobson, *Associate Surgeon*

Ruth B. Campbell, *Associate Surgeon*
James R. Lloyd, *Associate Surgeon*
Donald J. Murphy, *Assistant Surgeon*
Paul E. Derleth, *Assistant Surgeon*
Theodore M. Mattson, *Assistant Surgeon*
Homer M. Smathers, *Assistant Surgeon*
Joseph L. Posch, *Assistant Surgeon*
Robert D. Larsen, *Assistant Surgeon*
Paul G. Firnschild, *Assistant Surgeon*
Frank W. Prust, *Assistant Surgeon*
Ward M. Smathers, *Assistant Surgeon*
Herbert J. Robb, *Assistant Surgeon*
Frederick W. Rau, *Assistant Surgeon*
Thomas M. Flake, *Assistant Surgeon*
Robert P. Lilly, *Clinical Assistant Surgeon*
C. Jackson France, *Clinical Assistant Surgeon*
Robert D. Allaben, *Clinical Assistant Surgeon*
Vincent J. Gallant, *Clinical Assistant Surgeon*
Raymond C. Read, *Clinical Assistant Surgeon*

SECTION OF THORACIC SURGERY

F. D. Dodrill, *Chief of Section, Surgeon*
Jay C. Day, *Surgeon*
Paul V. O'Rourke, *Associate Surgeon*
Raymond J. Barrett, *Associate Surgeon*
Francis S. Gerbasi, *Assistant Surgeon*

SECTION OF PROCTOLOGY

Norman D. Nigro, *Chief of Section, Surgeon*
Jesse T. Harper, *Surgeon*
George T. Bradley, *Surgeon*
George L. Walker, *Surgeon*

SECTION OF NEURO SURGERY

Aage E. Nielsen, *Chief of Section, Surgeon*
Philip J. Huber, *Surgeon*

SECTION OF PLASTIC SURGERY

William G. McEvitt, *Chief of Section, Surgeon*
Edward J. Hill, *Surgeon*
Harold W. Jaffee, *Assistant Surgeon*
Donald I. Kapetansky, *Clinical Assistant Surgeon*

DEPARTMENT OF ANESTHESIOLOGY

Alexander B. Stearns, *Chief of Department, Anesthesiologist*
Ivan B. Taylor, *Anesthesiologist*
Ferdinand J. Greifenstein, *Associate Anesthesiologist*
Marvin H. Primack, *Clinical Assistant Anesthesiologist*
Rolf W. Donath, *Clinical Assistant Anesthesiologist*
Gerhard C. Endler, *Clinical Assistant Anesthesiologist*
Grant J. Withey, *Clinical Assistant Anesthesiologist*
Edward T. Glowacki, *Clinical Assistant Anesthesiologist*
Thomas E. Ryan, *Clinical Assistant Anesthesiologist*

DEPARTMENT OF ORTHOPEDIC SURGERY—JUNE 1, 1963

Frederick J. Fischer, *Chief of Department, Surgeon*
Francis P. Walsh, *Surgeon*
J. Gilbert Reid, *Surgeon*
A. Jackson Day, *Surgeon*
James J. Horvath, *Surgeon*
John M. Pendy, *Assistant Surgeon*
H. Ross Hume, *Assistant Surgeon*
L. Carl Sultzman, *Assistant Surgeon*
Loyal W. Jodar, *Clinical Assistant Surgeon*
William E. Siebert, *Clinical Assistant Surgeon*
Richard H. Hall, *Clinical Assistant Surgeon*
William R. Fulgenzi, *Clinical Assistant Surgeon*

DEPARTMENT OF UROLOGY

Frank B. Bicknell, *Chief of Department, Surgeon*
Benjamin W. Dovitz, *Surgeon*
Edward J. Shumaker, *Surgeon*
Harold V. Morley, *Surgeon*
Robert C. Thumann, Jr., *Surgeon*
Murray S. Mahlin, *Associate Surgeon*
George R. Sewell, *Assistant Surgeon*
George L. Reno, *Clinical Assistant Surgeon*
William H. Rattner, *Clinical Assistant Surgeon*
Albert J. Tactac, *Clinical Assistant Surgeon*

DEPARTMENT OF OPHTHALMOLOGY

Windsor S. Davies, *Chief of Department, Surgeon*
Wesley G. Reid, *Surgeon*
Frederick A. Lauppe, *Surgeon*
Leland F. Carter, *Surgeon*
Edmond L. Cooper, *Surgeon*
Walter G. Neeb, *Surgeon*
Lester E. McCullough, *Surgeon*
Horace L. Weston, *Surgeon*
James L. Frey, *Surgeon*
Albert E. Vossler, *Surgeon*
Robert J. Crossen, *Associate Surgeon*
Albert D. Ruedemann, Jr., *Associate Surgeon*
Quentin P. Hamilton, *Associate Surgeon*
Gomer P. Evans, *Associate Surgeon*
Maurice J. Hauser, *Assistant Surgeon*
Sidney L. Stone, *Assistant Surgeon*
Thomas G. Varbedian, *Clinical Assistant Surgeon*
Thomas H. Galantowicz, *Clinical Assistant Surgeon*
Herbert D. Sherbin, *Clinical Assistant Surgeon*

DEPARTMENT OF OTORHINOLARYNGOLOGY

Lyle G. Waggoner, *Chief of Department, Surgeon*
I. Jerome Hauser, *Surgeon*
William A. Summers, *Surgeon*
James E. Coyle, *Surgeon*
Ned I. Chalat, *Surgeon*
Gerardus J. Beekhuis, *Associate Surgeon*
James T. Mimura, *Assistant Surgeon*
Dieter Wendling, *Assistant Surgeon*
Richard M. Kommel, *Clinical Assistant Surgeon*
Martin B. Trotsky, *Clinical Assistant Surgeon*
John A. Fushman, *Clinical Assistant Surgeon*
George J. Viscomi, *Clinical Assistant Surgeon*

SECTION OF ORAL AND DENTAL SURGERY

Haven F. Doane, *Chief of Section, Dental Surgeon*
Carroll W. Kennedy, *Dental Surgeon*
Arthur T. Watson, *Assistant Dental Surgeon*
Malcolm W. Campbell, *Clinical Assistant Dental Surgeon*

DEPARTMENT OF PEDIATRICS

Edgar E. Martmer, *Chief of Department, Physician*
Edward A. Wishropp, *Physician*
Daniel Budson, *Physician*
Wilfred S. Nolting, *Physician*
Harold B. Rothbart, *Physician*
Irving Posner, *Physician*
Irving F. Burton, *Physician*
Carolyn S. Salisbury, *Physician*
Samuel J. Levin, *Physician*
Henry Siegel, *Associate Physician*
Louis M. Harley, *Associate Physician*
David B. Levy, *Associate Physician*
Robert P. Richardson, *Associate Physician*
Malcolm J. Kelson, *Assistant Physician*
Wyman C. C. Cole, Jr., *Assistant Physician*

Morris Starkman, *Assistant Physician*
James W. Collins, *Assistant Physician*
Lula Belle T. Stewart, *Assistant Physician*
Louis F. Heyman, *Clinical Assistant Physician*
Frederick W. Fitzpatrick, *Clinical Assistant Physician*
Paul M. Zavell, *Clinical Assistant Physician*
Richard J. Snyder, *Clinical Assistant Physician*
Mary V. McDermott, *Clinical Assistant Physician*
Calier H. Worrell, *Clinical Assistant Physician*
Byron A. Andreou, *Clinical Assistant Physician*

DEPARTMENT OF OBSTETRICS AND GYNECOLOGY

Leonard P. Heath, *Chief of Department, Surgeon*
Harold C. Mack, *Senior Surgeon*
G. Harry Agnew, *Surgeon*
Edward I. Mintz, *Surgeon*
Harold B. Rice, *Surgeon*
Laurel S. Eno, *Surgeon*
Robert W. McClure, *Surgeon*
Morton R. Lazar, *Surgeon*
Donald N. Morgan, *Surgeon*

Panfilo C. DiLoreto, *Surgeon*
Harvey D. Lynn, *Surgeon*
Lorraine A. Sievers, *Associate Surgeon*
Warren R. Moore, *Associate Surgeon*
Berj H. Haidostian, *Associate Surgeon*
Robert K. Whiteley, *Assistant Surgeon*
John Y. Teshima, *Assistant Surgeon*
Darrell Statzer, *Assistant Surgeon*
Georg H. E. Klutke, *Assistant Surgeon*
Anthony T. Salvaggio, *Assistant Surgeon*

Harvey A. Krieger, *Clinical Assistant Surgeon*

Kenneth I. Ranney, *Clinical Assistant Surgeon*

Addison E. Prince, *Clinical Assistant Surgeon*

Harold L. Katzman, *Clinical Assistant Surgeon*

James G. Kornmesser, *Clinical Assistant Surgeon*

Don R. Krohn, *Clinical Assistant Surgeon*

John A. Tulloch, *Clinical Assistant Surgeon*

Edward T. Turner, Jr., *Clinical Assistant Surgeon*

DEPARTMENT OF RADIOLOGY

James C. Cook, *Chief of Department, Radiologist*
W. George Belanger, *Radiologist*
E. Frederick Lang, *Radiologist*
Karl K. Latteier, *Radiologist*
Joseph O. Reed, Jr., *Radiologist*
Kenneth L. Krabbenhoft, *Radiologist*
Arch H. Hall, *Radiologist*
David P. Corbett, *Clinical Assistant Radiologist*
George A. Kling, *Clinical Assistant Radiologist*

DEPARTMENT OF PATHOLOGY AND RESEARCH

John R. McDonald, *Chief of Department, Pathologist*
Andrew R. W. Climie, *Associate Pathologist*
Nicolai Rachmaninoff, *Associate Pathologist*
Thadeus Jarkowski, *Associate Pathologist*

NOTES

1. George B. Catlin, *The Story of Detroit* (Detroit, 1926), p. 433. Gas illumination was introduced in Detroit in 1849. The first gas streetlights were installed in 1851.
2. *Detroit Daily Advertiser*, February 2–15, 1859.
3. Catlin, *Story of Detroit*, p. 656.
4. Silas Farmer, *The History of Detroit and Michigan* (Detroit, 1884), I. On page 378 appears a picture of the Duffield residence at 333 Woodward Avenue. It was built in 1846 and torn down in 1883. The caption erroneously places the house on the east side of Woodward. High Street, at the time Duffield lived there, was known as George Street. The present location is between Vernor Highway and Duffield Street.
5. Rev. George Duffield, Diary, March 19, 1859, p. 1 (In Burton Historical Collection, Detroit Public Library).
6. Farmer, *History of Detroit*, I, 50, 218, 646, 917. *Detroit in Its World Setting* (Detroit: Detroit Public Library, 1953), p. 149.
7. Farmer, *History of Detroit*, I, 374.
8. For accounts of the civic activities of Dr. Duffield's visitors, see Farmer, *History of Detroit*, I and II, various references under index of names.
9. Minutes of the Meetings of the Board of Trustees of Harper Hospital, 1859–74, pp. 21–22.
10. Walter Harper Deed, Liber 75 of Deeds, at folios 608–14, Register of Deeds Office, Wayne County, Michigan, February 4, 1859.
11. *The Encyclopaedia Britannica* (14th ed.; Chicago, 1937), IX, 152; *Encyclopedia Americana* (New York and Chicago, 1951), II, 104.
12. Harper Hospital Trustees' Minutes 1859–74, p. 59.
13. Harper Hospital Trustees' Minutes 1859–74, pp. 21–22.
14. Harper Hospital Trustees' Minutes 1859–74, p. 312. See inserted statement by R. W. King, based on a paper handed him by D. B. Duffield in July, 1874.
15. See note 10, above.
16. *Detroit Daily Advertiser*, February 8, 1859.
17. *The Detroit Free Press*, February 9, 1859.
18. In Harper Hospital Archives, Harper Hospital Library.
19. Harper Hospital Trustees' Minutes 1859–74, February 17, 1859.
20. Nancy Martin Deed, March 10, 1859; in Harper Hospital Trustees' Minutes 1859–74, March 15, 1859.
21. Information furnished July 16, 1962 by Philip Langwald, secretary. Department of Water Supply, City of Detroit.
22. Harper Hospital Trustees' Minutes 1859–74, February 28, 1859.
23. Harper Hospital Trustees' Minutes 1859–74, February 28, 1859.
24. *Detroit Daily Advertiser*, April 5, 1859.
25. *Detroit Daily Advertiser*, April 6, 1859.

Chapter 2

1. *Harper Hospital Annual Report for 1913* (Detroit, 1913), p. 27.
2. Harper Hospital Historical Scrapbook II (Harper Hospital Archives), p. 12.
3. Catlin, *The Story of Detroit*, pp. 479, 480.
4. *Detroit Daily Advertiser*, February 8, 1859.
5. *Detroit Advertiser and Tribune*, August 30, 1867.

6. *Detroit Advertiser and Tribune*, August 30, 1867.
7. *Detroit Advertiser and Tribune*, August 30, 1867.
8. Campau Family Papers (Burton Historical Collection), November 10, 1831.
9. *Harper Hospital Annual Report for 1913*, pp. 27–36.
10. *Detroit Advertiser and Tribune*, August 30, 1867.
11. *Detroit Advertiser and Tribune*, August 30, 1867.
12. *The Detroit Free Press*, February 9, 1859.
13. See *City of Detroit Directories*.
14. *The Detroit Free Press*, December 20, 1862.
15. *The Detroit Free Press*, July 30, 1871.
16. Harper Hospital Trustees' Minutes 1859–74, May 3, 1866.
17. *Detroit Advertiser and Tribune*, August 30, 1867.
18. *Detroit Advertiser and Tribune*, August 30, 1867.
19. Harper Hospital Trustees' Minutes 1859–74, August 30, 1867.
20. Farmer, *History of Detroit*, I, 657.
21. Harper Hospital Trustees' Minutes 1859–74, p. 312.
22. *Detroit Advertiser and Tribune*, August 30, 1867.
23. Harper Hospital Trustees' Minutes 1874–83, pp. 42 ff.
24. Harper Hospital Trustees' Minutes 1874–83, pp. 42 ff.
25. Harper Hospital Trustees' Minutes 1874–83, pp. 42 ff.
26. Harper Hospital Trustees' Minutes 1874–83, pp. 42 ff.
27. *The Maquoketa Community Press*, Maquoketa, Iowa, July 31, 1962.
28. Harper Hospital Trustees' Minutes 1874–83, p. 116.
29. Harper Hospital Trustees' Minutes 1874–83, p. 171.
30. Harper Hospital Trustees' Minutes 1874–83, p. 171.
31. *The Maquoketa Community Press*, July 31, 1962.
32. Clipping, *The Detroit Free Press*, n.d., but about July, 1874. In Harper Hospital Trustees' Minutes 1874–83, p. 289.
33. See Walter Harper Deed in Harper Hospital Trustees' Minutes 1859–74, February 3, 1859.
34. Harper Hospital Trustees' Minutes 1859–74, p. 312.

Chapter 3

1. *Detroit Advertiser and Tribune*, February 10, 1875.
2. *The Detroit Free Press*, February 10, 1875.
3. George B. Catlin, "Nancy Martin" (MS in the Catlin Papers, Burton Historical Collection).
4. Catlin, "Nancy Martin." (MS in Burton Historical Collection).
5. *Detroit Advertiser and Tribune*, February 10, 1875.
6. *Detroit Advertiser and Tribune*, February 10, 1875.
7. *Detroit Advertiser and Tribune*, February 10, 1875.
8. Catlin, "Nancy Martin" (MS in Burton Historical Collection).
9. *Detroit Advertiser and Tribune*, February 10, 1875.
10. *Detroit Advertiser and Tribune*, February 10, 1875.
11. Catlin, "Nancy Martin" (MS in Burton Historical Collection).
12. Farmer, *History of Detroit*, I, 793–95.
13. Farmer, *History of Detroit*, I, 793–95.
14. Harper Hospital Historical Scrapbook I (Harper Hospital Archives), p. 56.
15. Catlin, "Nancy Martin" (MS in Burton Historical Collection).
16. *Detroit Advertiser and Tribune*, February 10, 1875.
17. *The Detroit Free Press*, December 28, 1914.
18. *The Detroit Free Press*, December 28, 1914.
19. Catlin, "Nancy Martin" (MS in Burton Historical Collection).
20. *The Detroit Free Press*, May 14, 1859.

21. Elizabeth Anne Ash McFadden, "My Recollection of Nancy Martin" (MS in Harper Hospital Archives), August 1, 1934.
22. *Detroit Advertiser and Tribune*, February 10, 1875.
23. *The Detroit Free Press*, May 16, 1861.
24. Wayne County Probate Court Records, File No. 7597, Liber 85, p. 227.
25. C. B. Burr, ed. *Medical History of Michigan* (Minneapolis-St. Paul, 1930), II, 603.
26. *Detroit Advertiser and Tribune*, February 10, 1875.
27. Catlin, "Nancy Martin" (MS in Burton Historical Collection).
28. *Harper Hospital Annual Report for 1913*.
29. Harper Hospital Trustees' Minutes, 1859–74, September 7, 1867.
30. Catlin, "Nancy Martin" (MS in Burton Historical Collection).
31. *Detroit Advertiser and Tribune*, February 10, 1875.
32. *Harper Hospital Annual Report for 1913*.
33. Harper Hospital Trustees' Minutes 1859–74, April 2, 1872.
34. Harper Hospital Trustees' Minutes 1859–74, December 3, 1872.
35. *Detroit Advertiser and Tribune*, February 10, 1875.
36. *The Detroit Free Press*, February 12, 1875.
37. *The Detroit Free Press*, February 12, 1875.
38. Harper Hospital Trustees' Minutes 1859–74, p. 41.
39. Harper Hospital Trustees' Minutes 1859–74, newspaper clipping, not dated, not identified.

Chapter 4

1. Frank B. Woodford, *Mr. Jefferson's Disciple* (East Lansing, 1953), pp. 3–7.
2. Woodford, *Mr. Jefferson's Disciple*, p. 38.
3. M. Agnes Burton, ed. *Proceedings of the Land Board of Detroit* (Detroit, 1915), p. 17.
4. Agnes Burton, *Proceedings*, p. 48.
5. Records, City Engineer, City of Detroit.
6. Farmer, *History of Detroit*, I, 40–41.
7. M. Agnes Burton, *Proceedings*, p. 73.
8. Farmer, *History of Detroit*, I, 41.
9. See Nancy Martin Deed, March 10, 1859.
10. Harper Hospital Trustees' Minutes 1859–74, p. 59.
11. *Harper Hospital* (n.p., 1886), p. 79.
12. Plat of Harper's Greenfield property, Wayne State University Archives.
13. Farmer, *History of Detroit*, I, 40–41.
14. See Walter Harper Deed, February 4, 1859.
15. Harper Hospital Trustees' Minutes 1859–74, pp. 23–24.
16. Harper Hospital Trustees' Minutes 1859–74, pp. 27–28.
17. Harper Hospital Trustees' Minutes 1859–74, pp. 32–33.
18. Harper Hospital Trustees' Minutes 1859–74, p. 43.
19. Harper Hospital Trustees' Minutes 1859–74, p. 43. See also Joseph Jackson, *Encyclopedia of Philadelphia* (Harrisburg, 1932), III, 887.
20. Harper Hospital Trustees' Minutes 1859–74, pp. 32–33.
21. *Harper Hospital Bulletin*, XI, First Series (December, 1900), p. 2.
22. *Harper Hospital Bulletin* (December, 1900), p. 2.
23. *Harper Hospital* (1886), p. 71.
24. Harper Hospital Trustees' Minutes 1859–74, pp. 45, 48.
25. Harper Hospital Trustees' Minutes 1859–74, pp. 45, 48.
26. Harper Hospital Trustees' Minutes 1859–74, pp. 48, 56.
27. *Harper Hospital* (1886), p. 71.
28. *Harper Hospital* (1886), p. 71.
29. Harper Hospital Trustees' Minutes 1874–83, p. 277.

30. *Harper Hospital* (1886), p. 71; also Harper Hospital Trustees' Minutes 1859–74, p. 66.
31. Harper Hospital Trustees' Minutes 1859–74, p. 3.
32. *Harper Hospital* (1886), p. 79.
33. Catlin, *The Story of Detroit*, p. 480.
34. Farmer, *History of Detroit*, I, 667–68.
35. Harper Hospital Trustees' Minutes 1859–74, p. 312.
36. *The Detroit Free Press*, March 15, 1903.
37. *The Detroit Free Press*, March 15, 1903.
38. Harper Hospital Trustees' Minutes 1859–74, p. 312.
39. D. B. Duffield to Rev. George Duffield, Detroit, September 15, 1858 (Duffield Papers, Burton Historical Collection).
40. *Evening News*, Detroit, February 15, 1883.
41. Farmer, *History of Detroit*, I, 667–68.
42. Farmer, *History of Detroit*, I, 667–68.
43. Harper Hospital Trustees' Minutes 1859–74, p. 312.

Chapter 5

1. *Detroit Advertiser and Tribune*, February 9, 1859.
2. C. M. and M. Agnes Burton, eds. *Wayne County and the City of Detroit* (Chicago-Detroit, 1930), II, 1323.
3. *Detroit in Its World Setting*, pp. 74, 91, 107, 123.
4. Graeme O'Geran, *A History of the Detroit Street Railways* (Detroit, 1931), pp. 21–45.
5. Burton, *Wayne County*, II, 1323.
6. Helen Clapsattle, *The Doctors Mayo* (Minneapolis, 1941), p. 65.
7. Farmer, *History of Detroit*, I, 45.
8. Farmer, *History of Detroit*, I, 45.
9. Burr, *Medical History*, I, 681.
10. Burr, *Medical History*, I, 682.
11. Burr, *Medical History*, I, 683–85.
12. Burton, *Wayne County*, II, 1179.
13. *Harper Hospital Bulletin*, X, First Series, (February, 1900), 79.
14. Farmer, *History of Detroit*, I, 48.
15. Farmer, *History of Detroit*, I, 48.
16. Burr, *Medical History*, II, 338, 760, 827.
17. See annual reports for years indicated in *Harper Hospital Bulletin*.
18. James Dale Johnston, comp. *The Detroit City Directory* (Detroit, 1855).
19. Burr, *Medical History*, II, 221.
20. *Detroit Advertiser and Tribune*, March 29, 1867.
21. Edward G. Martin, *St. Mary's Hospital 1845–1945* (Detroit, 1945), 48.
22. William Edgar (MS in Burton Historical Collection)
23. Burr, *Medical History*, II, 599.
24. Burr, *Medical History*, II, 599.
25. Farmer, *History of Detroit*, I, 648–49.
26. George Paré, *The Catholic Church In Detroit, 1701–1888* (Detroit, 1951), 410.
27. Paré, *Catholic Church*, p. 410.
28. Martin, *St. Mary's Hospital*, pp. 50–64.
29. Martin, *St. Mary's Hospital*, pp. 50–64.
30. Martin, *St. Mary's Hospital*, pp. 50–64.
31. Farmer, *History of Detroit*, I, 653.
32. Burr, *Medical History*, I, 711.
33. Paré, *Catholic Church*, p. 666.
34. Catlin, *The Story of Detroit*, p. 479.

35. Farmer, *History of Detroit,* I, 923–24.
36. *The Detroit Free Press,* May 27, 1857.
37. Farmer, *History of Detroit,* I, 923–24.
38. Burr, *Medical History,* II, 645.
39. Malcolm T. MacEachern, *Hospital Organization and Management* (Chicago, 1957), p. 29.
40. MacEachern, *Hospital Organization,* p. 29.
41. "A History of the Hospital Movement," n.d. (Harper Hospital Archives).
42. MacEachern, *Hospital Organization,* p. 10.
43. Thomas Neville Bonner, *Medicine in Chicago 1850–1950* (Madison, 1957), p. 153.
44. MacEachern, *Hospital Organization,* p. 16.
45. MacEachern, *Hospital Organization,* p. 18.
46. George Worthington Adams, *Doctors In Blue* (New York, 1952), p. 221.
47. MacEachern, *Hospital Organization,* p. 18.
48. Clapsattle, *Doctors Mayo,* p. 138.
49. Clapsattle, *Doctors Mayo,* p. 116.
50. Burr, *Medical History,* I, 345.
51. Burr, *Medical History,* I, 599, 672.
52. Burr, *Medical History,* I, 345.
53. Bonner, *Medicine in Chicago,* p. 153.
54. Adams, *Doctors in Blue,* pp. 153 ff., 221.

Chapter 6

1. Harper Hospital Trustees' Minutes 1859–74, p. 46.
2. Dumas Malone, ed., *Dictionary of American Biography* (New York, 1934), XIV, 289.
3. Harper Hospital Trustees' Minutes 1859–74, p. 60.
4. Harper Hospital Trustees' Minutes 1859–74, p. 60.
5. *The Detroit Free Press,* December 20, 1862.
6. Harper Hospital Trustees' Minutes 1859–74, p. 66.
7. Farmer, *History of Detroit,* I, 654.
8. *Detroit Daily Advertiser,* February 18, 1859.
9. Harper Hospital Trustees' Minutes 1859–74, p. 67.
10. Jean Louise Datson, *"The History of Union Hospitals During the Civil War"* (Master's thesis, Wayne State University, 1947), pp. 56 ff.
11. Adams, *Doctors in Blue,* p. 153.
12. *Detroit Advertiser and Tribune,* July 22, 1862.
13. *Detroit Advertiser and Tribune,* August 5, 1862.
14. Stub Book No. 840, p. 22 in U.S. Surgeon General, Records of Harper's, St. Mary's, U.S. General Hospitals and Detroit Barracks Post Hospital 1864–66 (Burton Historical Collection).
15. *Michigan Adjutant General Report for 1864* (Lansing, 1865), pp. 849–84.
16. C. S. Tripler to Asst. Surgeon Gen. Wood, May 14, 1863, Record Group 92, Office of Surgeon General, War Department, National Archives.
17. George Fuller, ed. "Message of Gov. Blair to the Legislature, January 7, 1863," *Messages of the Governors of Michigan* (Lansing, 1926), II, 469.
18. *Michigan Adjutant General Report for 1864,* pp. 867–68.
19. *Michigan Adjutant General Report for 1863,* pp. 477–79.
20. Joseph Tunnicliff to Austin Blair, November 16, 1863 (Blair Papers, Burton Historical Collection).
21. Leartus Conner, "Comments on Detroit Doctors by those who knew them when practicing" (MS in Burton Historical Collection)
22. *Detroit Advertiser and Tribune,* July 19, 1862.
23. Tunnicliff to Blair, October 9, 1863.
24. Tunnicliff to Blair, August 17, 1863.

25. Tunnicliff to Blair, August 3, 1863.
26. Tunnicliff to Blair, August 17, 1863.
27. Tunnicliff to Blair, August 17, 1863.
28. Tunnicliff to Blair, August 17, 1863.
29. Tunnicliff to Blair, October 9, 1863.
30. Tunnicliff to Blair, August 3, 1863; also February 2, 1864.
31. Tunnicliff to Blair, January 24, 1864.
32. Tunnicliff to Blair, January 24, 1864.
33. Tunnicliff to Blair, October 9, 1863.
34. Harper Hospital Trustees' Minutes 1859–74, p. 72.
35. Duffield Diary, April 7, 1864.
36. Duffield Diary, April 7, 1864.
37. Harper Hospital Trustees' Minutes 1859–74, p. 73.
38. *Harper Hospital* (1886), p. 74.
39. *Harper Hospital* (1886), p. 74.
40. Harper Hospital Trustees' Minutes 1859–74, pp. 78–79.
41. Harper Hospital Trustees' Minutes 1859–74, p. 80.
42. *The Detroit Free Press,* June 9, 1864.
43. Duffield Diary, May 26, 1864.
44. Duffield Diary, May 31, 1864.
45. Duffield Diary, June 4, 1864.
46. Harper Hospital Trustees' Minutes 1859–74, p. 74.
47. *Harper Hospital* (1886), pp. 73–74.
48. Frank B. Woodford, *We Never Drive Alone* (Detroit, 1958), p. 143.
49. Harper Hospital Trustees' Minutes 1859–74, p. 83.

Chapter 7

1. Datson, "Union Hospitals," p. 77.
2. "Report of Dr. Joseph Tunnicliff, January 20, 1864," *Michigan Adjutant General Reports for 1863,* pp. 485–86.
3. *Detroit Advertiser and Tribune,* October 11, 1864.
4. Datson, "Union Hospitals," p. 57.
5. Datson, "Union Hospitals," p. 57.
6. *Detroit Advertiser and Tribune,* October 11, 1864.
7. *Detroit Advertiser and Tribune,* October 11, 1864.
8. Stub Book No. 836, p. 230.
9. John Robertson, *Michigan in the War* (Lansing, 1882), p. 115.
10. Michigan Adjutant General, *Record of Service of Michigan Volunteers in the Civil War* (Kalamazoo, 1905), Vol. XXXV.
11. *Michigan Volunteers,* XXVII, p. 53.
12. *Michigan Volunteers,* XXVII, p. 116.
13. Stub Book No. 834, p. 836.
14. Stub Book No. 835.
15. Stub Book No. 840, pp. 169–245.
16. *Michigan Adjutant General Report for 1864,* p. 857.
17. Frank B. Woodford, *Father Abraham's Children* (Detroit, 1961), pp. 93–96, 101–12.
18. Stub Book No. 836, pp. 5–10.
19. *Michigan Adjutant General Report for 1864,* pp. 856, 874.
20. Stub Book Nos. 835–37, 839 *passim.*
21. The order for this transfer, now framed, is a cherished Harper Hospital memento of the Civil War (Harper Hospital Archives).
22. Stub Book Nos. 835–37, 839 *passim.*
23. Newspaper clipping, not identified (in Biographical Index, Burton Historical Collection).

24. Robertson, *Michigan in the War,* pp. 98–99, 115; Stub Book Nos. 835–41.
25. Charles Lanman, *Red Book of Michigan* (Detroit, 1871), p. 217.
26. William J. Stapleton Jr., "Record of meeting held by Dr. Frederic Schreiber and others, 1938" (Wayne State University Archives), p. 30.
27. Stub Book No. 840, p. 49.
28. Adams, *Doctors in Blue,* p. 188.
29. *Michigan Adjutant General Report for 1864,* p. 859.
30. *Michigan Adjutant General Report for 1864,* p. 857.
31. Adams, *Doctors in Blue,* p. 188.
32. Stub Book No. 836, p. 114.
33. *Michigan Adjutant General Report for 1864,* p. 856.
34. Stub Book No. 835.

Chapter 8

1. MacEachern, *Hospital Organization,* p. 5; Burr, *Medical History,* II, 766.
2. Adams, *Doctors in Blue,* pp. 113, 115.
3. Stub Book No. 836, p. 88.
4. Stub Book No. 834, p. 9.
5. Adams, *Doctors in Blue,* p. 150.
6. *Harper Hospital Bulletin,* VI, First Series (February, 1896), 56.
7. Duffield Diary, May 23, 1865.
8. *The Detroit Free Press,* December 28, 1864.
9. *Michigan Adjutant General Report for 1864,* pp. 899–900.
10. Adams, *Doctors in Blue,* p. 167.
11. Adams, *Doctors in Blue,* p. 165.
12. Stub Book No. 834, p. 9.
13. Stub Book No. 834, p. 9.
14. Frank Gross, Diary, January 1, 1864–August 23, 1865 (Michigan Historical Collections, University of Michigan, Ann Arbor).

Chapter 9

1. Harper Hospital Trustees' Minutes 1859–74, p. 87.
2. Harper Hospital Trustees' Minutes 1859–74, p. 88.
3. Duffield Diary, November 30, 1865.
4. Harper Hospital Trustees' Minutes 1859–74, p. 89; Col. B. C. Card to Rev. George Duffield, December 8, 1865 (Duffield Papers, Burton Historical Collection).
5. Duffield Diary, December 12, 1865.
6. Duffield Diary, December 12, 1865.
7. Harper Hospital Trustees' Minutes 1859–74, p. 90.
8. Harper Hospital Trustees' Minutes 1859–74, p. 91.
9. Harper Hospital Trustees' Minutes 1859–74, p. 93.
10. Duffield Diary, December 4, 1865; Harper Hospital Trustees' Minutes 1859–74, p. 95.
11. Harper Hospital Trustees' Minutes 1859–74, p. 99.
12. *The Detroit Free Press,* November 27, 1865.
13. Harper Hospital Trustees' Minutes 1859–74, p. 95.
14. *Harper Hospital* (1886), pp. 75, 76; also *Constitution and Rules of the Harper Hospital* (Detroit, 1866), p. 20.
15. Harper Hospital Trustees' Minutes 1859–74, p. 96.
16. *Constitution and Rules,* p. 25.
17. Harper Hospital Trustees' Minutes 1859–74, p. 105.
18. *Constitution and Rules,* p. 1.
19. *Constitution and Rules,* pp. 4–6.
20. *Constitution and Rules,* pp. 6–7.

21. *Constitution and Rules,* pp. 10–16.
22. Lanman, *Red Book,* p. 202; Robert Spiro, "History of the Michigan Soldiers' Aid Society 1861–1865" (Unpublished doctoral dissertation, University of Michigan, 1959), pp. 16–17.
23. Spiro, "Soldiers' Aid Society," pp. 313, 317.
24. *Michigan Adjutant General Annual Report for 1864* (Michigan State Archives), pp. 3–5.
25. Spiro, "Soldiers' Aid Society," pp. 208–26, 330.
26. Spiro, "Soldiers' Aid Society," p. 453.
27. Spiro, "Soldiers' Aid Society," pp. 429, 431–32.
28. Valeria Campbell to Dr. C. R. Agnew, April 23, 1867 (Campbell Papers, Box 8, Michigan Historical Collections, Ann Arbor).
29. Harper Hospital Trustees' Minutes 1859–74, p. 92.
30. Harper Hospital Trustees' Minutes 1859–74, p. 92.
31. Harper Hospital Trustees' Minutes 1859–74, p. 101.
32. Campbell Papers, Box 7.
33. Campbell Papers, Box 7.
34. Harper Hospital Trustees' Minutes 1859–74, p. 108.
35. Harper Hospital Trustees' Minutes 1859–74, p. 105.
36. Harper Hospital Trustees' Minutes 1859–74, p. 105.
37. Harper Hospital Trustees' Minutes 1859–74, p. 108.
38. Harper Hospital Trustees' Minutes 1859–74, p. 121.
39. Harper Hospital Trustees' Minutes 1859–74, p. 121.
40. Harper Hospital Trustees' Minutes 1859–74, p. 121.
41. Harper Hospital Trustees' Minutes 1859–74, p. 109.
42. Harper Hospital Trustees' Minutes 1859–74, p. 112.
43. Harper Hospital Trustees' Minutes 1859–74, p. 121.
44. Spiro, "Soldiers' Aid Society," p. 322.
45. Harper Hospital Trustees' Minutes 1859–74, p. 122.
46. Senate Resolution No. 131, Committees on State Affairs and Finance, Michigan State Legislature, February 21, 1867, *Journal of Session of 1867–8.*
47. Harper Hospital Trustees' Minutes 1859–74, p. 125.
48. Michigan State Military Board, Minutes, April 9, 1867 (Michigan State Archives, Lansing).
49. Military Board Minutes, April 9, 1867.
50. Military Board Minutes, April 9, 1867.
51. Military Board Minutes, April 9, 1867.
52. Military Board Minutes, April 9, 1867.
53. Campbell Papers, Box 7.
54. Military Board Minutes, April 9, 1867.
55. Michigan State Soldiers' Home Clothing Receipts, 1867 (Harper Hospital Archives).
56. Robertson, *Michigan in the War,* p. 105.

Chapter 10

1. *Detroit Advertiser and Tribune,* May 28, 1866.
2. *Detroit Advertiser and Tribune,* May 28, 1866.
3. *Detroit Advertiser and Tribune,* May 28, 1866.
4. *Detroit Advertiser and Tribune,* May 28, 1866.
5. Harper Hospital Trustees' Minutes 1859–74, p. 114.
6. *Detroit Advertiser and Tribune,* May 28, 1866.
7. Gladys Gearhart, "History of Harper Hospital and Farrand Training School," *Harper Hospital Bulletin,* I, Second Series (July, 1921), 3.
8. Harper Hospital Trustees' Minutes 1859–74, frequent entries, for example, p. 196
9. Harper Hospital Trustees' Minutes 1859–74, pp. 196, 202, 205.

10. Harper Hospital Trustees' Minutes 1859–74, p. 128.
11. Gearhart, "Harper Hospital."
12. Harper Hospital Trustees' Minutes 1859–74, p. 109.
13. Harper Hospital Trustees' Minutes 1859–74, p. 187.
14. Harper Hospital Trustees' Minutes 1859–74, p. 153.
15. Harper Hospital Trustees' Minutes 1859–74, pp. 153, 198.
16. Harper Hospital Trustees' Minutes 1859–74, p. 153.
17. Harper Hospital Trustees' Minutes 1859–74, p. 153.
18. Harper Hospital Trustees' Minutes 1859–74, pp. 215, 219.
19. Harper Hospital Trustees' Minutes 1874–83, p. 276.
20. Farmer, *History of Detroit*, I, 933.
21. Harper Hospital Trustees' Minutes 1859–74, p. 194.
22. Harper Hospital Trustees' Minutes 1859–74, p. 195.
23. Harper Hospital Trustees' Minutes 1874–83, p. 271.
24. Harper Hospital Trustees' Minutes 1859–74, p. 282.
25. Charles F. Clark, comp. *Charles F. Clark's Annual City Directory of . . . City of Detroit* (Detroit, 1867), p. 35.
26. Harper Hospital Trustees' Minutes 1859–74, p. 103.
27. Harper Hospital Trustees' Minutes 1859–74, p. 116.
28. Harper Hospital Trustees' Minutes 1859–74, p. 118.
29. Harper Hospital Trustees' Minutes 1859–74, p. 130.
30. Harper Hospital Trustees' Minutes 1859–74, p. 163.
31. Harper Hospital Trustees' Minutes 1859–74, p. 184.
32. Harper Hospital Trustees' Minutes 1859–74, p. 205.
33. Harper Hospital Trustees' Minutes 1859–74, p. 228.
34. *Detroit Post*, February 4, 1874.
35. Harper Hospital Trustees' Minutes 1859–74, p. 209.
36. Harper Hospital Trustees' Minutes 1859–74, p. 217.
37. Harper Hospital Trustees' Minutes 1859–74, p. 223.
38. Harper Hospital Trustees' Minutes 1859–74, pp. 196, 204.
39. Gearhart, "Harper Hospital"; see also Harper Hospital Trustees' Minutes 1849–74, p. 217.
40. Plinn F. Morse, "Communication System Within Harper Hospital 1864–1948" (Miscellaneous Folder No. 1, Harper Hospital Archives).
41. Harper Hospital Trustees' Minutes 1859–74, p. 200.
42. Gearhart, "Harper Hospital."
43. Harper Hospital Trustees' Minutes 1859–74, p. 161.
44. Harper Hospital Trustees' Minutes 1859–74, p. 161.
45. Harper Hospital Trustees' Minutes 1859–74, p. 165.
46. Harper Hospital Trustees' Minutes 1883–93, p. 6.
47. Harper Hospital Trustees' Minutes 1859–74, p. 123.
48. Harper Hospital Trustees' Minutes 1859–74, p. 137.
49. Harper Hospital Trustees' Minutes 1859–74, p. 137.
50. Farmer, *History of Detroit*, I, 661.
51. Harper Hospital Scrapbook No. II, p. 21.

Chapter 11

1. See *Harper Hospital Annual Reports* 1866–84. These will be found in various places, including the Detroit newspapers. Most of the statistics are in the Harper Hospital Trustees' Minutes 1859–74 and 1875–83.
2. Harper Hospital Scrapbook No. II, p. 12.
3. Harper Hospital Patients Records, 1874–78 (Harper Hospital Archives).
4. Harper Hospital Scrapbook No. I, p. 3.
5. Harper Hospital Scrapbook No. I, p. 50.

6. Harper Hospital Trustees' Minutes 1859–74, p. 160.
7. See reports of annual meetings in Harper Hospital Trustees' Minutes.
8. *Harper Hospital Bulletin*, I, First Series (February, 1891), 55.
9. *Harper Hospital Bulletin*, I (February, 1891), 55.
10. Harper Hospital Patients Register, 1870–76 (Harper Hospital Archives).
11. *Harper Hospital Bulletin*, I, First Series (February, 1891), 55.
12. *Harper Hospital Bulletin*, I (February, 1891), 55.
13. All cases described are taken from Harper Hospital Patients Records 1874–78 (Harper Hospital Archives).
14. *Harper Hospital Bulletin*, I, Second Series (December, 1921), 6.
15. Harper Hospital Trustees' Minutes 1859–74, pp. 127, 145, 168.
16. Harper Hospital Trustees' Minutes 1859–74, p. 150.
17. Harper Hospital Trustees' Minutes 1859–74, p. 222.
18. *Harper Hospital Bulletin*, I, Second Series (December, 1921), 6.
19. Harper Hospital Trustees' Minutes 1859–74, pp. 263, 294.
20. Harper Hospital Trustees' Minutes 1874–83, p. 31.
21. Harper Hospital Trustees' Minutes 1874–83, p. 31.
22. Burton, *City of Detroit*, III, 38.
23. *Harper Hospital Bulletin*, I, Second Series (December, 1921), 6.
24. Burton, *The City of Detroit*, III, 38.
25. Harper Hospital Trustees' Minutes 1859–74, p. 237.
26. Harper Hospital Trustees' Minutes 1859–74, p. 239.
27. Harper Hospital Trustees' Minutes 1859–74, p. 252.
28. Harper Hospital Trustees' Minutes 1859–74, p. 255.
29. Harper Hospital Trustees' Minutes 1859–74, p. 114.
30. Harper Hospital Trustees' Minutes 1859–74, p. 231.
31. Harper Hospital Trustees' Minutes 1859–74, p 246.
32. Harper Hospital Trustees' Minutes 1874–83, p. 23.
33. Harper Hospital Trustees' Minutes 1874–83, p. 41.
34. Harper Hospital Trustees' Minutes 1874–83, pp. 137–39.
35. Burton, *Wayne County*, 449.
36. Spiro, "Soldiers' Aid Society," pp. 19–20.
37. Harper Hospital Trustees' Minutes 1859–74, p. 88.
38. T. A. McGraw to Hon. Charles Goreham, Marshall, Mich., March 29, 1867 (Marshall College Papers, Michigan Historical Collections).
39. Harper Hospital Trustees' Minutes 1859–74, p. 139.
40. Fannie Anderson, "A History of the College of Medicine of Wayne State University (MS, Wayne State University Archives), p. 5.
41. Newspaper clipping, not identified, in fly leaf of Harper Hospital Trustees' Minutes 1859–74.
42. Anderson, "College of Medicine," p. 8.
43. Harper Hospital Trustees' Minutes 1859–74, p. 287.
44. Harper Hospital Trustees' Minutes 1883–93, p. 164.
45. Anderson, "College of Medicine," p. 9.
46. Anderson, "College of Medicine," pp. 13, 17; Harper Hospital Trustees' Minutes 1883–93, pp. 200, 204.
47. Burr, *Medical History*, I, 546.
48. Burr, *Medical History*, I, 546.
49. Anderson, "College of Medicine," pp. 31–36.
50. Harper Hospital Medical Staff Minutes 1885–1909, p. 34.

Chapter 12

1. Rufus Clark, *Annals of St. Paul's Church* (Detroit, 1904), p. 80; Burr, *Medical History*, II, 602; Farmer, *History of Detroit*, I, 656.

2. Harper Hospital Trustees' Minutes 1859–74, p. 112.
3. Harper Hospital Trustees' Minutes 1859–74, p. 144.
4. Harper Hospital Trustees' Minutes 1859–74, p. 236; Farmer, *History of Detroit*, I, 661; Burr, *Medical History*, II, 605.
5. Harper Hospital Trustees' Minutes 1874–83, p. 70.
6. Harper Hospital Trustees' Minutes 1859–74, p. 314; 1874–83, p. 1; Farmer, *History of Detroit*, I, 599.
7. Harper Hospital Trustees' Minutes 1859–74, p. 314; Farmer, *History of Detroit*, I, 659–60.
8. Harper Hospital Trustees' Minutes 1874–83, p. 86.
9. Harper Hospital Trustees' Minutes 1874–83, p. 36; Farmer, *History of Detroit*, I, 587; Clark, *St. Paul's Church*, p. 107.
10. Harper Hospital Trustees' Minutes 1874–83, p. 208.
11. Harper Hospital Trustees' Minutes 1874–83, p. 281.
12. Harper Hospital Trustees' Minutes 1874–83, p. 285.
13. Harper Hospital Trustees' Minutes 1883–93, pp. 81, 197; Burr, *Medical History*, II, 606.
14. *The Detroit Free Press*, March 19, 1879.
15. *The Detroit Free Press*, February 28, 1879; April 4, 1879; April 20, 1879; April 27, 1879.
16. *The Detroit Free Press*, April 4, 1879.
17. Harper Hospital Trustees' Minutes 1874–83, p. 178.
18. Harper Hospital Trustees' Minutes 1874–83, p. 185.
19. *The Detroit Free Press*, May 13, 1879.
20. M. M. Quaife, *This Is Detroit* (Detroit, 1951), p. 195.
21. Harper Hospital Trustees' Minutes 1874–83, p. 199.
22. Harper Hospital Trustees' Minutes 1859–74, pp. 142–43.
23. Harper Hospital Trustees' Minutes 1859–74, p. 142.
24. Harper Hospital Trustees' Minutes 1859–74, p. 150.
25. Harper Hospital Trustees' Minutes 1859–74, p. 150.
26. Burton, *City of Detroit*, III, 692.
27. *Harper Hospital* (1886), pp. 92–93.
28. Harper Hospital Trustees' Minutes 1859–74, p. 287.
29. Harper Hospital Trustees' Minutes 1874–83, p. 245.
30. Harper Hospital Trustees' Minutes 1883–93, p. 5.
31. Harper Hospital Trustees' Minutes 1859–74, p. 137.
32. Harper Hospital Trustees' Minutes 1874–83, p. 240; 1883–93, pp. 5–6.
33. *Harper Hospital* (1886), p. 77.
34. *Harper Hospital* (1886), p. 74.
35. Harper Hospital Subscription Book (Harper Hospital Archives).
36. Harper Hospital Trustees' Minutes 1859–74, pp. 292–93.
37. Harper Hospital Trustees' Minutes 1874–83, p. 257; *Harper Hospital* (1886), p. 78.
38. *Harper Hospital* (1886), p. 78.
39. Harper Hospital Trustees' Minutes 1874–83, p. 107.
40. Harper Hospital Trustees' Minutes 1874–83, p. 253.
41. *Harper Hospital* (1886), p. 79.
42. Harper Hospital Trustees' Minutes 1874–83, p. 245.
43. Harper Hospital Trustees' Minutes 1874–83, p. 260.
44. Harper Hospital Subscription Book.
45. Harper Hospital William Kieft Coyl Free Hospital Record Book (Harper Hospital Archives), pp. 1–4.
46. Harper Hospital Coyl Book, pp. 1–4.
47. Harper Hospital Coyl Book, pp. 21–22.
48. Farmer, *History of Detroit*, II, 1137.
49. Harper Hospital Coyl Book, pp. 21–22.

50. *Detroit News and Tribune,* April 27, 1913.
51. *Harper Hospital Bulletin,* XIX, First Series (July, 1909), 353.
52. Harper Hospital Coyl Book, p. 7.
53. Harper Hospital Coyl Book, p. 8.
54. Harper Hospital Coyl Book, p. 13.
55. Harper Hospital Coyl Book, p. 48.
56. Harper Hospital Coyl Book, p. 52.
57. Harper Hospital Coyl Book, p. 20.
58. Harper Hospital Coyl Book, p. 72.
59. *Harper Hospital Bulletin,* V, First Series (February, 1895), 91.
60. *Harper Hospital Bulletin,* XIX, First Series (July, 1909), 353.

Chapter 13

1. Harper Hospital Trustees' Minutes 1859–74, p. 288.
2. Harper Hospital Trustees' Minutes 1874–83, p. 245.
3. Harper Hospital Trustees' Minutes 1883–93, p. 11.
4. Harper Hospital Trustees' Minutes 1883–93, p. 19.
5. Harper Hospital Trustees' Minutes 1874–83, pp. 260–61.
6. Harper Hospital Trustees' Minutes 1874–83, p. 280; also, see Harper Hospital Building Committee Minutes 1883–93, p. 300.
7. "Annual Report for 1882" in Harper Hospital Trustees' Minutes 1883–93, pp. 5–6.
8. *Detroit Post and Tribune,* February 8, 1882.
9. Duffield Papers (Burton Historical Collection).
10. Harper Hospital Building Committee Minutes 1883–93, p. 301.
11. *Harper Hospital* (1886), pp. 79–81.
12. Harper Hospital Building Committee Minutes, p. 303.
13. Harper Hospital Building Committee Minutes, p. 308.
14. Harper Hospital Building Committee Minutes, p. 306.
15. *Harper Hospital* (1886), p. 82.
16. Harper Hospital Trustees' Minutes 1883–93, pp. 24–25.
17. Harper Hospital Trustees' Minutes 1883–93, p. 25.
18. Harper Hospital Trustees' Minutes 1883–93, p. 24.
19. Harper Hospital Trustees' Minutes 1883–93, p. 32.
20. *Harper Hospital* (1886), pp. 82–83.
21. Harper Hospital Trustees' Minutes 1883–93, p. 41.
22. Farmer, *History of Detroit,* I, 659.
23. Harper Hospital Trustees' Minutes 1883–93, p. 26.
24. Harper Hospital Trustees' Minutes 1883–93, pp. 37, 39, 45, 47.
25. *The Detroit Free Press,* June 20, 1884.
26. Newspaper clippings, not identified, in Harper Hospital Scrapbook II.
27. Newspaper clippings, not identified, in Harper Hospital Scrapbook II.
28. *Harper Hospital* (1886), pp. 80–81.
29. See note 26, above.
30. Gearhart, "Harper Hospital," p. 2.
31. See note 26, above.
32. *The Detroit Free Press,* clipping, undated, in Harper Hospital Scrapbook II.
33. Harper Hospital Trustees' Minutes 1883–93, pp. 9, 10.
34. *Harper Hospital* (1886), p. 86.
35. Burr, *Medical History,* II, 647.
36. H. Fulton, "History of Nursing in Harper Hospital" (Harper Hospital Archives).
37. *Harper Hospital* (1886), p. 86.
38. *Harper Hospital* (1886), p. 87.
39. *Harper Hospital* (1886), p. 87.
40. *Harper Hospital* (1886), pp. 88–91.

41. Agnes G. Deans and Anne L. Austin, *The History of the Farrand Training School For Nurses* (Detroit, 1936), p. 36.
42. Deans and Austin, *Farrand Training School*, p. 47.
43. Farrand Training School Student Records 1884–96 (Harper Hospital Archives).
44. Farrand Training School Student Records 1884–96 (Harper Hospital Archives).
45. Deans and Austin, *Farrand Training School*, p. 41.
46. Deans and Austin, *Farrand Training School*, p. 42.
47. *Harper Hospital Bulletin*, V, First Series (February, 1895), 79.
48. Deans and Austin, *Farrand Training School*, p. 41.
49. Harper Hospital Trustees' Minutes 1883–93, pp. 71–72.
50. Fulton, "Nursing in Harper Hospital."
51. *Harper Hospital Bulletin*, V, First Series (February, 1895), 79–84; also for an account of Mrs. Gretter and the Farrand School under her administration, see Helen W. Munson, "Lystra E. Gretter," *American Journal of Nursing*, IL, (June, 1949), 344–48.
52. Deans and Austin, *Farrand Training School*.
53. Deans and Austin, *Farrand Training School*, pp. 34, 73; *Harper Hospital Bulletin*, I, Second Series (October, 1921), 6; V, (2nd Quarter, 1925), 8.
54. Harper Hospital Trustees' Minutes 1897–1913, p. 113.
55. Deans and Austin, *Farrand Training School*, pp. 153–58; *Harper Hospital Bulletin*, I, Second Series (July, 1921), 7; Farrand Training School Student Records (Harper Hospital Archives), p. 30.
56. *Leucocyte*, II (January, 1896), 15; see also *Annual Reports for the Farrand Training School for Nurses*, and specifically that for 1903 in *Harper Hospital Bulletin*, XIV, First Series (February, 1904), 103–04.
57. *Harper Hospital Bulletin*, XIII, First Series (February, 1898), 65.
58. *The British Journal of Nursing*, XXIX (October 3, 1903), 267.

Chapter 14

1. Schreiber Meeting (Wayne State University Archives).
2. Harper Hospital Trustees' Minutes 1883–93, p. 7.
3. Harper Hospital Trustees' Minutes 1883–93, p. 8.
4. Harper Hospital Trustees' Minutes 1883–93, p. 33.
5. Harper Hospital Trustees' Minutes 1883–93, p. 108.
6. Harper Hospital Trustees' Minutes 1883–93, p. 67.
7. Harper Hospital Medical Staff Minutes 1885–1909 (Harper Hospital Archives), p. 39.
8. Harper Hospital Medical Staff Minutes 1885–1909, p. 45.
9. Harper Hospital Medical Staff Minutes 1885–1909, p. 81.
10. Harper Hospital Medical Staff Minutes 1885–1909, p. 95.
11. Harper Hospital Medical Staff Minutes 1885–1909, p. 24.
12. Clapsattle, *Doctors Mayo*, p. 109.
13. Harper Hospital Medical Staff Minutes 1885–1909, p. 37.
14. Burr, *Medical History*, II, 422, 604.
15. *Harper Hospital Bulletin*, I, First Series (February, 1891), 57.
16. This sketch of Dr. J. H. Carstens is drawn from the following sources: Burr, *Medical History*, I, 15, 529–31, 778; II, 188, 348, 422, 472, 519, 540; *Leucocyte*, I (October, 1894), 14; *Detroit Journal*, January 15, 1917; *Harper Hospital Bulletin*, XVII, Third Series (September–October, 1959), 263; interview, the authors with Dr. Louis J. Hirschman, October 27, 1962, Traverse City, Michigan. Dr. Hirschman was a student, staff colleague, and son-in-law of Dr. Carstens.
17. Statistics taken from *Harper Hospital Annual Reports* 1890–1911. These will be found in the *Harper Hospital Bulletin* for the years indicated. For 1922, see *Harper Hospital Bulletin*, II, Second Series (February, 1922), 8.
18. Harper Hospital Medical Staff Minutes 1885–1909, p. 101.

19. Dr. Louis J. Hirschman interview, October 27, 1962.
20. *Harper Hospital Bulletin*, IX, First Series (February, 1899), 56.
21. *Harper Hospital Bulletin*, VII, First Series (February, 1897), 70.
22. Newspaper clipping, not identified, in Harper Hospital Scrapbook I, p. 75.
23. Clapsattle, *Doctors Mayo*, p. 135.
24. Burr, *Medical History*, I, 746.
25. Burr, *Medical History*, I, 746.
26. *The Detroit Free Press*, January 9, 1900.
27. *Harper Hospital Bulletin*, XI, First Series (June, 1900), 5.
28. *Harper Hospital Bulletin*, IX, First Series (December, 1898), 35.
29. *Harper Hospital Annual Reports* 1892–1911.
30. Harper Hospital Medical Staff Minutes 1885–1909, p. 48.
31. Minutes 1883–93, pp. 115, 121; also Louis J. Hirschman interview. Dr. Hirschman recalled the old streetcars on the hospital grounds during his medical school days, about 1898.
32. *Harper Hospital Bulletin*, XI, First Series (December, 1900).
33. *Harper Hospital Bulletin*, IV, First Series (April, 1894), 58; (February, 1894), 111.
34. *Harper Hospital Bulletin*, VII, First Series (February, 1897), 91.
35. Louis J. Hirschman interview.
36. Harper Hospital Medical Staff Minutes 1885–1909, p. 97.
37. Harper Hospital Medical Staff Minutes 1885–1909, pp. 102–03.
38. *Detroit Tribune*, January 14, 1902.
39. Harper Hospital Trustees' Minutes 1897–1913, p. 93.
40. Harper Hospital Trustees' Minutes 1897–1913, p. 103.
41. Harper Hospital Scrapbook I, p. 66.
42. *Detroit Tribune*, May 19, 1902.
43. *Detroit Journal*, March 18, 1904.
44. Harper Hospital Scrapbook I, pp. 81–2.
45. Harper Hospital Scrapbook I, p. 86.
46. Harper Hospital Scrapbook I, p. 85.
47. Burr, *Medical History*, II, 609–10.
48. *Harper Hospital Bulletin*, VII, First Series (February, 1897), 70.

Chapter 15

1.   Harper Hospital Trustees' Minutes 1859–74, p. 130.
2.   E. H. L. Corwin, *The American Hospital* (New York, 1946), p. 165.
3.   Harper Hospital Trustees' Minutes 1859–74, p. 132.
4.   Harper Hospital Trustees' Minutes 1859–74, p. 131.
5.   *Detroit Advertiser and Tribune*, February 29, 1868.
6.   *Detroit Advertiser and Tribune*, February 29, 1868.
7.   Harper Hospital Trustees' Minutes 1859–74, p. 158.
8.   Corwin, *American Hospital*, p. 176.
9.   *Leucocyte*, II (October, 1895), 13.
10. Corwin, *American Hospital*, p. 171.
11. Harper Hospital Trustees' Minutes 1883–93, p. 73.
12. Harper Hospital Medical Staff Minutes 1885–1909, p. 48.
13. Harper Hospital Trustees' Minutes 1883–93, p. 115.
14. Harper Hospital Trustees' Minutes 1883–93, p. 130.
15. Harper Hospital Trustees' Minutes 1883–93, p. 131.
16. *Harper Hospital Annual Report for 1890.*
17. *Harper Hospital Bulletin*, II, First Series (February, 1892), 43 ff.
18. Harper Hospital Medical Staff Minutes 1885–1909, pp. 74, 76.
19. *Harper Hospital Bulletin*, III, First Series (February, 1893), 40.
20. *Harper Hospital Annual Report for 1894.*

21. Information supplied by Barbara Coe Johnson, Director of Libraries, Harper Hospital, November 5, 1962.

22. *Harper Hospital Bulletin,* VIII, First Series (August, 1897), 23.

23. *Harper Hospital Bulletin,* II, Second Series (July, 1922), 2, 12.

24. *Harper Hospital Bulletin,* III, Second Series (April, 1923), 8.

25. *Harper Hospital Bulletin,* III, Second Series (June, 1923), 13.

26. Alice H. Walker, "Harper Hospital Out-patient Department Extends Its Clinic Service," *The Modern Hospital,* XXIX, No. 2 (August, 1927), 1.

27. *Harper Hospital Annual Report for 1887;* also Harper Hospital Trustees' Minutes 1883–93, p. 91.

28. Harper Hospital Trustees' Minutes 1883–93, p. 126.

29. Preston M. Hickey, "History of the Detroit College of Medicine," *Leucocyte,* I, (December, 1894), pp. 4, 5.

30. Interview with J. Milton Robb, M.D., August 14, 1962.

31. Harper Hospital Trustees' Minutes 1883–93, pp. 144, 161, 184, 211, 215.

32. *Harper Hospital Bulletin,* III, First Series (February, 1893), 43.

33. *Detroit News,* July 24, 1887; July 25, 1887; Harper Hospital Trustees' Minutes 1883–93, pp. 100, 103.

34. *The First Fifty Years—The Grace Hospital* (Detroit, 1938).

35. Schreiber Meeting, p. 15.

36. Schreiber Meeting, p. 15.

37. *Harper Hospital Bulletin,* IV, First Series (February, 1894), 68.

38. *Harper Hospital Annual Report for 1895,* p. 4.

39. Louis J. Hirschman interview.

40. *Leucocyte,* I (October, 1894), 11.

41. *Harper Hospital Bulletin,* IX, First Series (February, 1899), 48.

42. Harper Hospital Trustees' Minutes 1914–23, May 22, 1914. Although the trustees authorized the purchase of an automobile ambulance, Dr. Louis J. Hirschman says it was donated by Trustee C. A. Black.

43. Harper Hospital Trustees' Minutes 1914–23, June 19, 1918.

44. Harper Hospital Trustees' Minutes 1883–93, pp. 92, 94, 95, 135.

45. Harper Hospital Trustees' Minutes 1883–93, pp. 97, 99, 100.

46. Harper Hospital Trustees' Minutes 1883–93, pp. 195–96.

47. Harper Hospital Trustees' Minutes 1883–93, p. 225.

48. *Leucocyte,* III (October, 1896), 16.

49. Quaife, *This Is Detroit,* p. 47; Harper Hospital Trustees' Minutes 1883–93, pp. 160, 184.

50. Harper Hospital Trustees' Minutes 1883–93, p. 218.

51. *Harper Hospital Bulletin,* II, First Series (August, 1891), 18.

52. *Leucocyte,* I (October, 1894), 11.

53. Harper Hospital Trustees' Minutes 1897–1913, p. 32.

54. Marion H. Wells, "Then and Now—Harper Hospital Library," *Harper Star,* Vol. I (September, 1950); also "Rough Copy of Talk with Mrs. Parmalee Regarding Early History of Library, July 24, 1950" (MS in Harper Hospital Archives).

55. Interview with Barbara Coe Johnson, Director of Libraries, Harper Hospital, November 8, 1962.

56. Harper Hospital Trustees' Minutes 1883–93, p. 167.

57. Harper Hospital Medical Staff Minutes 1885–1909, p. 66; Harper Hospital Trustees' Minutes 1883–93, p. 176.

58. Harper Hospital Medical Staff Minutes, 1885–1909, p. 70.

59. *Harper Hospital Bulletin,* XIII, First Series (December, 1902), 44.

60. Harper Hospital Medical Staff Minutes 1885–1909, p. 100.

61. Harper Hospital Medical Staff Minutes 1885–1909, p. 134; Harper Hospital Trustees' Minutes 1897–1913, p. 195.

62. Harper Hospital Trustees' Executive Committee Minutes 1915–45, April 4, 1919.

63. Harper Hospital Trustees' Minutes 1934–43, February 19, 1941.
64. Harper Hospital Trustees' Minutes 1883–93, p. 170.
65. Georgiana Downes, *Administratrix, etc.,* v. *The Harper Hospital,* 101 Michigan, p. 555. For the general significance of this case, see also *National Hospital Record* (June, 1903), p. 27.

Chapter 16

1. *Harper Hospital Bulletin,* XXI, First Series (September, 1910), 54.
2. *Detroit News,* February 10, 1892.
3. Harper Hospital Trustees' Minutes 1883–93, p. 236.
4. *Harper Hospital Bulletin,* XI, First Series (February, 1901), 50.
5. Harper Hospital Trustees' Minutes 1883–93, p. 236; *Detroit News,* February 10, 1892.
6. Harper Hospital Scrapbook II, p. 35.
7. Harper Hospital Scrapbook II, p. 37.
8. Harper Hospital Trustees' Minutes 1897–1913, p. 30.
9. *Harper Hospital Bulletin,* III, Second Series (April, 1923), 16.
10. Harper Hospital Trustees' Minutes 1897–1913, p. 295.
11. *Harper Hospital Bulletin,* VI, First Series (February, 1896), 48; II, Second Series (February, 1922), 7; Harper Hospital Trustees' Minutes 1897–1913, p. 1.
12. *Harper Hospital Bulletin,* XIV, First Series (December, 1903), 40.
13. Harper Hospital Trustees' Minutes 1897–1913, pp. 43, 49.
14. Harper Hospital Trustees' Minutes 1897–1913, p. 73.
15. Harper Hospital Trustees' Minutes 1897–1913, pp. 79, 80.
16. Harper Hospital Trustees' Minutes 1897–1913, pp. 101, 119.
17. *Detroit Journal,* May 27, 1903; *Evening News,* October 28, 1903.
18. *Harper Hospital Bulletin,* XIV, First Series (December, 1903), 39–56.
19. *Harper Hospital Bulletin,* XIV, First Series (December, 1903), 53.
20. Harper Hospital Trustees' Minutes 1897–1913, pp. 165, 166, 167, 177; *Harper Hospital Bulletin,* XXII, First Series (June, 1911), 14.
21. Harper Hospital Trustees' Minutes 1897–1913, p. 207.
22. Harper Hospital Trustees' Minutes 1897–1913, p. 208.
23. Harper Hospital Trustees' Minutes 1897–1913, p. 216.
24. "History of Henry Ford Hospital" (n.d., n.p., typescript, 2 pp., furnished authors by Henry Ford Hospital, 1962).
25. *What Detroit Needs Most* (Detroit, 1912).
26. Harper Hospital Trustees' Minutes 1897–1913, p. 222.
27. Harper Hospital Trustees' Minutes 1897–1913, p. 245.
28. *Harper Hospital Bulletin,* XXII, First Series (June, 1911), 14.
29. Harper Hospital Trustees' Minutes 1897–1913, p. 293.
30. Harper Hospital Trustees' Minutes 1897–1913, p. 264.
31. Harper Hospital Trustees' Minutes 1897–1913, p. 293.
32. Harper Hospital Trustees' Minutes 1897–1913, p. 262.
33. Harper Hospital Trustees' Minutes 1914–23, May, 25, 1916.
34. Wayne Smith, "Joseph L. Hudson Memorial Building of Harper Hospital, Detroit," *The Modern Hospital,* V (August, 1915), 1–7.
35. Typescript material not otherwise identified (Harper Hospital Archives).
36. Burr, *Medical History,* II, 630; Harper Hospital Trustees' Minutes 1914–23, May 18, 1915.
37. Harper Hospital Trustees' Minutes 1914–23, September 4, 1914; Harper Hospital Medical Staff Executive Committee Minutes, 1910–16, p. 133; Harper Hospital Trustees' Minutes 1914–1923, May 18, 1915.
38. Harper Hospital Trustees' Minutes 1914–23, Dec. 11, 1917.
39. *What Detroit Needs Most* (Detroit, 1912).

40. See Harper Hospital Scrapbook I, pp. 55–66, 72 for newspaper clipping on this matter.
41. Burr, *Medical History,* II, 610.
42. Harper Hospital Trustees' Minutes 1897–1913, p. 276.
43. Harper Hospital Trustees' Minutes 1897–1913, pp. 277–80.
44. Harper Hospital Trustees' Minutes 1897–1913, pp. 281–83.
45. Burr, *Medical History,* II, 610.
46. Harper Hospital Trustees' Minutes 1897–1913, p. 232.
47. Harper Hospital Trustees' Minutes 1897–1913, p. 289; 1914–23, Dec. 16, 1915, Jan. 1, 1916.
48. Harper Hospital Trustees' Minutes 1897–1913, p. 95.
49. Harper Hospital Medical Staff Executive Committee Minutes 1910–16, p. 94.

Chapter 17

1. Harper Hospital Medical Staff Minutes 1885–1909, pp. 116, 122–23.
2. Harper Hospital Trustees' Minutes 1897–1913, p. 197.
3. Harper Hospital Scrapbook I, p. 135.
4. W. F. Metcalf, "Observations on the General Principles of Hospital Organization," *Journal of the Michigan State Medical Society,* VIII (May, 1904), 230–40.
5. Harper Hospital Medical Staff Executive Committee Minutes, 1910–16, p. 2.
6. Harper Hospital Trustees' Minutes 1897–1913, pp. 218–19.
7. Harper Hospital Trustees' Minutes 1897–1913, p. 222.
8. Harper Hospital Trustees' Minutes 1897–1913, p. 226.
9. *Harper Hospital Bulletin,* XXI, First Series (September, 1910), 54; I, Second Series (April, 1921), pp. 5–6.
10. Harper Hospital Trustees' Minutes 1897–1913, p. 219.
11. *Harper Hospital Bulletin,* XXIII, Second Series (July, 1912), 21.
12. Harper Hospital Medical Staff Executive Committee Minutes, 1910–16, p. 41.
13. Harper Hospital Trustees' Executive Committee Minutes 1915–45, p. 59.
14. Harper Hospital Trustees' Minutes 1914–23, April 8, 1919.
15. Harper Hospital Trustees' Executive Committee Minutes 1915–45, p. 64.
16. Harper Hospital Trustees' Executive Committee Minutes 1915–45, pp. 65 ff.
17. *The Detroit Free Press,* November 18, 1919.
18. Harper Hospital Scrapbook I, p. 104; Harper Hospital Trustees' Executive Committee Minutes 1915–45, pp. 92, 93, 123.
19. *Detroit News,* February 17, 1921.
20. *Detroit News,* February 17, 1921.
21. *Harper Hospital Bulletin,* I, Second Series (April, 1921), 1.
22. *Harper Hospital Bulletin,* III, Second Series (April, 1923), 2; also, Harper Hospital Trustees' Executive Committee Minutes 1915–45, pp. 180–81.
23. Owen C. Foster, M.D., and Laurence A. Chrouch, M.D. "The Obstetrical and Gynecological Department of Harper Hospital," *Harper Hospital Bulletin,* V, Third Series (June, 1947), 47; also for obstetrical statistics see "the largest number of deliveries in the obstetrical history of Harper Hospital occurred in 1947," in *Harper Hospital Bulletin,* VI, Third Series (November–December, 1948), 156.
24. Harper Hospital Trustees' Executive Committee Minutes 1915–45, p. 74.
25. *Harper Hospital Bulletin,* V, Second Series (Spring, 1926), 15.
26. *Harper Hospital Bulletin,* XIII–XVI, Third Series (1955–1956), 46.
27. *Harper Hospital Bulletin,* I, Second Series (July, 1921), 4.
28. *Harper Hospital Bulletin,* I, First Series (June, 1890), 5.
29. *Harper Hospital Bulletin,* X, First Series (February, 1900), 76.
30. Harper Hospital Trustees' Minutes 1897–1913, p. 204; *Harper Hospital Bulletin,* XX, First Series (December, 1909), 39.
31. *Harper Hospital Bulletin,* V, Second Series (Second Quarter, 1925), 5.

32. Harper Hospital Bulletin, V, Second Series (Second Quarter, 1925), 5.
33. *Harper Hospital—An Obligation and An Opportunity* (Detroit, 1926), p. 15; *Harper Hospital Bulletin*, XVIII, Third Series (March–April, 1960), 2; Harper Hospital Trustees' Executive Committee Minutes 1915–45, p. 223; *Harper Hospital Bulletin*, V, Second Series (Second Quarter, 1925), 5; *The Detroit Free Press*, January 16, 1921; *Detroit News*, February 2, 1923; H. C. Saltzstein, "A Brief History of Our Animal Laboratory," *Harper Hospital Bulletin*, IX, Third Series (July–August, 1951), 131 ff.; Harper Hospital Trustees' Minutes 1944–53, January 14, 1947; 1934–43, April 9, 1934; Harper Hospital Trustees' Executive Committee Minutes 1914–45, p. 223, and other various issues of *Harper Hospital Bulletin* from 1941 to 1962.
34. Schreiber Meeting, 1938 (Wayne State University Archives).
35. Dr. Louis J. Hirschman, interview, October 27, 1962.
36. *Detroit News*, n.d., in Harper Hospital Scrapbook I.
37. Harper Hospital Trustees' Minutes 1897–1913, p. 84; also Hirschman.
38. *Detroit News*, n.d., in Harper Hospital Scrapbook I.
39. *Harper Hospital Bulletin*, XIV, Second Series (February, 1903), 51.
40. *Harper Hospital Bulletin*, XV, First Series (February, 1904), 70.
41. Burr, *Medical History*, II, 867.
42. *Harper Hospital Bulletin*, V, Second Series (1st Quarter, 1925), 5.
43. Harper Hospital Trustees' Minutes 1914–23, April 8, 1915. The working arrangement between Hickey and his successors and Harper Hospital also was described to the authors by Dr. Kenneth L. Krabbenhoft, of Lawrence Reynolds & Associates, in an interview, October 16, 1962.
44. *Harper Hospital Bulletin*, II, Second Series (February, 1922), 2.
45. *Harper Hospital Bulletin*, IV, Second Series (April, 1924), 10.
46. *Harper Hospital Bulletin*, V, Second Series (2nd Quarter, 1925), 12; *Detroit Times*, January 9, 1933.
47. *Harper Hospital Bulletin*, XIII, Second Series (July, 1912), 20; Harper Hospital Trustees' Executive Committee Minutes 1915–45, p. 127.
48. Harper Hospital Trustees' Minutes 1944–53, February 13, 1951.
49. See various annual reports and record of appointments in Minutes.
50. *Harper Hospital Bulletin*, II, Second Series (February, 1922), 12.
51. *Harper Hospital Bulletin* III, Second Series (April, 1923), 7.
52. *Harper Hospital* Bulletin, III, Second Series (April, 1923), 7.
53. *Harper Hospital Bulletin*, V, Second Series (1st Quarter, 1925), 6.
54. *Harper Hospital Bulletin*, II, Second Series (February, 1922) 8.
55. *Harper Hospital Bulletin*, IV, Second Series (April, 1924), 7.
56. *Harper Hospital Bulletin*, IV, Second Series (April, 1924), 9.
57. *Harper Hospital Bulletin*, V, Second Series (1st Quarter, 1925), 4.
58. Harper Hospital Trustees' Minutes 1934–43, September 18, 1936; December 18, 1936.
59. Harper Hospital Trustees' Minutes 1944–53, May 22, 1953.
60. Harper Hospital Trustees' Minutes 1944–53, October 22, 1953.
61. Dean Gordon H. Scott, interview, January 3, 1963.
62. *Harper Hospital Bulletin*, XXIII, First Series (October, 1912), 7–12.
63. Harper Hospital Medical Staff Executive Committee Minutes 1910–16, June 23, 1913, p. 92.
64. Harper Hospital Medical Staff Executive Committee Minutes 1910–16, p. 98; Harper Hospital Trustees' Minutes 1914–23, May 22, 1913.
65. *Harper Hospital Bulletin*, V, Second Series (2nd Quarter, 1925), 11.
66. *Harper Hospital Bulletin*, V, Second Series (2nd Quarter, 1925), 11.
67. *Harper Hospital Bulletin*, III, Second Series (April, 1923), 7.
68. "Annual Report, Out-patient and Social Service Departments," (MS in Harper Hospital Archives), 1946.
69. *Harper Hospital Bulletin*, I, Second Series (October, 1921), 2.
70. *Harper Hospital Bulletin*, I, Second Series (October, 1921), 2.

71. *Harper Hospital Bulletin,* I, Second Series (April, 1921), p. 5; I (July, 1921), 7.
72. *Harper Hospital Bulletin,* I, Second Series (October, 1921), p. 1.
73. *Harper Hospital Bulletin,* I, Second Series (October, 1921), p. 1.
74. *Detroit Journal,* October 15, 1921.
75. Harper Hospital Trustees' Executive Committee Minutes 1915–45, p. 120.
76. *Harper Hospital Bulletin,* V, Second Series (Spring, 1926), 20.
77. Harper Hospital Trustees' Executive Committee Minutes 1915–45, p. 211.
78. Harper Hospital Trustees' Executive Committee Minutes 1915–45, pp. 219 ff.
79. Harper Hospital Trustees' Executive Committee Minutes 1915–45, pp. 219 ff.
80. Harper Hospital Trustees' Minutes 1934–43, February 17, 1943.
81. *Harper Hospital Annual Statistical Report 1951* (Harper Hospital Archives), p. 2.

Chapter 18

1. *Detroit News,* April 26, 1898.
2. Deans and Austin, *Farrand Training School,* pp. 162–65.
3. *New York Journal,* September 2, 1898.
4. Janet Mitchell, n.d. (MS in Harper Hospital Scrapbook II).
5. *Harper Hospital Bulletin,* IX, First Series (February, 1899), 84.
6. Harper Hospital Trustees' Minutes 1897–1913, p. 20.
7. Deans and Austin, *Farrand Training School,* p. 168.
8. Deans and Austin, *Farrand Training School,* p. 169.
9. Harper Hospital Trustees' Minutes 1914–23, July 5, 1916.
10. War Department Order No. 6, June 29, 1917 (Harper Hospital Archives); see also *The Detroit Free Press,* May 25, 1917.
11. Agnes G. Deans, "War Service," in Scrapbook "World War I Nursing Service" (MS in Harper Hospital Archives, n.d.).
12. Harper Hospital Trustees' Minutes 1914–23, June 12, 1917.
13. Harper Hospital Trustees' Minutes 1914–23, July 17, 1917.
14. *The Detroit Free Press,* May 16, 1917.
15. Deans, "War Service."
16. Deans, "War Service."
17. Deans, "War Service." See also Harper Hospital Scrapbook I, p. 98, and American Red Cross Scrapbook (Harper Hospital Archives).
18. Deans and Austin, *Farrand Training School,* p. 171.
19. Harper Hospital Trustees' Minutes 1914–23, April 9, 1918; Harper Hospital Scrapbook I, p. 99.
20. Burr, *Medical History,* II, 869.
21. Deans, "War Service."
22. Harper Hospital Trustees' Executive Committee Minutes 1915–45, p. 52.
23. Harper Hospital Trustees' Executive Committee Minutes 1915–45, pp. 71–72.
24. Deans and Austin, *Farrand Training School,* p. 173.
25. Teresa Curley, Scrapbook (Harper Hospital Archives).
26. *The Detroit Free Press,* March 10, 11, 1919.
27. Louis J. Hirschman to authors, interview, Traverse City, Michigan, October 27, 1962.
28. Harper Hospital Trustees' Minutes 1914–23, September 12, 1916.
29. James Deming Smith, interview, Detroit, November 30, 1962.
30. *Harper Hospital Bulletin,* II, Second Series (July, 1922), 3.
31. *Harper Hospital Bulletin,* I, Second Series (May, 1921), 3.
32. Deans and Austin, *Farrand Training School,* p. 97.
33. *Detroit News,* April 9, 1922.
34. *Harper Hospital Bulletin,* II, Second Series (July, 1922), 3 ff.
35. *Detroit News,* October 23, 1936.
36. Harper Hospital Trustees' Minutes 1914–23, May 29, 1922.
37. *Detroit Saturday Night,* May 27, 1922.

38. *Harper Hospital Bulletin,* IV, Second Series (April, 1924), 5.
39. Harper Hospital Trustees' Executive Committee Minutes 1915–45, p. 156.
40. Harper Hospital Trustees' Executive Committee Minutes 1915–45, pp. 161, 162, 163.
41. Harper Hospital Trustees' Executive Committee Minutes 1915–45, p. 166; *Harper Hospital Bulletin,* V, Second Series (1st Quarter, 1925), 5.
42. Harper Hospital Trustees' Minutes 1924–33, April 20, 1925; Harper Hospital Trustees' Executive Committee Minutes 1915–45, p. 169.
43. Harper Hospital Trustees' Minutes 1924–33, September 17, 1925.
44. Harper Hospital Trustees' Minutes 1924–33, November 10, 1925.
45. Harper Hospital Trustees' Executive Committee Minutes 1915–45, p. 171.
46. *Harper Hospital Bulletin,* V, Second Series (Spring, 1926), 3.
47. Harper Hospital Trustees' Minutes 1924–33, October 3, 1927; November 17, 1927.
48. Journal, Brush Building (Harper Hospital Archives).
49. Harper Hospital Trustees' Minutes 1924–33, April 26, 1917; June 7, 1927.
50. Harper Hospital Trustees' Minutes 1924–33, February 22, 1928; April 3, 1928.
51. *The Detroit Free Press,* May 13, 1928.
52. *Harper Hospital Bulletin,* V, Second Series (Spring, 1926), 4.
53. *Harper Hospital, An Obligation and An Opportunity* (Detroit: Harper Hospital, 1926), p. 23.

Chapter 19

1. *Harper Hospital Bulletin,* IV, First Series (February, 1894), 54.
2. *Harper Hospital Bulletin,* V, First Series (February, 1895), 94.
3. Program, Complimentary Banquet in Honor of Dr. John Henry Carstens, September 26, 1911 (Wayne State University Archives), p. 357.
4. Harper Hospital Trustees' Minutes 1914–23, May 25, 1916; May 9, 1920.
5. Harper Hospital Trustees' Minutes 1914–23, June 12, 1931; October 12, 1931; November 17, 1931.
6. Harper Hospital Trustees' Minutes 1914–23, March 6, 1933.
7. Smith, November 30, 1962.
8. Harper Hospital Trustees' Minutes 1924–33, July 7, 1933.
9. Harper Hospital Trustees' Minutes 1924–33, December 30, 1932.
10. Deans and Austin, *Farrand Training School,* p. 192; Harper Hospital Trustees' Minutes 1924–33, May 22, 1933.
11. Harper Hospital Trustees' Minutes 1934–43, April 4, 1936.
12. Lystra E. Gretter to Senator James Couzens, Detroit, June 7, 1935 (Harper Hospital Archives).
13. Senator James Couzens to Lystra E. Gretter, Washington, June 10, 1935 (Harper Hospital Archives).
14. Harper Hospital Trustees' Minutes 1934–43, January 8, 1937.
15. *Detroit News,* November 8, 1948.
16. Harper Hospital Trustees' Minutes 1934–43, May 19, 1941.
17. Harper Hospital Trustees' Minutes 1944–53, April 24, 1947.
18. Labor Scrapbook (Harper Hospital Archives).
19. Bulletin "Notice To All Employes," April 20, 1948 (Harper Hospital Archives).
20. Bulletin "To Employes of Harper Hospital," June 1, 1948 (Harper Hospital Archives).
21. "To Employes of Harper Hospital."
22. *Detroit News,* November 8, 1948.
23. Labor Scrapbook.
24. *The Detroit Free Press,* February 13, 1949.
25. "The Harper," August 3, 1948 (Harper Hospital Archives), p. 3.
26. *Harper Hospital Bulletin,* IV, Second Series (April, 1924), 4.
27. Robert M. Cunningham, *The Blue Cross Story* (Chicago, 1958), p. 6.
28. Cunningham, *Blue Cross Story,* pp. 4–6.

29. Lawrence Drake and Alice Hanna, *The History of Michigan Hospital Service* (Detroit, 1952), pp. 14–17.
30. Harper Hospital Trustees' Minutes 1934–43, October 3, 1938.
31. Harper Hospital Trustees' Minutes 1934–43, January 6, 1939.
32. *Background of Michigan Blue Cross-Blue Shield* (Detroit, 1962), pp. 4, 5.
33. *Harper Hospital Bulletin,* III, Second Series (November, 1923), 8.
34. Harper Hospital Trustees' Executive Committee Minutes 1915–45, February 13, 1924.
35. *Harper Hospital Bulletin,* IV, Second Series (April, 1924), 14.
36. Stewart Hamilton to Major General James C. Magee, Detroit, March 19, 1940; Lt. Col. Francis M. Fitts, M.C., to Hamilton, Washington, June 18, 1940 (Harper Hospital Archives).
37. Coral Bremer, "History of the Nursing Service, 17th General Hospital (U.S.)," (MS in Harper Hospital Archives, August, 1945).
38. Bremer, "Nursing Service."
39. Bremer, "Nursing Service."
40. Bremer, "Nursing Service."
41. Colonel H. R. Carstens, interview, Detroit, November 10, 1962.
42. Bremer, "Nursing Service."
43. Carstens, November 10, 1962.
44. Harper Hospital Trustees' Minutes 1934-43, December 16, 1941; January 18, 1942; April 7, 1942; May 18, 1942; October 26, 1942; June 21, 1943.
45. Roy A. Frakes, "The Harper Hospital Auxiliary," in *Nursing Outlook,* 10 (May, 1962), 326–27.

Chapter 20

1. Harper Hospital Trustees' Minutes 1944–53, June 19, 1950.
2. Harper Hospital Trustees' Minutes 1944–53, December 21, 1949.
3. Harper Hospital Trustees' Minutes 1944–53, February 14, 1950.
4. *The Michigan Society of Architects Monthly Bulletin,* XXXII (June, 1958), pp. 17–32.
5. *Detroit News,* May 5, 1937; November 10, 1937.
6. *Detroit News,* December 29, 1942.
7. Edgar Hughes Norris, *The Medical Science Center of Wayne University* (Detroit, July 7, 1943).
8. *The Detroit Free Press,* November 24, 1943.
9. Wendell Anderson, Progress Report of Medical Science Center of Wayne University to the Board of Education (MS in Wayne State University Archives).
10. *Detroit Times,* March 26, 1953; *Detroit News,* June 28, 1955; January 26, 1956.
11. George E. Cartmill to Ray R. Eppert, Detroit, August 30, 1954. Copy furnished authors by Mr. Cartmill.
12. George E. Cartmill, interview, Detroit, January 2, 1963.
13. *The Detroit Free Press,* May 24, 1956; *Detroit News,* June 3, 1956; July 7, 1956. Also Ray R. Eppert to authors, Detroit, December 27, 1962.
14. *Detroit Times,* March 20, 1960.
15. Anthony J. J. Rourke, *Proposed Detroit Medical Center* (Detroit, 1960), pp. R2–R12.
16. *Detroit News,* April 20, 1961; *The Detroit Free Press,* April 20, 1961.
17. Rourke, *Medical Center,* R-4.
18. Rourke, *Medical Center,* p. R-4.
19. Harper Hospital Trustees' Minutes 1914–23, p. 8.

BIBLIOGRAPHY

Official Archives of Harper Hospital

The extensive files of official Harper Hospital records were the basic source of information in this book. Fortunately, the Hospital over the years recognized the value of its records and preserved most of them intact. The bound volumes of the Minutes of the Board of Trustees run from 1859 to the present time, with the exception of one missing volume covering the years 1893–97. The entries vary according to the style of the recording secretaries, but are in general very comprehensive. They include the important decisions taken by the Board, monthly and annual reports, copies of important documents, and correspondence. The Minutes of the Executive Committee of the Board of Trustees, 1914–45, and the Minutes of the Medical Staff, 1885–1916, are also important sources of hospital history.

The Harper Hospital Archives contains most of the basic financial records of the institution, including general ledgers, cash books, fund-raising records, audits, property and equipment appraisals, and studies of patient costs for the period after 1874. Prior to that time one must rely upon the financial reports which appear in the trustees' minutes. These records give a day-by-day account of the business of running a hospital—the expense of patient care, food, personnel, buildings, drugs and equipment, etc. For example, the Treasurer's Ledger, 1884–89, gives complete details on the construction of the Harper building on John R Street and comparative costs of hospital administration for the years 1887, 1888, and 1889. Similar records are available for the J. L. Hudson Memorial Building, the Buhl building, and the Brush Street building. Also helpful are the special ledgers kept to record bequests, endowments, and other contributions to the institution.

Patient records are comprehensive for the first seventy-five years of Harper's existence and give valuable data on the patient, listing residence, occupation, vital statistics, as well as diagnosis and treatment.

General Background

A wide variety of publications on Detroit is available as background material for the Harper story. Silas Farmer, *A History of Detroit and Michigan* (Detroit, 1884) is the best history of Detroit up to 1880 and gives good accounts of prominent Detroiters and local institutions. George B. Catlin, *The Story of Detroit* (Detroit, 1926) and C. M. and M. Agnes Burton, *History of Wayne County and the City of Detroit* (5 vols., Chicago, 1930) give a more up-to-date treatment of Detroit's history. Friend Palmer, *Early Days in Detroit* (Detroit, 1906) is particularly useful for biographical data on Detroiters. Other volumes which have useful information are: Charles Lanman, *Red Book of Michigan* (Detroit, 1871); Paul Leake, *History of Detroit* (3 vols., Chicago, 1912); Robert B. Ross and George B.

Catlin, *Landmarks of Detroit, A History of a City* (Detroit, 1898). For an account of Detroit in the early half of the nineteenth century see Floyd Dain, *Every House a Frontier* (Detroit, 1956) and Frank B. Woodford, *Mr. Jefferson's Disciple* (East Lansing, 1953).

The city directories of Detroit contain valuable data on business and industry, and persons living in the city. The maps inserted in the directories are particularly helpful in showing graphically the physical development of Detroit. *Detroit in its World Setting: A 250 Year Chronology, 1701–1951* (Detroit, 1953) gives the annual highlights of the social, political, scientific, and cultural developments in Detroit, Michigan and the United States in general.

C. B. Barr, *Medical History of Michigan* (2 vols., Minneapolis and St. Paul, 1930) is a reservoir of information on medicine, hospitals, and physicians, although it must be used cautiously because of inaccuracies. Samuel P. Duffield and Edward W. Jenks, "Medical History of Detroit from 1701–1864," *Detroit Illustrated* (Detroit, 1891) pp. 73–81 is an account by two informed contemporaries. For accounts of other Detroit hospitals, see Edward G. Martin, *Early Detroit St. Mary's Hospital, 1845–1945* (Detroit, 1945) and *The First Fifty Years of the Grace Hospital* (Detroit, 1938). George Paré, *The Catholic Church in Detroit, 1701–1888* (Detroit, 1951) also contains detailed information on St. Mary's Hospital.

Medical History

The standard sources for the history of American medicine are Henry E. Sigerist, *American Medicine* (New York, 1934) and Richard Skyrock, *The Development of Modern Medicine* (2 ed., New York, 1947). Thomas N. Bonner, *Medicine in Chicago* (Madison, Wis., 1957) is an outstanding work of its kind and was useful as a source of medical history in another midwestern metropolis. The sections "Birth of Modern Medical Science, 1850–1900," and "Socio-Medical Problems" were especially helpful. See also Richard A. Leonardo, *History of Surgery* (New York, 1943); Irmengarde Eberle, *Modern Medical Discoveries* (1948); Morris Fishbein, *Frontiers of Medicine* (New York, 1933); and Thomas N. Bonner, "The Social and Political Attitudes of Midwestern Physicians, 1840–1940," *Journal of the History of Medicine and Allied Sciences,* VII (April, 1953), 133–64.

The best historical account of hospitals in the United States is E. H. L. Corwin, *The American Hospital* (New York, 1943). Another is Malcolm T. MacEachern, *Hospital Organization and Management* (Chicago, 1957). Statistical data on Harper and other United States hospitals are available from a variety of sources. The first list of hospitals appeared in J. M. Toner, "Statistics of Hospitals of the United States, 1872–3," *Transactions of the American Medical Association,* XXIV (1873), 314–33. The next compilation of hospitals came out in 1903 in the *Standard Medical Directory.* In 1906, the first edition of the *American Medical Directory* appeared under the auspices of the American Medical Association. The *American Medical Association Journal* (April 16, 1921), pp. 1083–85 contains a summary compilation of Detroit and Michigan hospitals.

Historical studies of other American hospitals were useful for comparative data. Alan M. Chesney, *The Johns Hopkins Hospital and the Johns Hopkins Medical School* (2 vols., Baltimore, 1943) was particularly helpful for its details about the founding and early history of the great Baltimore hospital in the 1870's and 1880's during the period when Harper was undergoing similar developments. Joseph Hirsh and B. Doherty, *The First 100 Years of Mount Sinai Hospital of New York, 1852–1952* (New York, 1952); Nathaniel W. Faxon, *The Massachusetts General Hospital* (Cambridge, Mass., 1959); and *The Presbyterian Hospital of the City of Chicago, 1883–1943* (Chicago, 1943) describe the origins of other major United States hospitals. Helen Clapsattle, *The Doctors Mayo* (Minneapolis, 1941) and Abraham Flexner, *I Remember: The Autobiography of Abraham Flexner* (New York, 1940) are standard works in medical history.

Medical journals and periodicals provided basic data on all phases of Harper's history. The news notices and articles by Harper personnel describe research at Harper, staff activities, medical controversy, and other related hospital developments in Detroit and Michigan. Especially revealing of the period prior to 1900 are *The Detroit Review of Medicine*, 1866–76; *The Detroit Lancet*, 1878–87; and its successor, *The American Lancet*, 1887–95; *Physician and Surgeon*, 1878–1915; and *The Medical Advance*, 1877–80, succeeded by *Leonard's Illustrated Medical Journal*, 1880–1906.

The Michigan State Medical Society Journal (1901) is the best source of medical developments in Michigan at large and contains scores of articles by the Harper staff. *The Detroit Medical Journal*, 1901–20 and *The Detroit Medical News*, 1909–   , the organ of the Wayne County Medical Society, are also excellent sources of local hospital history. See also *American Medical Association Journal*, 1883–   . *The Leucocyte*, a publication of the Detroit College of Medicine from 1894 to 1922, holds many references pertinent to Harper Hospital history.

The Modern Hospital, 1913–   ; *Hospitals*, the Journal of the American Hospital Association, 1927–   ; and *Hospital Management*, 1916–   are the standard journals of hospital administrators. These journals give important background information on hospital and medical problems and also include accounts of Harper Hospital. See, for example, Wayne Smith, "The Joseph L. Hudson Memorial Building of Harper Hospital, Detroit," *The Modern Hospital*, V (August, 1915), 1–7.

The Detroit Free Press, The Detroit Advertiser and Tribune, Detroit Post and Tribune, The Detroit News, and *Detroit Saturday Night* contain hundreds of significant articles on Harper Hospital's history. The papers published annual reports of the Hospital, biographical sketches of its founders and officials, descriptions of new buildings and services, and general news stories. Many newspaper references to Harper are in the indexed Burton and Palmer scrapbooks in the Burton Historical Collection of the Detroit Public Library; the J. H. Carstens, H. Leonard, and Walter Cree scrapbooks in the Wayne State University Archives; and the Harper scrapbooks in the Harper Hospital Archives.

Founders of Harper Hospital

Biographical data on Walter Harper and Nancy Martin are unusually scarce and for the most part inaccurate. Brief obituaries of Walter Harper are found in *Harper Hospital* (Detroit, 1886), 97–98 and the *Detroit Advertiser and Tribune,* August 30, 1867. Similar data about his life are found in Agnes Deans and Mary Austin, *History of Farrand Training School for Nurses* (Detroit, 1936); Farmer, *History of Detroit and Michigan,* I (Detroit, 1884), 657–58; Catlin, *Story of Detroit* (Detroit, 1926), 479–80; and *Harper Hospital, Report for the Year Ending December 31, 1913,* 27–36. The public announcement of his bequest for a hospital appeared in *The Detroit Free Press,* February 9, 1859 and *The Detroit Daily Advertiser,* February 8 and 9, 1859. The original deed was recorded February 4, 1859 in Liber 75 of folios 608–614 in the Register's Office, County of Wayne.

Walter Harper's whereabouts in Detroit can be traced through the *City of Detroit Directories,* 1841–67. *Harper Hospital* (Detroit, 1886), 70–71, details the sale of Harper's property in Detroit and Philadelphia and his annuity arrangement with the trustees. Other minor references appear in *The Detroit Free Press,* December 20, 1862 and July 30, 1871, and in the Reading Room File, Burton Historical Collection.

Nancy Martin was better known to Detroiters than Walter Harper was, and her name appeared often in newspapers and other publications. Typical of the biographical sketches of Nancy Martin is Farmer, *History of Detroit and Michigan,* I (Detroit, 1884), 793–95; *Harper Hospital* (Detroit, 1886), 98–100; and Palmer, *Early Days in Detroit* (Detroit, 1906), 26–28. Similar accounts are found in Ross and Catlin, *Landmarks of Detroit* (Detroit, 1898), 494; C. F. Warner, *Picturesque Detroit and Environs,* (Northampton, Mass., 1893); Milo Quaife, *Builders of Detroit* (Detroit, 1951), 28–30; *Harper Hospital, Report for Year, 1913,* 27–36; and C. M. Burr, *Medical History of Michigan,* II, 603.

Detailed reports of the Martin gift can be found in Harper Hospital Trustees' Minutes, March 10, 1859 and *Detroit Daily Advertiser,* April 4, 5, and 6, 1859. The deed is listed in the Wayne County Probate Court Records. File No. 7597, Liber 85, p. 227.

Romanticized accounts of Nancy Martin's life are written in "Four Noble Women," *Detroit Journal* (May 16, 1896) and N. H. Bowen, "How Huckster Nancy Helped Give Harper Hospital to Detroit," *Detroit Saturday Night,* May 27, 1922; and Elizabeth Anne Ash McFadden, "My Recollection of Nancy Martin" (MS in Harper Hospital Archives) Detroit, August 1, 1934. Other references to Nancy Martin's public life appear in *The Detroit Free Press,* May 14, 1859, May 16, 1861, February 10, 1875, March 15, 1903, and December 28, 1914; *Detroit Advertiser and Tribune,* February 10, 1875; and the *Lansing Republican,* February 12, 1875.

Harper as a Civil War Hospital

In addition to the minutes of the Board of Trustees the best source on the origin and establishment of Harper Hospital is the George Duffield Papers in the Burton Historical Collection. The following entries in the Duffield Diaries refer to the founding of the Hospital: April 7 and 9, 1864; May 26 and 31, 1864; June 4, 1864; May 23, 1865; November 30, 1865, and December 12 and 14, 1865. See also the correspondence between Duffield and his son, Divie B. Duffield. Farmer, *History of Detroit and Michigan*, I (Detroit, 1884), 667–68 credits Mrs. Isabella Stewart, Duffield's daughter, with persuading Walter Harper and Nancy Martin to give their land for a hospital. A similar account is found in *Detroit Evening News,* February 15, 1883, in an interview with Dr. Morse Stewart. Other references to the early plans for a hospital are found in *Detroit Daily Advertiser,* February 18, 1859, July 19, 1862, July 22, 1862, and August 5, 1862. The University of Michigan proposal to establish Harper Hospital as the clinical department of the University of Michigan Medical School is described in *The Detroit Free Press,* December 20, 1862.

The standard work on Civil War medicine is George W. Adams, *Doctors in Blue: The Medical History of the Union Army in the Civil War* (New York, 1952). Jean L. Datson, "History of Union Hospitals During the Civil War," unpublished Master's thesis, Wayne State University, Detroit, 1947, contains an account of war hospitals and, in particular, a description of Harper Hospital. *The Medical and Surgical History of the War of the Rebellion, 1861–1865* (6 vols., Washington, 1875–88) is of major importance to Civil War medical practices and hospitals. John Robertson, *Michigan in the Civil War* (Lansing, 1882) and Charles Lanman, *Red Book of Michigan* (Detroit, 1871) give background information on the war and the need for hospital service in Michigan.

The Records of the Office of the Surgeon General, War Department, Record Group 92 and 94, National Archives, contain many documents relating to the establishment of an army hospital in Michigan and its transfer in December, 1865 back to the Board of Trustees. See, for example, Charles Tripler's letter to Surgeon General William A. Hammond, October 25, 1862 containing specifications and plans for a 200-bed hospital in Detroit, and Tripler to Colonel R. L. Hood, Assistant Surgeon General, May 11, 1863. The Austin Blair Papers in the Burton Historical Collection hold many letters relating to the establishment of Harper Hospital and describe the powerful influence exerted by Senators Zachariah Chandler and Jacob Howard to have the army hospital located in Detroit. The Adjutant General's Files in the Michigan Historical Commission Archives also reflect the state-wide campaign for the construction of a Michigan hospital. *The Michigan Adjutant General, Annual Reports* (Lansing, 1862–66) give facts on the establishment of Harper, including the correspondence and reports of Joseph Tunnicliff, Michigan military agent at Washington, D.C.; James M. Edmunds, President of the Michigan Soldiers' Relief Association of Washington, D.C.; Luther Willard, agent at Nashville, Tennessee; J. B. Gilman, agent at Cincinnati, Ohio; and Benjamin Vernor, agent at Detroit. Governor Blair's official war messages are in George N. Fuller, ed. *Messages of the Governors of Michigan,* Vol. II (Lansing, 1927). Vivian T. Messner, "Public Life of Austin Blair, War Governor of Michigan, 1845-1863," unpublished Master's thesis, Wayne State University, Detroit, 1934, offers timely background data on Michigan's official war policy.

Robert Spiro, "History of the Michigan Soldier's Aid Society, 1861-1865," unpublished Ph.D. dissertation, University of Michigan, 1959, is the definitive work on this agency which worked actively for hospital accommodations and which in 1866 transferred its patients to Harper. The reports, correspondence, and other papers of the Michigan Soldiers' Aid Society in the Burton Historical Collection and the James V. Campbell Papers, University of Michigan Historical Collections, describe the work of the Society in Detroit and other Michigan cities. For details of the Michigan Soldiers' Home, located at Harper Hospital in 1866, see Minutes of the State Military Board, 1859-90, Records of the Michigan Military Establishment, Michigan Historical Commission Archives and *The Michigan Adjutant General Annual Reports,* 1867-90.

An account of the construction of the Hospital in 1864 is given in *The Detroit Free Press,* June 9, 1864. The barracks buildings are described first-hand in the *Detroit Advertiser and Tribune,* October 11, 1864.

The details of running Harper as a military hospital are given in the Records of the United States Surgeon General, "United States General Hospitals of Harper's, St. Mary's, and Detroit Barracks Post Hospitals, 1864-1866" in the Burton Historical Collection. Included in this voluminous collection are correspondence, reports, daily and weekly patients' reports, and receipts for food, clothing, and hospital supplies. Also of interest for a study of nineteenth-century medicine is the Harper Hospital Prescription Book, December 3, 1864 to April 15, 1865, Burton Historical Collection.

Service and pension records of soldier patients at Harper are located in the Civil War Record and Pension Office, National Archives; Records of the Michigan Military Establishment, Michigan Historical Commission Archives; and in Michigan Adjutant General, *Record of Service of Michigan Volunteers in the Civil War, 1861-1865* (46 vols., Kalamazoo, 1905). A first-hand description by a soldier-patient at Harper Hospital during the summer of 1865 is found in the Diary of Frank Gross, January 1, 1864 to August 23, 1865 (MS in the University of Michigan Historical Collections).

Harper as a Civilian Hospital

In addition to official institutional archives, the history and development of Harper Hospital are described in numerous publications. *The Annual Reports* of the Board of Trustees give accounts of the operation of the Hospital, inauguration of new services and programs, financial and staff data, and information on patient care. Although there is apparently no complete set of these reports as separate publications, copies of many of them appeared in Detroit newspapers and medical journals, such as *Medical Age, Physician and Surgeon,* and the *Detroit Medical Journal.* Starting in 1890, the annual reports appeared in the *Harper Hospital Bulletin.* The *Bulletin* was issued in three series: the first, 1890–1912; the second, 1921–26; and the third, 1942–55. In addition to periodic official reports, the *Bulletin* contains medical case studies by staff members, news notices, and biographical sketches of prominent staff members.

Other official Harper publications contain pertinent material. *The Constitution and By Laws of the Harper Hospital, Together with a Report and Statement of the Board of Trustees* (Detroit, 1866) explains early medical practices at Harper and lists members of the first civilian hospital medical staff. The book *Harper Hospital,* published anonymously by the Board of Trustees in 1886, gives an excellent report of the origins and early history of the Hospital, including copies of the Harper and Martin deeds, Articles of Incorporation, and Bylaws and Regulations, as well as lists of trustees and officers, biographical descriptions of Nancy Martin, Walter Harper, and deceased trustees. Data on land transactions, financial operation of the institution up to 1884, and the details of the construction of the John R building, 1882–84, are also offered.

The Fiftieth Anniversary of Harper in 1913 witnessed a number of historical accounts of the Hospital. The most extensive is "Harper Hospital, A Short History of the Beginnings and Up to its Fiftieth Anniversary," *Harper Hospital Report for 1913,* pp. 27–36. See also "Harper Hospital, Fifty Years Service," *Detroit News and Tribune,* April 27, 1913; "Fifty Years of Harper Hospital," *The Detroit Free Press,* December 28, 1913; and Walter J. Cree, "Harper Hospital," *Detroit Medical News,* XXVI (January 14, 1935), 9, 19. A study of the Hospital is found also in the Catlin Papers, Burton Historical Collection. Other historical works are "History of Harper Hospital," *Detroit Lancet, VIII* (1884–85), 24–25; Gladys Gearhart, "History of Harper Hospital and Farrand Training School," *Harper Hospital Bulletin,* I, Second Series (July, 1921) 3 and Agnes G. Deans and Anne Austin, *The History of the Farrand Training School for Nurses* (Detroit, 1936), 11–30.

The construction and dedication of new buildings are adequately documented in official Harper records. See, for example, Treasurer's Journal, 1884; Contributors' Journal, 1878–1907; and Purchase Ledger—Furnishing of New Building, 1884—all in the Harper Hospital Archives. For other contemporary accounts of the 1884 building, see *Detroit Lancet,* VI (1882–83) p. 217 and VIII (1884–85) 24–25; and *The Detroit Free Press,* March 15, 1882 and January 20, 1884. The definitive study of hospital construction, which was the reference used by the Harper trustees in plans for the 1884 building, is Josh Billings, Norton Folsom, Joseph Jones, Caspar Morris, and Stephen Smith, *Hospital Plans: Five Essays Relating to the Construction, Organization and Management of Hospitals* (New York, 1875).

Plans for the construction of the J. L. Hudson Memorial and Buhl buildings in 1912 and the future development of Harper are covered in an official Harper publication, *What Detroit Needs Most* (Detroit, 1912). For other accounts of the two buildings see "Buhl and Hudson Buildings," *Michigan State Medical Society Journal,* X (1911), 321, 580; "Greater Harper Hospital," *ibid.,* XI (1912), 321; "The

Buhl Building," *Leucocyte,* XXI (January 15, 1914), 80; and "The New Harper Hospital," *ibid.,* XXII (January 15, 1915), 91–96. See also *Detroit News and Tribune,* April 27, 1913 and *The Detroit Free Press,* December 28, 1914. Among the official Harper records, see Journal: J. L. Hudson Memorial, 1911–14; Ledger, Buhl and Hudson Buildings, 1912–13; and *Harper Hospital Bulletin,* 1911–12.

For data on the Brush Street building, opened in 1928, see *Harper Hospital, An Obligation and an Opportunity* (Detroit, 1926); "The Brush Street Building," *Michigan State Medical Society Journal,* XXVII (1928), 387; *The Detroit News,* May 13, 17, 1928; and *The Detroit Free Press,* May 13, 1928. See also Journal, Brush Street Building, 1926–28, Harper Hospital Archives, and *Harper Hospital Bulletin,* 1924–26.

The Out-patient Department at Harper is described in *Detroit Medical News* XXV (May 7, 1934), 14 ff.; and Out-patient Reports and Out-patient Journal, 1894–96 in Harper Hospital Archives. See also "Free Dispensary for Poor at Harper's," *The Detroit Free Press,* January 4, 1868.

For a description of Harper's early ambulance service, see Ambulance Journal, 1893–96, Harper Hospital Archives; *24th Annual Report of Harper Hospital for 1887; 32nd Annual Report of Harper Hospital for 1895; The Detroit Free Press,* May 15, 1887; "Harper's Ambulance Service," *Physician and Surgeon,* XIV (1892), 27; *Leucocyte,* VI (October 15, 1897), 31; and *Detroit Medical News,* XXV (February 12, 1934), p. 9. See also Schreiber Interview Transcript, 1938, in Wayne State University Archives; and Plinn F. Morse, "Communication System within Harper Hospital, 1864–1948" (MS in Harper Hospital Archives).

William F. Metcalf's proposals for the reorganization of Harper Hospital are carefully documented in the minutes of the Board of Trustees and the Executive Committee of the Medical Staff. See also *Harper Hospital Bulletin,* XXII (June, 1911), 14; William Metcalf, "Observations on the General Principles of Hospital Organization," *Michigan State Medical Society Journal,* VIII (May, 1909), 230–40; and Schreiber Interview (Transcript, Wayne State University Archives). For reaction of the Detroit press to the controversy, see J. H. Carstens' Scrapbook, 1908–13, Wayne State University Archives.

For the story of the Detroit General Hospital, which subsequently became Henry Ford Hospital, see W. L. Graham, "The Henry Ford Hospital, Detroit," *Hospital Management,* XVIII (November, 1924), 28–34 and "The Detroit General Hospital," *Detroit Medical Journal,* XII (May, 1912), 173–75. Metcalf's part in the development of this hospital is recounted in the Ford Hospital Papers, Ford Motor Company Archives. See, for example, Homer E. Safford to Mrs. Henry Ford, May 24, 1914 and June 4, 1914.

The proposed merger of Harper Hospital and the Detroit General Hospital is explained in *Detroit Medical Journal,* X (1910) 118, 274; XIII (1913), 447–48; *Leucocyte,* XXI (1913), 79; and *The Detroit News,* March 8, 1910.

The most comprehensive contemporary account of the issue of "fee splitting" is in the *Detroit Medical Journal, XII* (October, 1912), 341–49. In this article, the views of Drs. Theodore A. McGraw, Walter P. Manton, Harold Wilson, Charles G. Jennings, and Frederick W. Robbins are presented. The action of Harper Hospital is found in Board of Trustees' Minutes, November 4, 1912; *Detroit Medical Journal,* XII (December, 1912), 438; and "Fee Splitting," *Michigan State Medical Society Journal,* XI (1913) 59.

The closed hospital controversy was given widespread coverage in the medical journals and the daily press. For Harper's official stand on the issue, see the Board of Trustees' Executive Committee Minutes, 1919–21; *Harper Hospital Bulletin,* I Second series (April, 1921), 1; and III (April, 1923), 2. For other accounts, see J. G. R. Manwaring, "The Community Hospital," *Michigan State Medical Society Journal,* XIX (April, 1920) 165–67; "The Closed Hospital," *Detroit Medical Journal,* XX (1919), 20; and "The Evolution in Medical Practice and the Open Hospital Idea," *ibid.,* XXI (1920), 22–24.

The Closed Hospital Bill, sponsored by Dr. O. G. Johnson, state senator from Fostoria, Michigan, is described in *Michigan State Medical Society Journal,* XX (May, 1921), 215 and *Detroit Saturday Night,* March 21, 1921. See also "A Letter Relating to Closed Hospitals," *Michigan State Medical Society Journal,* XX (March, 1921), 106–07; (April, 1921), pp. 135–37; *The Detroit News,* February 12, 1919; and *The Detroit Free Press,* November 18, 1919. Angus McLean presented his views on the closed hospital and fee splitting in "President's Address, 1921: The Existing Relations Between the Medical Profession and the Public and the Future Tendency," *Michigan State Medical Society Journal,* XX (June, 1921), 225–31.

Harper in the World Wars

Harper Hospital's World War I unit, Base Hospital 17, received enthusiastic publicity. The most comprehensive source of information on its activities is found in Wayne County Medical Society, *War Bulletin,* August 1, 1917–March, 1919. See, for example, I (August 1, 1917) 5; (August 15, 1917), 6–7; (September 1, 1917), 7–8; (September 15, 1917), 6; (October 15, 1917), 6; (November 1, 1917), 6–9; XX (August 1, 1918), 8; (September 1, 1918) 11; (October–November 1918), 10–12; and (March, 1919), 2. The *Detroit Medical Journal* also gives much space to the activities of Base Hospital 17. See XVIII (February, 1917), 86; (July, 1917), 282–86; (September, 1917), 342–43; XX (April, 1919), 157; and "Major Hirschman's Return," XIX (November, 1918), 397–98. War Department Order No. 6, June 29, 1917, which assigned Base Hospital 17 to overseas duty, is in Harper Hospital Archives. Scrapbooks in the Archives also relate to the war efforts of Harper and the Farrand Training School for Nurses. A list of the staff of doctors and nurses is given in *Michigan State Medical Society Journal,* XVIII (May, 1919), 277–78. For other references to the Harper Unit see *ibid.,* XVI (1917), 295–96, 387, 422, and XVIII (1919), 279–80. Other accounts appear in Deans and Austin, *History of Farrand Training School for Nurses,* 168–69; and Henry B. Selleck, *A Golden Century of Medicine* (Detroit, 1949), 34–35. For newspaper stories of the Harper Unit, see *The Detroit Free Press,* May 16, 1917, May 25, 1917, and March 10 and 11, 1919. Biographical studies of Dr. Angus McLean, the head of Base Hospital 17, were written in *Detroit Saturday Night,* October 23, 1926; *The*

Detroit Free Press, April 12, 1933; and the Reading Room File, Burton Historical Collection.

Harper Hospital also organized Base Hospital 17 again during World War II. Its service is documented in the Henry Carstens Collection, Wayne State University Archives; and *Harper Hospital Bulletin,* 3 Series 1942-55. See also "Stewart Hamilton and the United States Army" (Typescript), 1940, and Carol Bremer, "History of Nursing Service in the 17th General Hospital" (Typescript), August, 1945, Harper Hospital Archives.

Medical Education at Harper Hospital

The most reliable account of the Detroit College of Medicine, the forerunner of the Wayne State University College of Medicine, which was located in the original barracks buildings and closely affiliated with Harper, is Fannie Anderson, "History of the College of Medicine of Wayne State University" (MS in Wayne State University Archives), 1958. Also of value is Fannie Anderson, "History of Wayne State University College of Medicine," *Bulletin of Wayne University College of Medicine and the Detroit Receiving Hospital,* II (March, 1955), 20-32; (June, 1955), 64-72.

Other early studies of the Detroit College of Medicine which cover the relationship of the College to Harper Hospital, but which must be used with caution, are Preston M. Hickey, "History of the Detroit College of Medicine," *Leucocyte,* I (December, 1894), 1-10; J. H. Carstens, "Detroit College of Medicine," *ibid.,* XXV (1918), 89-92; and Frank B. Walker, "Detroit College of Medicine," *Erythrocyte* (Detroit, 1913), pp. 10-12. The official records of the College, including minute books, correspondence files, reports, catalogs, bulletins, etc. in the Wayne State University Archives, also describe the close association between Harper and Wayne State University. The plans for the establishment of the medical school and the agreement between the two institutions are explained in the Harper Hospital Trustees' Minutes, November 14, 1865, April 11, 1868, April 6, 1875, and February 1, 1881. See also "Detroit Preparatory School of Medicine Planned," *Detroit Advertiser and Tribune,* May 15, 1865.

The definitive work on the Farrand School is Agnes Deans and Anne L. Austin, *History of the Farrand Training School for Nurses* (Detroit, 1936). Also of value is Gladys Gearhart, "History of Harper Hospital and Farrand Training School," *Harper Hospital Bulletin,* I, Second Series (July, 1921), 2-5; (October, 1921), 8; (December, 1921), 10; and H. Fulton "History of Nursing in Harper Hospital" (Typescript), Harper Hospital Archives. The official reports of the Farrand School were published in the *Harper Hospital Bulletin.* See also the following official records in the Harper Hospital Archives: Student Records, 1884-96; Practical Nursing Notes of Lystra Gretter, 1894; the Gretter Papers; Farrand Scrapbooks, and the volumes devoted to the Alumnae Association of the Nurses School. Miscellaneous copies of announcements, annual reports, and other Farrand School publications in the Burton Historical Collection have some value.

For an account of the Harper nurses in the Spanish-American War, see *Harper Hospital Bulletin,* IV, First Series (February, 1899), 48–49, 78, and 84–85. The references to Harper Hospital in World War I and World War II, cited above, also give accounts of Harper nurses in Base Hospital 17.

Other pertinent references to the Farrand School are "The Farrand School of Nursing, Harper Hospital," *British Journal of Nursing,* XXIX (October 3, 1903) 267, and Helen W. Munson, "Lystra E. Gretter," *American Journal of Nursing,* IL (June, 1949), 344–48.

Detroit Medical Center

The first proposals for a medical center were presented by A. M. Smith, *Shall Detroit Be a Great Medical Teaching Center?* (Detroit, 1937) from a series of articles which *The Detroit News* originally published. The best examination of the proposals in 1943 is given in George F. Pierrot, "The Medical Center of Wayne University," *Detroit Trust Company Quarterly* (Spring, 1944), pp. 12–14 and Edgar Norris, *The Medical Science Center of Wayne University* (Detroit, 1943). The Warren Bow Papers in the Wayne State University Archives contain extensive files on the plans. See especially "Progress Report of the Medical Center of Wayne University to the Board of Education" by Wendell Anderson. For newspaper reaction to the plans see *The Detroit News,* December 29, 1942 and *The Detroit Free Press,* November 24, 1943.

There is also comprehensive documentation for new plans for a medical center in the 1950's. The most extensive files are in the Wayne State University Archives, and the best published account of the Center proposal is "The Detroit Medical Center," *The Michigan Society of Architects, Monthly Bulletin,* XXXII (June, 1958). See also Charles Blessing, *ibid.;* Gordon H. Scott, "The Detroit Medical Center," *Michigan Challenge* (April, 1962), p. 10; and Anthony J. J. Rourke, *Proposed Detroit Medical Center* (Detroit, 1960). For public reaction to the Center idea, see *The Detroit Times,* March 26, 1953, March 20, 1960; *The Detroit News,* June 28, 1955, January 26, 1956, May 24, 1956, June 3, 1956, July 7, 1956, July 17, 1956, and April 20, 1961; and *The Detroit Free Press,* May 24, 1956, June 17, 1960, and April 20, 1961.

Biographical Data

On the staff members of Harper Hospital, there is a wealth of biographical data which gives not only valuable information on individuals and their research projects, but also insights into the operation of the Hospital during the past century. The most useful guides for the earlier period are Howard A. Kelly, *Cyclopedia of American Medical Biographies* (2 vols. Philadelphia, 1912); Kelly and Walter Burrage, *American Medical Biographies* (3 vols. Baltimore, 1920); and Lloyd Thompson and W. S. Downs, *Who's Who in American Medicine* (New

York, 1925). The American College of Surgeons *Yearbook* (Chicago, 1950) also offers interesting facts concerning the Harper staff at that time. C. B. Burr, *Medical History of Michigan* (2 vols. Minneapolis, 1930) is also helpful.

The finest single collection on Harper and Detroit physicians is the Medical Biography Collection in the Wayne State University Archives. The nucleus of this collection is the papers of the Detroit Academy of Medicine. In addition, the Archives has an extensive biographical index to the major medical journals in Detroit and Michigan, compiled by Fannie Anderson of the Wayne State University Medical School Library. Also of value are the scrapbooks of J. Henry Carstens, C. Henri Leonard, and Walter Cree. Included also in the Archives are transcripts of a number of interviews and reminiscences, which provide personal observations on Harper personnel. The interview, for example, recorded in the home of Dr. Frederic Schreiber, Grosse Pointe, March 23, 1938 by Drs. Schreiber, William Donald, Stephen H. Knight, Andrew Biddle, Angus McLean, Don Campbell, Parker, Ridland, and Mr. Stanislas Keenan, gives a vivid picture of medical practice in Detroit from 1885 to 1915. The William J. Stapleton Papers also contain biographical information.

The Burton Historical Collection also has rich sources on the Harper staff. The Reading Room File contains clippings, photographs, and other printed material on all of the major staff members. For the Civil War records of Theodore A. McGraw, George P. Andrews, Edward W. Jenk, see Record Group No. 94, Office of Adjutant General, War Department, National Archives. See also "A Record of My Army Experience, Written for My Children" by Theodore A. McGraw (Typescript, Wayne State University Archives).

INDEX